ANGLO-SAXON ORNAMENTAL METALWORK
700–1100 IN THE BRITISH MUSEUM

ANGLO-SAXON ORNAMENTAL METALWORK 700-1100

IN THE BRITISH MUSEUM

BY

DAVID M. WILSON, M.A., F.S.A.

Assistant Keeper of British and Medieval Antiquities

with appendices by

R. L. S. BRUCE-MITFORD, M.A., F.S.A.

Keeper of British and Medieval Antiquities

and

R. I. PAGE, M.A., Ph.D.

Fellow of Corpus Christi College and Lecturer in the Department of Anglo-Saxon,
University of Cambridge

THE TRUSTEES OF THE BRITISH MUSEUM

1964

PRINTED IN GREAT BRITAIN BY
WILLIAM CLOWES AND SONS LTD
LONDON AND BECCLES

PREFACE

The present volume is the first in a series of six or seven planned to cover the antiquities of the later Saxon period, including the Celtic antiquities. The division between early and late Saxon has been fixed at the year A.D. 700 for practical purposes, as explained by Mr. Wilson in his Introduction. The British Museum collection of late Saxon antiquities in general is unrivalled. Its collection of Hiberno-Saxon and Irish metalwork is the finest outside Dublin, and its collection of Viking antiquities the most important outside Scandinavia. These volumes will therefore be of major importance. Other volumes envisaged are on pottery, on tools and weapons and on Viking antiquities, all being individual volumes of the *Catalogue of Antiquities of the Later Saxon Period*.

In connection with the present volume we are particularly indebted to our colleagues in the British Museum Research Laboratory whose skill in reconstructing and elucidating many of the objects described has made a major contribution. We are also greatly indebted to our colleagues in the Department of Coins and Medals, who have been continuously consulted.

The Trustees have been fortunate in obtaining the collaboration of Dr. R. I. Page, of the Department of Anglo-Saxon in the University of Cambridge, who has written a special chapter on inscriptions that occur on the ornamental metalwork covered by the volume.

R. L. S. BRUCE-MITFORD,
Keeper of British and Medieval Antiquities.

FOREWORD

The copyright of the following photographs is acknowledged: Rheinisches Landes-museum, Bonn, pl. I*b*; Historisk Museum, Bergen, pls. I*c*, II*d*, III*d* and *e*; Hitchin Museum, pl. II*a*; Sir Thomas Kendrick, pl. II*b*, VIII*b* and X*e*; Leicester City Museum, pl. III*a*; National Museum, Copenhagen, pl. III*c*, IX*a*; National Museum of Anti-quities of Scotland, pl. IV*d*; Ashmolean Museum, Oxford, pl. IV; Pitt-Rivers Museum, Oxford, pl. VII; Trinity College, Cambridge, pl. VIII*a*; Universitetets Oldsaksamling, Oslo, pl. VIII*a*; Museum of Archaeology and Ethnology, Cambridge, pls. X*b* and *c*; Gotlands Fornsal, Visby, pl. X*d*; D. M. Wilson, pls. I*a* and IX*b*. All the other photographs used in the catalogue are copyright of the British Museum.

The copyright of the following drawings is acknowledged: Mrs. Eva Wilson, figs, 1, 2, 5, 6, 7, 11-14, 33, 38-45, 53 and 54; National Museum of Antiquities of Scotland, fig. 2. The other drawings are copyright of the British Museum and were done by Miss M. Miller and Mr. C. O. Waterhouse. The index has been prepared by Miss J. M. Davis of the Department of British and Medieval Antiquities; her co-operation is much appreciated.

The author of the catalogue wishes to thank the curators of museums and collections, too numerous to mention, in Great Britain, the Republic of Ireland, Spain, France, Austria, Germany, Belgium, Holland, Sweden, Norway, Denmark and Finland, who have helped him in many ways. He is particularly grateful for help received from Holger Arbman of Lund and Michael Dolley and Peter Lasko of London who have answered questions without number.

D. M. WILSON
January 1962

CONTENTS

LIST OF FIGURES

LIST OF PLATES

Between pp. 116 *and* 117.

PLATE

  I. (*a*) The Gandersheim Casket. *Herzog Anton Ulrich Museum, Brunswick.*

      (*b*) Bronze mount of unknown provenance. *Rheinisches Landesmuseum, Bonn.*

      (*c*) Gilt-bronze mount from Bjørke churchyard, Hjørundfjord, Møre, Norway. *Historisk Museum, Bergen.*

  II. (*a*) Silver-gilt pin from St. Andrew's Street, Hitchin, Hertfordshire. *Hitchin Museum.*

      (*b*) Fragment of a stone cross from Brixworth, Northamptonshire. *Brixworth Church.*

      (*c*) A lost hanging-bowl from the River Witham, Lincolnshire.

      (*d*) Bronze fragment from Lunde, Vangen, Voss, Hordaland, Norway. *Historisk Museum, Bergen.*

CHAPTER I

THE COLLECTION OF ANGLO-SAXON ORNAMENTAL METALWORK, OF THE PERIOD 700–1100, IN THE BRITISH MUSEUM

THE SCOPE OF THE CATALOGUE

This catalogue lists all the objects in the British Museum of precious metal or decorated bronze, made in an Anglo-Saxon context in the period between 700 and 1100. Objects of iron inlaid or embellished with precious metal are also included, but objects of iron embellished in the same metal with patterns or inscriptions (e.g. pattern-welded sword-blades) are not included. The only objects of non-precious, undecorated metal listed in the catalogue are bronze objects which occur in hoards of predominantly Anglo-Saxon character. Decorated objects of non-Anglo-Saxon character found in such hoards are not included here[1]: in the case of Anglo-Saxon objects found in hoards which are predominantly of Viking character only the Anglo-Saxon objects are included.[2] Objects made under Celtic influence in England (e.g. Hiberno-Saxon pennanular brooches) are not included here but will be listed in a future catalogue.

All judgments concerning the objects are discussed in the introductory chapters. The catalogue proper is completely factual; the only judgements made in this section (other than the insertion of a rough date for general guidance at the end of each entry) concern matters of disputed provenance or of identification of substances and materials. Page references are given under each entry of the discussion or mention of the object in the introductory chapters. The catalogue is arranged alphabetically under find-places; unprovenanced objects are arranged in their order of accession and are placed at the end of the catalogue.

All objects listed in the catalogue are illustrated by photographs—line drawings are used to amplify and illustrate certain points not immediately obvious from the photographs; they are in no way intended to duplicate the photographs.

The catalogue is complete to December 1961.

HISTORY OF THE COLLECTION

The collection of the great polymath, Sir Hans Sloane, which formed the nucleus round which the British Museum has been formed, passed into the hands of the nation in 1753. It contained two pieces of late Saxon ornamental metalwork, Ædred's finger-ring (no. 30) and a pair of tweezers from Reculver (no. 62). It is hardly surprising that the

---

[1] This applies only in one instance—a penannular brooch in the Trewhiddle hoard, Wilson and Blunt (1961), pl. xxviii, b.

[2] Only one object is affected under this heading—Cuerdale (No. 13).

hard-pressed staff of what was then the Department of Natural and Artificial Productions were not particularly interested in a very minor part of their collections and made no effort to acquire available late Saxon objects (such as the Bramham Moor ring sold in 1762 for £15 and now in the National Museum at Copenhagen[1]). The two Sloane objects were the only eighteenth-century acquisitions of late Saxon ornamental metalwork and it was not until between 1810 and 1816 that the newly formed Department of Antiquities and Coins and Medals acquired its third piece, the Kirkoswald brooch (no. 28). The method of acquisition of this piece is obscure but it is possible that it was purchased by the Museum at the Gough Sale in 1810. With the gift of Æthelwald's seal (no. 18) in 1822 by Mr. Hudson Gurney, a Vice-president of the Society of Antiquaries, the records of method of acquisition become slightly more detailed and acquisition itself more frequent. In 1829 the Earl of Radnor gave the Museum one of its more famous pieces, the ring of King Æthelwulf, the father of Alfred the Great (no. 31). Few objects were acquired in the thirties or forties, although the acquisition of the great Viking age hoard from Cuerdale in 1841 gave a considerable impetus to the study of the antiquities of the late Anglo-Saxon period (only one object from this hoard (no. 13) is included in this catalogue). The gradual emergence of the Department of British and Medieval Antiquities and Ethnography during the years between 1861 and 1866 ushered in the greatest period of the collection's growth under the Keepership of Augustus Wollaston (later Sir Wollaston) Franks, who had come to the Museum in 1851. Franks was at once the greatest Keeper and greatest consistent benefactor of the Department and his first gift of a piece of late Saxon metalwork was made as early as 1862. It was presumably his great personal friendship with Albert Way and his active participation in the affairs of the newly founded Archaeological Institute that was responsible, four years later, for the gift by that Institute of (among other things) the Witham pins (no. 19), one of the key pieces in the study of the subject. Meanwhile in 1856 the Department had acquired the collection of that remarkable antiquary Charles Roach Smith.[2] Roach Smith's collection was to a great extent made up of finds from London and a number of late Saxon objects came to the Museum with it (nos. 34, 38–40, 43 and 47–9). Late Saxon material continued to trickle into the Department, and in 1880 the most important collection of late Saxon ornamental metalwork ever found in this country, the Trewhiddle hoard (nos. 90–103), was given to the Museum by Mr. J. J. Rogers in recognition of Franks's services to the National Collections. Another important hoard, from Sevington, Wiltshire (nos. 67–79), was given in 1888 and in 1893 Franks gave the Museum the splendid Fetter Lane sword hilt (no. 41). Franks retired in 1896 and died in 1897. Among the many objects he bequeathed to the Museum were a number of ornaments of late Saxon origin including Queen Æthelswith's ring (no. 1), which was acquired by Franks from Canon Greenwell. Franks was succeeded in the Keepership by Charles Hercules (later Sir Hercules) Read and his first appointment was Reginald Allender Smith, whose interest in late Saxon antiquities and in Scandinavian archaeology resulted in a number of papers on the subject and in a number of important acquisitions over the next forty years. Acquisitions by Smith included the Hammersmith bronze (no. 42), the Beeston Tor hoard (nos. 2–7),

[1] Wilson (1959b), 163. [2] 1807–90.

2

the Ixworth disc (no. 25), and the Pitney brooch (no. 60), deposited on loan by Miss Dudham.

On Read's retirement in 1921 Thomas Downing (now Sir Thomas) Kendrick was appointed as Assistant Keeper and, in the year in which Kendrick succeeded Smith as Keeper (1938), he published his book *Anglo Saxon Art to A.D. 900*. It was natural, therefore, that the collections of late Saxon metalwork should continue to grow under his hands and those of his successors. Between 1940 and 1960 the Museum acquired a number of outstanding pieces, the Scales Moor sword-pommel (no. 65), the Strickland brooch (no. 152), the Sutton, Isle of Ely, brooch (no. 83) (which had been lost for 250 years), the Fuller brooch (no. 153) (which had been denounced as a forgery earlier in the century by Read and Smith, but which was proved to be ancient by scientific research), and the King's School, Canterbury, brooch (no. 10). Meanwhile, soon after the Second World War, the Museum had acquired on permanent loan the bulk of the large group of last Saxon antiquities excavated by (Sir) Charles Peers at Whitby Abbey (nos. 105–32). The most recently acquired object is the Pershore censer cover, first published just over two hundred years ago and acquired in the saleroom in 1960 (no. 56).

AN EVALUATION

This collection is without parallel. About a quarter of the total known corpus of late Saxon ornamental metalwork is in the British Museum, including many of the key pieces. One of the most important objects not included in the Museum is the Alfred Jewel, found in Newton Park, Somerset, in 1693, which has been one of the chief treasures of the University of Oxford since it was found. The Museum lacks a mounted sword of the Abingdon type (The Abingdon sword is in the Ashmolean Museum, other examples are in the Ipswich Museum, the Sheffield City museum, the Trondheim Museum and in Universitetets Oldsaksamling, Oslo—less elaborate examples are known elsewhere). The Ormside bowl in the Yorkshire Museum, with the Rupertus cross at Bischofshofen in Austria (which may be English) and the now lost hanging bowl from the River Witham, are objects for which the British Museum has no parallel material.

These are the chief lacunae of the collection. On the other hand its importance can be gauged from the fact that of the large silver disc brooches, which form one of the most important fields of study within the corpus, the Museum has six out of the seven existing examples (the other example was found in Stockholm towards the end of the last century and is in Statens Historiska Museum, Stockholm). Of the commonest type of late Saxon metal objects—strap-ends—38 out of a provisional total of 103 are in the collection. Further, every technical process known to Anglo-Saxon metalwork is represented in the collection. The Museum also has all the major hoards of late Saxon metalwork found in England, including the only known metalworker's hoard (Sevington, nos. 67–79) and the key hoard, from an art-historical point of view, the Trewhiddle hoard (nos. 90–103).

It is further interesting that, since the beginning of this century, the most important writings on the subject of late Saxon ornamental metalwork have been either produced by, or assisted by, members of the staff of the Museum. Even Shetelig and Brøndsted, who produced two of the most important studies of this material from the point of view

3

of the Viking art-historian, acknowledge their debt to Reginald Smith, indeed Smith wrote a foreword to Brøndsted's book.[1] Smith and two of his successors, T. D. Kendrick and R. L. S. Bruce-Mitford, have produced a considerable literature on the subject. This part of the collection, therefore, has been constantly re-examined and documented for more than half a century, so that there is little for the compiler of this catalogue to do but collate the material and add a few further facts. The chief additions to be made in this catalogue consist of more precise details concerning the history and provenance of each object, a matter which has sometimes in the past been neglected. It has been the intention of the compiler to collect all the known facts about the objects and bring them together so that this unique collection should be more readily available to students.

PAGAN BURIALS

It is quite possible that some objects buried in graves, in the traditional pagan Saxon manner, should have been included in this catalogue if it were to be kept strictly within the earlier date of its title. The dates which appear in the title, however, are merely ciphers: it is reasonably obvious to the specialist that, if indeed there are any eighth-century objects found in pagan graves, they belong to a different series than that of the 700–1100 period.

[1] Brøndsted (1924).

CHAPTER II

THE ART OF THE METALWORKER

In 1924 Brøndsted published *Early English Ornament*—a translation and revision of his doctor's thesis, which had been published four years earlier.[1] The book was basically a study of English zoomorphic and foliate ornament of the period between 650 and 1100. Brøndsted largely ignored both figural and interlaced designs,[2] but dealt with all forms of decorative art—metalwork, sculpture and manuscript illumination—particularly in so far as they were considered to relate to the Scandinavian material. Brøndsted's book has never been superseded and cannot easily be replaced. Sir Thomas Kendrick's survey of Anglo-Saxon art from the end of the Roman period to *c.* 1100[3] was a more general study intended for a wider public and was not intended to replace Brøndsted's work. Together with a number of papers by Reginald Smith, R. L. S. Bruce-Mitford and a handful of others, these books form the basis for all studies of Anglo-Saxon ornamental metalwork of the period covered by this catalogue. The study still rests firmly on Brøndsted's work. Although a surprising number of his judgments are valid to-day, the methods he used to achieve them, and the material he used as evidence, are no longer the best available; it seems best, therefore, to start again at the beginning, examining the problems of this metalwork in the light of the British Museum's collections, with reference mainly to the material and but little to the ideas and theories of previous writers on the subject.

THE METHODS OF DATING OF ANGLO-SAXON ORNAMENTAL METALWORK OF THE PERIOD 700–1100

I have argued elsewhere[4] that there is only one primary method of dating this material —when the name of a known historical person is inscribed in a primary position on an object, as for instance on the Æthelwulf ring (no. 31). There can be little doubt that such an object was manufactured during the life-time, reign, episcopate, etc., of the person mentioned.

All other methods are secondary to this, providing in the majority of cases a latest possible date for the manufacture of the object only. The dating of an object found with the burial of a known historical person (e.g. St. Cuthbert[5]), of an object found in a hoard of coins (e.g. the Beeston Tor objects, nos. 2–7), or of an object which imitates in its design a coin type (e.g. Aelfric's Seal (no. 104)), is based on a *terminus post quem*.

A less reliable method of dating, but one that must sometimes be used, is to compare the ornament of the metalwork with similar motifs in accurately dated manuscripts or

---

[1] Brøndsted (1920).
[2] Brøndsted (1924), 11.
[3] Published in two volumes, Kendrick (1938*a*) and Kendrick (1949).

[4] Wilson (1959*a*), (1960*a*), 17-22 and Wilson and Blunt (1961), 106–8.
[5] Battiscombe (1956).

embroideries. Such dating, however, is even less reliable than dating by archaeological association, owing to the element of opinion which must enter into any comparison of motifs carried out in two very different mediums. This latter method is mainly useful in a period when other more accurate chronological yardsticks are not available. It is only valuable when an object is decorated with a motif to which there is no parallel, art-historical or typological, in the same medium.

The following objects of ornamental metalwork, made in England between 700 and 1100, bear an inscription associating them with a known historical personage: King Æthelwulf's ring (839 (or perhaps earlier)–858) (no. 31), Queen Æthelswith's ring (853 –4–888–9) (no. 1), Bishop Æthelwald's seal (middle of the ninth century) (no. 18) and, possibly, the Alfred jewel (871–99).[1] We must add to this list an object which was made on the Continent under strong Anglo-Saxon influence: the Tassilo chalice (777–88).[2]

The British Museum has no object of this period associated with the burials of historical personages, the only surviving object is a decorated bronze pin from the coffin of Archbishop Wolfstan of York (1002–23).[3] Two other finds dated in this way should however be mentioned as they directly concern the period under review, firstly the relics

[1] Kirk, (1948). The suggestion has occa-sionally been made that the Alfred referred to in the inscription on this object is not King Alfred of Wessex, but nobody has taken the suggestion seriously. There are, however, certain points in its favour: (a) the absence of the royal title in the inscription, (b) the Mercian taint in the dialect of the inscription (*mec* is a form which is extremely rare in late ninth-century Wessex texts) and (c) the com-parative ubiquity of the name 'Ælfred' in the Anglo-Saxon period. These three arguments are rather more telling than those of the protagonists of the King Alfred theory, which may be summed up in the words of Miss Kirk (1948), 'The inscription, the unusual magnificence of the gold-work, and the fact that the gem was found near Athelney in a part of the country frequently visited by Alfred all point in that direction' (p. 6). There is, then, a certain amount of doubt as to the identity of the Alfred who ordered the jewel to be made.

The identification by Pegge (1786) of a ring (now in the Victoria and Albert Museum) inscribed with the name Ahlstan, with Ahl-stan, Bishop of Sherborne 817–67, has not been challenged since it was made in 1773.

Pegge has been followed by *Gentlemen's Magazine*, xciii (1823), 483, *The Archaeologi-cal Journal*, xvi (1859), 194, *Proceedings of the Society of Antiquaries of London*, ser. 2, i, 107 and 277, Brøndsted (1924) 133–4, Jessup (1950), 133, *et alia*. It can no longer be held to be a valid recognition; there were far too many Ahlstans in the Anglo-Saxon period: I have therefore not included it in my list of well-dated objects, although I have accepted it elsewhere (Wilson (1960*a*), 20).

[2] Haseloff (1951) describes this object in detail; it is in the monastery of Krems-münster, Austria.

[3] Now in the Museum of the Society of Antiquaries of London. Tanner (1954) has drawn attention to Taylour's (1688) account of the finding of the gold chain and Crucifix of St. Edward the Confessor. The place of manu-facture of this object is not known but it was probably Byzantine. We have many references in literature to objects being found in the coffins of known Saxon personages (e.g. in Symeon of Durham's description of the open-ing of Acca's tomb at Hexham (in 740) *Symeonis monachi dunelmensis historia regum*, s.a. 740 (*Rolls Series*, lxxv, ii, 33)) but it would be impossible and out of context to list them here.

of St. Cuthbert (*d.* 687)[1] and possibly the crozier and ring of Bishop Ranulf Flambard of Durham (*d.* 1128).[2] The material from these two burials is of importance for the study of the earliest and latest phases of the metalwork treated here.

Late Saxon ornamental metalwork was found in coin hoards at Sevington (nos. 67–79), dated *c.* 850; Hon, Norway,[3] dated *c.* 855; Kirkoswald (no. 28), dated *c.* 855; Beeston Tor (nos. 2–7), dated *c.* 875; Trewhiddle (nos. 90–103), dated *c.* 872–5; Gravesend (no. 20), dated *c.* 872; Talnotrie, Kirkcudbrightshire,[4] dated *c.* 875; Cuerdale (no. 13), dated *c.* 903; Igelösa, Sweden,[5] dated *c.* 1005; Stockholm, Sweden,[6] dated *c.* 1025; Hurva, Skåne, Sweden (*c.* 1048),[7] Sutton, Isle of Ely (no. 83), dated 1066–87, and a hoard of which the associated objects have been lost, London, St. Mary Hill,[8] dated *c.* 1075. Another hoard, dated *c.* 970, from Tetney contains two undecorated silver strap tags (nos. 86 and 87).

These dates refer, of course, to the dates of deposition of the hoards; but there is no reason why a brooch found in a hoard deposited in 875 should not have been a hundred, or more, years old when it was buried.[9] Nevertheless, such dating provides a useful clue to the chronological position of a particular object.

The following objects are dated by the fact that they imitate coins: the two seals (nos. 18 and 104), dated to *c.* 865 and 978/9 respectively, the coin brooch found on the

[1] The relics of St. Cuthbert do not all belong to the same period; they are fully described and published in Battiscombe (1956).

[2] Kendrick (1938*b*). The identification by the excavators of 1874 (Fowler, 1880) of the grave as that of Ranulf Flambard depends entirely on secondary evidence. The site was recorded by Willis (1727) in a plan (pl. opp. p. 221), which was made before the destruction of the site of the burial in 1796, in which he apparently copied the engraved names on the stones in the chapter house (these names are listed in the *Rites of Durham*, Fowler (1903), but it is possible that Willis took his information from Davies (1672)). We cannot, however, be absolutely sure that these were the correct identifications, especially in the light of the fact that the stone covering the so-called coffin of Flambard, when it was excavated in 1874, was that of Bishop Geoffrey Rufus (1113–40), Flambard's successor. Similarly there are certain discrepancies between Willis's plan and *The Rites of Durham*. The tombs of 'Aydanus', 'Eadmund and Eadred', 'Willem's' (Carilef) are not on Willis's plan, although recorded as buried in the chapter house in *The Rites*. Further Raine (1852), 8, records that the tomb of Carilef (1081-96) was opened on the demolition of the Chapter House in (1795–6 ?). We have no evidence of the whereabouts of Carilef's tomb other than this one statement, the two tombs which should have been disturbed during this demolition were those of Hugh de Puiset (1153–95) and Philip of Poitiers (1197–1208). In view of these discrepancies it is difficult to know whether the identification of the crozier with Ranulf Flambard can be accepted. In any case there is no reason to suppose that the crozier buried with a bishop was necessarily the bishop's personal property.

[3] Holmboe (1835), Grieg (1929) 182–98. The chief English object found in this hoard, a gold finger-ring, is best illustrated by Brøgger (1920–1), fig. 8.

[4] Maxwell (1912–13).

[5] Bruce-Mitford (1956*a*), 201.

[6] Månadsbladet (Stockholm, *Kungl. Vitterhets Historie och Antikvitets Akadamien*), 1892, 172–4.

[7] Holmqvist (1951), fig. 38.

[8] Griffith (1786).

[9] For a more complete argument on this point see Wilson (1959*a*).

south side of Winchester Cathedral,[1] which can be dated after *c.* 920 (based on a coin of Heremod minted at Derby), and the coin brooch from Canterbury,[2] which is imitative of coins of Eadgar. Such dating is reasonable as coins had a limited life and were frequently, and at regular intervals, called in and reminted: further the owner of such an object would presumably wish to be up-to-date.

One object can be included in this list of dated metalwork as it is built round a coin of Edward the Elder—this is the brooch from Rome (no. 64) which has a *terminus post quem* of *c.* 915.[3]

It would be impossible to list all the well-dated Anglo-Saxon illuminated manuscripts. Between 698 and 850/900, however, only two important illuminated manuscripts can be dated on internal evidence[4]: the Lindisfarne Gospels (*c.* 698)[5] and the Leningrad Bede (*c.* 746)[6]. After 850/900 there are rather more well-dated manuscripts, but few can be dated to the period prior to the Benedictional of St. Æthelwold[7] (971–84) and the Charter of the New Minster (*post*-966).[8]

Accurate dating on purely palaeographical grounds is often of doubtful validity; but, if palaeography can be combined with other internal evidence, it is sometimes possible to date a manuscript more accurately. Ultimately the palaeographical study of illuminated manuscripts in relation, for example, to a well-dated charter series may produce an adequate, but never an absolute, chronology for English manuscript art. Much detailed work of this nature is being done but the study is as yet in its infancy.

It should be emphasised that art-history is often a more reliable guide than palaeography to the dating of manuscripts. This, however, is only true when a number of manuscripts from the same scriptorium are available for comparison.[9]

In a different medium, one of the two recorded groups of high-quality Anglo-Saxon embroidery (the stole and maniple of St. Cuthbert), can be dated on the basis of an inscription to between 909 and 916.[10]

Finally it should be mentioned that the Anglo-Saxon objects (nos. 105–32) found during the excavations at Whitby Abbey can be dated to the period between the foundation of the monastery in 657 and its destruction by the Danes in 867. A similar argument, which

[1] *The Numismatic Chronicle*, 1908, 83–4.

[2] *VCH Kent*, i, 382 and fig. 27.

[3] I am omitting here a pendant from Cerne Abbas, Dorset, published by Dolley (1957), which I consider to be a Viking import.

[4] This information is based on Lowe (1934–), *passim*.

[5] Kendrick *et alia* (1960).

[6] Lowe (1958).

[7] Wormald (1959).

[8] B.M. MS. Cotton Vesp. A.VIII (text printed by Dugdale (1846), illuminated page illustrated Kendrick (1949), pl. II). This document is a copy of the charter and the laws given by Edgar to the New Minster in 966 and is often said to have been written in that year. This may be so, for there is only one Anglo-Saxon charter in the manuscript (a charter of Henry I has been added later) and it seems unlikely that other charters would not have been inscribed in the manuscript if it was written at a later date. On the other hand this is a unique document and may well have been written for some special purpose at a later date. The answer will never be known, but at least we have a *terminus post quem* for the date of the manuscript.

[9] Cf., for example, the dating of the Book of Durrow in Kendrick *et al.* (1960), 255–7.

[10] Battiscombe (1956), 376.

associates the Gandersheim casket with the Abbey of Ely (destroyed by the Danes in 866), which has been used, *inter alia*, by Kendrick,[1] cannot be upheld in the light of recent evidence[2]; in any case the reading of the inscription is certainly not valid.

It can be seen that there are a large number of objects dated, by their presence in hoards or by the inscriptions upon them, to the ninth century. There is no such convincing series for the eighth or tenth centuries, when dating must depend on comparison with other arts; a few objects, however, are known from eleventh-century hoards. The only other direct help in dating the series is provided by the Anglo-Saxon antiquities which occur in Viking graves in Scandinavia,[3] which can sometimes provide a very rough *terminus ante quem*.[4] On this basis we must build up an art-historical sequence for late Saxon metalwork.

It might seem that the art-historian could be aided by parallels with sculpture and dated Hiberno-Saxon and Irish metalwork. Although there are sufficient parallels of ornament between Anglo-Saxon sculpture and metalwork, the sculpture cannot be dated any more closely than the metalwork. For instance, the identification of 'Acca's' cross at Hexham Abbey with the bishop of that name who died in 740 is by no means certain[5] and, apart from a few fragments of inscribed, but otherwise featureless, stone from Whitby Abbey,[6] there is no firm dating evidence available for Anglo-Saxon sculpture.[7] A more difficult problem is raised in any attempt to date Hiberno-Saxon and Irish metalwork; there is, for example, an element of doubt at many stages of our period as to the regional priority of a motif common to Anglo-Saxon and Hiberno-Saxon or Irish contexts. A number of Irish ecclesiastical objects (mainly of eleventh-century date) bear inscriptions, which give them a *terminus post quem*[8]; but the composite character of many of the objects, and the tenuous contact between Irish and English art at this late period, make for difficulties of interpretation which are almost insoluble.

On the basis of these arguments I shall attempt to build up a chronological view of the catalogued material.

THE CHRONOLOGICAL SEQUENCE OF ANGLO-SAXON ORNAMENTAL METALWORK

(i) *The eighth century.*

Towards the end of the seventh century gold as the chief medium of coinage in Europe was gradually replaced by other materials. In England gold first gave place to electrum which, in turn, was replaced in the early years of the eighth century by a silver and

[1] (1938a), 169.

[2] Fink (1957).

[3] See e.g. the now rather out-of-date and inaccurate lists published in Shetelig (1940), v.

[4] But on the problems of dating Viking graves see Almgren (1955) and Wilson (1959a).

[5] Cf. Kendrick (1938a), 134 n.

[6] Peers and Radford (1943), 40 ff.

[7] For a discussion of one particular piece of sculpture (the Bewcastle Cross), which has often been dated on the basis of its inscription, see Page (1960). The author dismisses completely the value of this inscription, and does so on philological, historical and common-sense grounds: in a similar manner, in another place Page (1959) examines the whole problem of dating on linguistic grounds in a most convincing manner.

[8] Raftery (1941), *passim*.

bronze coinage.[1] Ornaments of gold were apparently much less commonly produced in Europe after the disappearance of the gold coinage, which was presumably the chief source of the jeweller's raw material. Towards the end of the pagan Saxon period silver objects became more common in the cemetery material, while gold objects (other than finger-rings) after *c.* 700 are rare. This rarity must be ascribed in part to the fact that many fewer objects of the post-700 period survive as a result of the cessation of the pagan practice of accompanied burial, but it is striking that of the objects in the British Museum collections recorded in this catalogue (which forms a reasonable statistical sample) only twelve are of gold—and these are mainly small objects, such as finger-rings.

For about a century, and perhaps more, after the beginning of the period covered by this catalogue, the medium to which Anglo-Saxon metalworkers aspired was gold—wherever possible they gilded their metal. Such objects as the Witham pins (no. 19) (of gilt-silver) and the Whitby mounts (nos. 105 and 106) (of gilt-bronze) witness to this fact.

There is only one piece of metalwork of eighth century date which can be fixed chronologically—the Tassilo chalice.[2] This object is executed in a gilt-bronze, chip-carved technique, by a craftsman whom Haseloff has satisfactorily shown to have been under considerable Anglo-Saxon influence.[3] There can be no doubt that it was manufactured between the years 777 and 788.[4] Unfortunately, as Haseloff has shown, the very distinctive school of metalworker's art to which this object belongs is a Carolingian[5] facet of Anglo-Saxon art—a facet which has no exact parallels in the art of the Anglo-Saxon homeland. Parallels, then, can only be drawn in the most general fashion between the two different schools, but at least a firm date is provided for the technical aspects of both schools. The following objects in the British Museum collections are of gilded silver or bronze: the Witham pins (no. 19), a pair of so-called 'book-mounts' from Whitby (nos. 105–6), the Rome strap distributor (no. 63), the Ixworth disc (no. 25), the runic-inscribed mount from the Thames (no. 45), two fragments from Sevington (nos. 69 and 70), the Fetter Lane sword pommel (no. 41), the Reculver tweezers (no. 62) and the Gravesend cross (no. 20) (only the setting of the glass is gilt). Two gilt pieces of obviously later date (nos. 143 and 147) are omitted from this list. One other piece from Whitby (no. 107) is of the same design as nos. 105 and 106 and can be associated with it (it may have been gilt originally). A series of gilt objects of Anglo-Saxon origin found in Scandinavia are also of interest here as they occurred mainly in Viking contexts and were probably taken there during the earlier period of the Viking raids. These include objects from Støle,[6] Bjorke[7] (pl. I, *c*), Lunde[8] and Standal.[9] In various English Museums there are

[1] Grierson (1958), pl. VII. The use of gold coinage in England after 700 will be discussed by Messrs. Blunt and Dolley in a forthcoming paper.

[2] Haseloff (1951).

[3] *Ibid.*, 64–75.

[4] *Ibid.*, 1.

[5] See also, Werner (1959) and Wilson (1960e). The British Museum possesses three objects of this school, a bronze mount (Haseloff (1951), pl. 11, 5) a finger-ring (Wilson (1958b)) and a brooch (Mahr (1932), pl. 35, 1).

[6] (1) Shetelig (1940), v, 48 and fig. 47.

[7] *Ibid.*, 183 and fig. 150.

[8] *Ibid.*, 182 and fig. 148.

[9] *Ibid.*, 184 and fig. 154.

further parallels in the same technique, e.g. two roundels from Cambridge,[1] another fragment from Hauxton Mill, Cambs.,[2] and a similar, unpublished example from Ixworth, Suffolk in the Ashmolean Museum, while from Mildenhall comes a lead weight with a gilt-bronze top.[3] All these objects fit into the group formed of such objects as the Witham pins and the Ixworth brooch.

It is interesting that at about the same time the Hiberno-Saxon craftsmen of Scotland, northern Northumbria and Ireland were also working in the same materials with great competence. Such finds as that from Navan[4] illustrate the form which this technical advance took in Ireland, while the Scottish side of the story is illustrated by the St. Ninian's Island treasure.[5] There seems little doubt that the Hiberno-Saxon craftsmen based their technique on Anglo-Saxon prototypes, from which they evolved and developed their own style during the late seventh and eighth century. The ultimate origin of the articulated animals of the Hiberno-Saxon school is the ribbon style (Style II) ornament of seventh-century England, combined, as Mr. Bakka will re-emphasise in a forthcoming paper, with influences drawn from the inhabited vine scroll of the Mediterranean world.

The ornament on the heads of the Witham pins (no. 19) provides a convenient stylistic starting point for the study of the ornament of eighth-century metalwork. The pin-heads display many ornamental details which occur time and again in the Anglo-Saxon repertoire: the tendency to divide an area for decoration up into small fields, the speckling of the bodies of the animals which decorate the surfaces, the body caught up in interlaced ribbons and limbs, the form of the heads of the animals (with squared snout, bump over the eye, the occasional collared neck and the tongue developing into an interlaced ribbon), the blue glass eyes of the animals, the carefully executed interlace pattern (which fills one field) and the decoration of the borders by carefully executed, bored dots; all these are features which form the basis for the development of the Anglo-Saxon metal work from the seventh to the tenth centuries.

The quality of the craftsmanship of the Witham pins is high and, as is often the case in such circumstances, certain unique features are clearly to be seen, particularly on the (perhaps later) right-hand pin. Particularly noticeable are the animals—one of them rather shaggy—seen from above. The animal seen from above is a not uncommon feature of Anglo-Saxon art—it occurs on the finger-ring (no. 146) and on a ring from York in the Yorkshire Museum, and, although the head is seen in profile, it also occurs on the Fetter Lane sword hilt (no. 41). In the manuscripts it can be seen especially in the canon tables of the Leningrad Gospels,[6] a parallel which is interesting in the light of further similarities discussed below. The motif can also be seen on the Gandersheim casket (pl. I, *a*), which, as is shown below, is another very significant parallel. In sculpture an interesting parallel is provided by the Thornhill, Dumfries, cross fragment,[7]

[1] One published by Fox (1923), 297–8 and pl. XXXIV, 6 and *VCH. Cambridgeshire*, i, 324 and pl. XII, c and the other *ibid.*, 234 and pl. XI, c.

[2] *Ibid.*, 324 and pl. XII, a.

[3] *VCH Suffolk*, i, 345 and fig. 12.

[4] Mahr (1932), pl. 33.

[5] Cf. O'Dell, *et al.* (1959) and O'Dell (1960).

[6] Zimmermann (1918), pl. 323.

[7] Kendrick (1938*a*), pl. 93, 4.

but the difficulties of dating such sculpture invest this parallel with little significance. A strange feature is the shaggy naturalism, which is particularly noticeable on the animal (a dog), on the right but, apart from the very weak parallel one might draw between this animal and the equally shaggy animals on the (presumably contemporary) casket from Werden,[1] it is difficult to trace the origins of the motif, although it might be possible to see here the origin of the nicks which are so definite and prominent a feature of animals in ninth-century metalwork (cf. nos. 2 and 153).

The other two pin-heads demonstrate a feature which rarely occurs elsewhere in the metalwork of the South of England, this is the sharply everted, pointed wing. This feature can be seen on the fragment of a silver boss from Re, Nedre Stjørdalen, Nord-Trøndelag[2]—indeed the mount might come from the same workshop as the Witham pins. But for other parallels one must turn to the manuscripts. The motif can be seen in the Leningrad Gospels[3] which, with the Gandersheim casket, were the parallels drawn by Reginald Smith.[4] He also drew attention to the parallel with the Hedda stone in Peterborough Cathedral[5]—but this is perhaps a questionable parallel, for the reconstruction of the ornament used by Smith is not perhaps so certain as his illustration suggests. A very good comparative piece of sculpture is the displayed eagle built into the wall of the porch of the church at Brixworth, Northamptonshire (pl. II, b); this bird has similar wings to those on the Witham pins. In a broader sense one might compare, the wing of the animal portrayed next to the initial on fol. 3r of MS. Li.i.io (The Book of Cerne) in the Cambridge University Library (pl. III, b) or on fol. 22r of the same manuscript. These Southern English, eighth-century parallels (for such the Leningrad Gospels, the Book of Cerne, the Brixworth carving and the Gandersheim casket seem to be) are the sort of parallels to be expected for the ornament of the Witham pins. Elements of the art of the Witham pins, however, seem to occur in the Hiberno-Saxon corpus and attention should be drawn particularly to the bronze mount from Stromness which has similarly shaped wings on its much more formalised animal ornament.[6] The same feature is apparent, although it is perhaps better compared with the sharply everted legs of the animals on the Witham pins, in the series of penannular silver brooches of Hiberno-Saxon manufacture and rather later date which I have listed elsewhere.[7] The wings are more closely paralleled in a similar context on the Jedburgh shrine,[8] which Brøndsted[9] has already compared to the Gandersheim casket. In these two objects can be seen one of the links between Hiberno-Saxon and Anglo-Saxon art of the eighth century.

These pins, with the Gandersheim casket and the Hedda stone, were, as we have seen, used by Smith[10] to define an Anglian School of ornament, which is perhaps better described by Kendrick's term—'Mercian'.[11] Kendrick[12] pointed out the tendency of the

[1] Baum (1937), pl. XXXIII.
[2] Müller (1880), fig. 67; Rygh (1885), fig. 617; Åberg (1921), fig. 15; Smith (1925a), fig. 21.
[3] Zimmermann (1918), pl. 321.
[4] (1925a).
[5] Ibid., fig. 4.
[6] Romilly Allen (1903), fig. 22.
[7] Wilson (1958a).
[8] Radford (1955), pl. vi.
[9] (1924), 140.
[10] (1925a).
[11] (1938a), 164 ff.
[12] Ibid., 171.

Mercian artist to use and develop the Northumbrian style of ornament, instancing particularly the South Kyme, Lincolnshire carvings, where Hiberno-Saxon trumpet-spirals occur.[1] It has already been noticed that a developed trumpet-spiral occurs on the Gandersheim casket, which is so closely related to the Witham pins. Such distinct indications of Hiberno-Saxon elements are rare in Anglo-Saxon contexts—so rare in fact that it is difficult to define their southern distribution as a peculiarly Mercian trait. Indeed, if the spiral ornament of the Vespasian psalter (British Museum MS., Vespasian A.1) is taken into consideration,[2] one might more reasonably see this particular trait as one which occurs in Southern England as a whole. It would perhaps be wise to think of the cultural (if not political) unity of England at this period and not to confine a facet of art to narrow political boundaries. Elements of Hiberno-Saxon art can certainly be seen recurring in Anglo-Saxon contexts as late as the end of the eighth century (when the Vespasian psalter was presumably illuminated).

On the right-hand pin-head of the group from the Witham can be seen the beginning of a feature which occurs with some frequency in contemporary metalwork; this is the subordination of the body of the animal to the interlace pattern in a field (the body of the animal in the lower field of this pin-head has lost all importance—the head and the interlace take up the major portion of the decorative surface). An interesting occurrence of this motif is in the English sceatta series of the first half of the eighth century, where one side of a coin can bear a similar animal head with interlace pattern (pl. IV, c)[3]: this helps to confirm the eighth-century date of these objects, for the motif occurs at no other stage in the development of Anglo-Saxon art.[4] This tendency reaches the heights of absurdity on the metal binding-strips of the Gandersheim casket, where the only zoo-morphic element is an animal head at one end of the back of the ridge-pole—all the rest of the ornament is interlace of similar quality and style to that of the Reculver tweezers (no. 62). In its most interesting form it is seen on the fragment from Re, Stjørdalen, Nord Trøndelag, Norway[5]; here all the elements of the style of the Witham pins are repeated —particularly the form of the animals and the easy competence of the interlace—so that it might be possible to say that it came from the same workshop. The same head also occurs on the gilt-bronze plaque (perhaps from a box or a bookbinding) from Bjørke churchyard, Hjørundfjord, Møre, Norway (pl. I, c),[6] the ornament of which exhibits many of the features of the Witham pins—the scrolled terminals to the interlace, the chip carving, the precise placing of the dots along the median line of the borders of the field, etc.—and yet is of much coarser quality, though presumably from the same milieu as the Witham pins. It is perhaps closer to the Ixworth brooch (no. 25) to which we shall shortly return. The head on the Bjørke plaque, which is of the same form as that on the Gandersheim casket, is again paralleled on another object from Norway—a fragment in

[1] Clapham (1923), fig. 1.

[2] Zimmermann (1918), pl. 286, a. Presum-ably illuminated at Canterbury.

[3] Keary (1887), pl. III, 20–24.

[4] An interesting stage in the development is illustrated by one coin (*ibid.*, pl. III, 19).

Here the hind legs of the animal can be seen, but are all that survive—other than ribbon—of the body of the animal.

[5] Smith (1925a), fig. 21.

[6] Bøe (1932).

the form of a quadrant of bronze from Lunde, Vangen, Voss, Hordaland (pl. II, *d*), which was found in a richly furnished grave.[1]

The Bjørke plaque is, as has been suggested, closely related to the Ixworth brooch which, after the Witham pins, is the chief representative of this group of objects in the British Museum. The treatment of the borders of the fields of the Ixworth Brooch and the form of the rivet in the centre, together with certain details of the interlace, are to be compared closely with those of the Bjørke plaque. The formal discipline of the Witham pins is missing, the animals are more freely drawn—more fantastic. The animal heads, unlike those on the Bjørke plaque or the Witham pins, are portrayed in a more abstract idiom. The division between cheek and eye and the naturalistic eye and ears of the Bjørke plaque and the crisply carved head of the Witham pins are replaced by heads drawn with great economy: with round staring eyes which dominate the field or with smaller, round eyes in a long curved eye socket, the ear is treated as a tendril and the lower jaw is scrolled. The bodies of the animals are more completely speckled than those on the Witham pins. There can be little doubt that in this East Anglian find we have yet another example of Anglian/Mercian art.

The Anglian/Mercian origin of objects of this sort is demonstrated geographically by a number of objects found in East Anglia which, while not so fine as the Ixworth, Lunde and Bjørke plaques, are nevertheless poor relations of it. Two bronze-gilt pinheads from Cambridge[2] and a fragment of a similar pinhead from Hauxton Mill, Cambridgeshire[3] can be taken together with the Kegworth, Leicestershire pin (pl. III, *a*), the Roos pinhead,[4] the fragment of a pinhead from Ixworth, Suffolk[5] as an expression, by poorer craftsmen, of the same school of metalwork—all are found in the Anglian/Mercian area. Certain less easily movable objects decorated in a similar style, such as the Brixworth carving and other pieces of monumental sculpture, also point to the same Anglian/Mercian distribution. But it is necessary to be extremely cautious in labelling the school with such a title, for the small bronze object from Whitby Abbey (no. 110), the cross from Croft in the North Riding of Yorkshire[6] (which has many of the elements of the Witham pins) and the cross shaft from St. Andrew Auckland, Co. Durham (which also has some of the same traits, e.g., the animals' heads of this school[7]) are in what was politically at this period Northumbria; so again it is impossible to confine these objects within narrow political boundaries.

Closely related to this group of objects are the chip-carved mounts from Whitby (nos. 105–7) distinguished by Peers and Radford as book-mounts.[8] The interlacing ribbons that form the borders and divisions of the fields of the two objects have animal-head terminals. The heads are treated in a manner similar to that on the Ixworth brooch the eyes are panelled with the same comma-like tail, but there are elements here which have not been noticed so far. The snouts, for example, are squared off in a manner more

[1] *Foreningen til norske fortidsmindesmerkers bevaring: Aarsberetning*, 1869, 45.

[2] *VCH Cambridgeshire*, i, pl. XI, c and XII, c.

[3] *Ibid.*, pl. XII, a.

[4] Kitson-Clark (1941*a*).

[5] Ashmolean Museum, Oxford.

[6] Stone (1955), pl. 10, b.

[7] *Ibid.*, pl. 6.

[8] (1943), 50–2, but see below pp. 58–59.

reminiscent of the Hiberno-Saxon School of metalwork represented in the St. Ninian's Island treasure.[1] It is interesting in this context to compare these two mounts, probably from the same mould, with a coarser example of similar design from the same site. This object (no. 107) has a much less crisp and skilful interlace and the animals' heads at the terminals of the ribbons have disappeared completely. Unlike the other two mounts it may originally have been gilded. A closely related object of unknown provenance is in the Rheinisches Landesmuseum, Bonn (pl. I, b). This object, which is exactly paralleled by a rather corroded item in the National Museum, Copenhagen, underlines the cruciform design and possible Christian significance of the Whitby mounts.

In parenthesis it is worth while stressing that the beaded wire collar of gold (no. 108), was found adhering to the back of this object. As the bronze mount was probably lost at the sack of Whitby in 867, it would seem probable that this object is one of the few pieces of beaded filigree wire found in an Anglo-Saxon context which can be dated to the late eighth or first half of the ninth century.

At this point we must consider the other gilt objects from the British Museum's collections which can be dated to the eighth century. Firstly, the silver gilt mount inscribed with a runic inscription from the River Thames (no. 45). This object, although famous runologically, has rarely been considered art-historically. It is remarkable in that it is one of the extremely rare three-dimensional animal heads found in Anglo-Saxon contexts. Its closest parallel was pointed out by Romilly Allen in 1904[2]: it is very similar in form and decoration to the label-stops in Deerhurst Church, Gloucestershire. The teeth, eyebrows and ears are all strikingly similar and from this parallel there can be little doubt as to its Saxon character, but the parallel does not help to date the object. Allen also pointed to the very convincing parallel with animals on certain Hiberno-Saxon brooches of the late ninth century.[3] This parallel is interesting in view of the close connection with another Hiberno-Saxon find which must now be discussed. With its blue glass eyes and plastic appearance, it has a superficial resemblance to the animal head on the spoon from the St. Ninian's Isle treasure,[4] a resemblance which is made more striking by the protruding tongue on both objects. Another quite striking resemblance is to be seen in the same hoard, for the uninscribed chape (pl. IV, a) has the same blue glass eyes, spiral hair, protruding tongue and open mouth with vicious teeth. The mouldings on the back of the Thames mount and on the snout of the animal heads of the chape are closely comparable—the same feature can be seen on the snouts of the animal heads on the inscribed St. Ninian's chape (pl. IV, b), where there is the same median incision on the ridge of the moulding. The inscription on these two objects might be generally compared in technique. Palaeographical[5] and art-historical tendencies to consider the two chapes as Northumbrian might enable us to compare them with the Thames mount, which is, of course, by reason of its inscription, Anglo-Saxon. Despite the new find from St. Ninian's Isle, which tends to colour the thoughts of present-day writers on these problems, we still do not know enough about the artistic content of Hiberno-Saxon metalwork at this

[1] O'Dell (1960), pls. 11 and 20.
[2] Romilly Allen (1904b), fig. 4.
[3] Ibid., 274 and fig. 5.
[4] O'Dell (1960), pl. 34 and 35.
[5] O'Dell et al. (1959), 250–55.

period in relationship to the pure Anglo-Saxon tradition. We note the occurrence of the blue glass eyes of the animals at St. Ninian's and on the Thames mount; the same feature occurs in Anglo-Saxon contexts on the Witham pins, on the Strickland brooch (no. 152) and (although the colour of the glass is not the same) on Æthelwald's seal (no. 18), but it is impossible to say where they originated; it seems probable that the animal style of the Celtic area derived from Anglo-Saxon sources and that, once the influence had made itself felt, there was a cross-fertilisation between the two areas. The St. Ninian's comparison helps to fit the Thames mount into an eighth-century context, a dating which could not perhaps have been made with any degree of certainty before the discovery of the St. Ninian's Isle hoard, as most of the parallels cited by Romilly Allen,[1] were of ninth-century date or even later.

The parallel between the knurled rivet heads on the Thames mount and the knurled rivet heads on the Ixworth brooch (no. 25) should be mentioned: similar rivet heads can also be seen on an insular ornament from Norway—the Hillesøy disc.[2] Certain general similarities with the dog-head finials of the Lindisfarne Gospels are of interest, the teeth are closely paralleled on fol. 90r.[3] and the attenuated ears with lobed ends on fol. 27r, 29r, fol. 95r, etc.[4]

Another gilt object to be considered is the Rome strap-distributor (no. 63), which has been discussed by only two authorities, Reginald Smith[5] and Gunther Haseloff.[6] In both cases their discussion of the object has been cursory; Reginald Smith dismissing it in a single sentence and Haseloff in a paragraph. This is not surprising as there are no distinct art-historical parallels to this piece. The boss-headed rivets, surrounded by beaded wire collars, are a common feature in Anglo-Saxon art from the seventh century onwards,[7] but this is also a well-known feature of Frankish jewellery and of Italian seventh-century jewellery, which provides some fairly close parallels to the setting of groups of collared rivets of this sort together.[8] The human masks on the arms of the object tend to confirm its insular identity. The object is tentatively retained here as falling within the purview of this catalogue, but, as it is unparalleled in technique and ornament, the identification is made with some hesitation.

The two gilt bronze objects from the Sevington hoard need not detain us long. The roundel cast in low relief with a series of backed, double-contoured C-shaped motifs (no. 70) is without exact parallel and, although backed C-shaped pieces of filigree do occur in insular filigree (e.g. on the King's School, Canterbury, brooch (no. 10)), they are of no immediate relevance to the object from Sevington. The nearest parallel of motif is provided by the brooch from London (no. 47), which may well belong to this period. Broadly speaking the Sevington object may possibly be included in the same

[1] (1904b).
[2] Sjøvold (1951).
[3] Kendrick, et al. (1960), fig. 44, e.
[4] Ibid., fig. 44, i–k.
[5] BMASG, 156.
[6] Haseloff (1950), 173–4.
[7] Cf. The Sutton Hoo buckle, [Bruce-

Mitford] (1956b), pl. 1; strap-tags from Seamer, Yorkshire, Wright (1865), pl. 18 (where the collars surround dome-shaped garnets); The Strickland brooch (no. 152), etc.
[8] Åberg (1923), figs. 187, 190, 191–3, etc.

group as the Ixworth brooch series, but the resemblance is slight. The scrap of torn sheet bronze from the Sevington hoard (no. 69) defies analysis.

The Gravesend cross (no. 20) is an interesting piece. Only the setting of the glass is gilt, but the whole object might be considered here. Its date of deposition is known, 872, but it may well have been made in the eighth century, or at least in an eighth-century tradition. The roughly scratched design on the arms of the cross can perhaps be compared with the similar scratched designs on the Sevington spoons (nos. 67 and 68), but the coarse quality of this design does not enable us to make distinct judgments; suffice it to say here that the presence of ornament of this sort on the arms of the cross, although roughly paralleled at Sevington, may well have been added later. The setting itself is best paralleled on the eighth-century Ormside bowl[1] and is merely a larger version of the similar settings on the Witham pins (no. 19). These parallels may be significant in that similar settings do not seem to occur in the later Anglo-Saxon metalwork, but seem to be confined to eighth-century objects. The glass contained in the setting is one of the few examples of *Reticella* glass found in a Christian Anglo-Saxon context[2] and one of the very few pieces of this type of glass found in a dated context.

Turning from the gilt objects for a moment it might be well to consider Kirkoswald trefoil here (no. 28). Although it was found in a hoard deposited in the ninth century it is, in my opinion, of eighth-century date. The object is unfortunately damaged, but the whole pattern can be reconstructed. At the end of one of the arms, in a setting on a boss, is a circular flat garnet—the last occurrence in Anglo-Saxon England of this semi-precious stone, which was so popular from the fifth to the seventh centuries. The Anglo-Saxon metalworker had excelled in the use of this stone, technically and aesthetically he led the rest of Europe in carving and setting garnets, but the source of garnets, perhaps for economic-political reasons, seems to have dried up towards the end of the seventh century and its use in Western Europe in the eighth century and later is rare.[3] The central boss and that which survives at the terminal of one arm are further embellished with an encrustation of annulets crowned by granules. The closest parallel to this is to be seen on a brooch (?) from Hauge, Sunelven, Møre, Norway[4] (pl. III, *e*), which was found in a Viking grave with a pair of oval brooches of Rygh type 652 and a number of other objects. The detail of the bosses on this object is very close to the detail of the Kirkoswald trefoil, indeed the central boss of the Hague object is an almost exact replica of that on the Kirkoswald mount. The borders are rather different—the Kirkoswald mount has a double border of twisted plain wire[5] crowned by a beaded band, whilst

[1] Kendrick (1938*a*), pl. 60.

[2] For a discussion of *Reticella* glass, see Arwidsson (1942), 97–9.

[3] It does, however, occur on a few eighth-century European objects, e.g. the Lindau Gospel cover, Nesbitt and Thompson (1883), pl. xlvii.

[4] *Foreningen til Norske fortidsmindesmerkers bevaring; Aarsberetning*, (1887) 105–6; Peter-sen (1928), fig. 144; Haseloff (1950), pl. xx, c; Holmqvist (1959), fig. 11. The object is in private possession and all who have written on the subject in recent years have based their remarks on a very good electrotype in the Bergen Museum (*inv. no.* 4445).

[5] Not beaded wire as stated by Haseloff (1950), 173.

the Hauge object has a border made up of a single strand of twisted and beaded wire, enclosing a thin strand of beaded wire. But despite these and other differences the parallel is very striking. Another close parallel to the technique of the bosses of the Kirkoswald brooch is provided by a small fragment from the great Danish hoard found at Terslev in 1911. This object (pl. III, *c*) has the same crowned annulet as on the Kirkoswald mount, but the annulets themselves are made up of twisted wire. Further, while the border of the Terslev fragment is of the same form and construction as the Kirkoswald border, the twisted strands are beaded. The presence of twisted beaded filigree on these two objects is of some importance for the technique does not occur on Anglo-Saxon objects of the period dealt with in this catalogue: there is, however, no reason why the technique should not have been used in the eighth century in England, for it occurs occasionally in pagan Anglo-Saxon metalwork; e.g. on the seventh century Taplow gold buckle.[1] Most of the filigree techniques of the Christian period seem to have been derived from pagan sources (on the Taplow buckle for example—together with twisted beaded wire— twisted plain wire, elaborate bossed settings for garnets and beaded wire annulets crowned with granules are used), but one technique of the Kirkoswald mount does not occur in the pagan corpus—the serrated band which forms the tendril-like pattern in the arms of the object. The serrated band soldered by one edge to a base plate is a common enough technique on the Continent from the beginning of the ninth century, but its earliest appearance in the British Isles is on the lost hanging bowl from the river Witham, only known from excellent drawings (pl. II, *c*). This object is almost certainly of eighth-century date,[2] but, even if it is later, it bears the same heavy serrated band filigree as the Kirkoswald brooch. Serrated band filigree is known on the Continent in the late eighth century—chiefly in Scandinavia[3]—but rarely does it have the weight and coarseness of the English examples. The bold quality of the Kirkoswald serrated band filigree appears to be an insular feature derived perhaps from the rather finer bands which can be seen in an Hiberno-Saxon context at an earlier period on the Tara brooch.[4] The ultimate origin of the technique, which does not seem to appear before the end of the seventh century, is probably to be found, as Stenberger has suggested,[5] in the walls of the cells of the cloisonné work of the pagan period. Not only is the serrated tape of the right shape, but the form of the decoration on many of the Scandinavian objects decorated in this manner is obviously derived from the cells of the cloisonné jewellery[6] and one is reminded of a number of Anglo-Saxon pendants, with cells but no garnets, which occur in late pagan contexts.[7] The cells of migration period cloisonné jewellery are not normally serrated, but the presence of filigree beaded wire as the walls of cells in enamel work can occasionally be seen in the Roman period—for instance at the terminals of the bracelet from Rhayader, Radnorshire[8]—showing that the idea cannot have been very far from

[1] Kendrick (1938*a*), pl. xxxiv, 5.

[2] Kendrick (1941*a*) thought of it as a ninth-century object, but current opinion would rather place it in the eight century, cf. O'Dell *et alia* (1959), 258 and Wilson (1960*c*), 24.

[3] E.g. Arbman (1937), pls. 57–9.

[4] de Paor (1958), pl. 24.

[5] (1958), 116.

[6] E.g. Stenberger (1958), fig. 10.

[7] E.g. Kendrick (1933*b*), pl. 1, 7.

[8] *British Museum, Guide to the Antiquities of Roman Britain*, 2nd edition, London 1958, pl. iii.

the mind of the craftsman. This is not the place to enter into a discussion of this technique and its origins, for the ground has already been adequately covered by Arbman,[1] Stenberger[2] and others: suffice it to say that, so long as only the Kirkoswald trefoil, the Tara brooch, the Witham hanging bowl and a handful of other objects executed in this technique, survive in an insular context, it is impossible to come to any firm conclusion as to its origins. It is, however, only technically that one can show that such an object as the Kirkoswald mount is of insular origin, owing to the universality of the motifs which embellish it.[3]

The vine-scroll of this piece, it has been argued by Haseloff[4] and Holmqvist,[5] 'has nothing to do with the Carolingian type, but must be specifically North English'. This may well be true but, unfortunately, the whole argument is based on the identification of an openwork piece of lead from Whitby Abbey as Anglo-Saxon—an identification which is probably wrong. Zarnecki[6] has suggested that a date c. 1200 would be correct for this piece. A thirteenth-century date would be so convincing both on art-historical and technical grounds, that I have omitted the object from this catalogue, together with another lead fragment from the same site which Haseloff also identified as Anglo-Saxon.[7] Haseloff has quite correctly argued that the clusters of granules, imitative of grapes, on the Kirkoswald brooch are an Anglo-Saxon feature; but the arguments of Friis-Johansen[8] and Arbman[9] in comparing the Kirkoswald trefoil with the filigree patterns of the cover of the psalter of Charles the Bald[10] cannot be ignored. There is an even closer parallel with the filigree ornament of the Cross of Victory at Oviedo.[11] Both the cross and the psalter cover, however, are later in date than the Kirkoswald object (even if a ninth-century date is given to it). If my eighth-century date for this object be accepted there is good evidence, despite the apparently false basis of Haseloff's argument, that he is right in identifying the motif as Anglo-Saxon: the argument, however, remains thin, for the Witham hanging bowl is the only technical and art historical parallel in the metalwork.[12]

The Fetter Lane sword pommel (no. 41) is one of the most splendid, and certainly

[1] (1937), 180–214.

[2] (1958).

[3] Haseloff, (1950), 173, makes much of the *Äquatorschnitt* which occurs on the Kirkoswald brooch. Although there is a median incision, produced by the serration of the wire, on a number of the beads of this brooch it is by no means a consistent feature and, if it is not an accidental feature, it is at least not *Äquatorschnitt sensu strictu*, for *Äquatorschnitt* is by definition a 'slight cut around each bead of the pearled filigree wire at its maximum diameter' (Haseloff, *loc. cit.*). It is I think therefore stretching the evidence too far to compare it with the true *Äquatorschnitt* first recognised by Schmid (1893, 16) or even with the Anglo-Saxon examples quoted by Haseloff (*loc. cit.*).

[4] (1950), 171–3.

[5] (1959), 43.

[6] (1957), 3–4, 42–3.

[7] Haseloff (1950), pl. xix, b.

[8] (1912), 244.

[9] (1937), 156.

[10] Arbman (1937), fig. 27.

[11] Schlunck (1950), fig. c (wrongly captioned).

[12] The Mosnæs brooch which Haseloff offers as a parallel (1950, pl. xx, a) cannot be identified as English, for it is not paralleled technically in the Anglo-Saxon corpus. The technique of the gold filigree plates and the three-dimensional centre are unknown in English contexts. The clinching point in the argument against its English origin is pro-

one of the most competently executed, pieces of late Anglo-Saxon metalwork to survive. Its quality sets it apart from any of its fellows and its ornament is in many respects difficult to parallel. The whirling snakes pattern is derived presumably from the spiral ornament so common in Celtic and Anglo-Saxon art. A four-element spiral, given zoomorphic characteristics by the addition of an eye, can be seen on the right-hand side of the main arch on fol. 8a of the Stockholm Codex Aureus.[1] On fol. 11a of the same manuscript the spiral is given zoomorphic character and two animal heads are opposed to each other in the centre of two of the many spiral patterns enclosed by the top left limb of the X in the *Christi* monogram. In the Rome Gospels (Vatican Barb. lat. 570) four whirling animal heads appear in two of the terminals of the X of the *Christi* monogram on fol. 18a, and in the centre of the large initial N on fol. 125a.[2] A similar zoomorphic two-element spiral occurs at the springing of the two main arches in the canon tables of the Leningrad Gospels (lat. F.v.I.N.8), fol. 12a and 12b,[3] and another at the bottom left-hand corner of fol. 30b of the Vespasian psalter (B.M. Cotton Vespasian A.1).[4] It is interesting that all these occurrences should be in late eighth-, or early ninth-, century English manuscripts. Whirling animal heads occur below the arms of the cross on the front of the sculptured slab from Aberlemno, Forfarshire,[5] but while it might be possible to draw a parallel with the Scottish boss style, typified by the Nigg slab,[6] this connection is very tenuous. The animal heads tell us little: basically their panelled features are rather close to those on the Witham pins (no. 19) or on other objects executed in the chip-carved style—the curved cheek-line is particularly well paralleled on the Whitby mount (no. 105). The whirling snakes motif can only be satisfactorily paralleled in metalwork in the early eighth-century series of English sceattas[7], and particularly on a hitherto unpublished coin in the British Museum (pl. IV, *c*). These coins, which date from the first half of the eighth century, also provide parallels for other features on the pommel. The barbed tail of the displayed animal on the back of the pommel is probably related to the fin-like barbs of

vided by the animal masks between the arms on the back of the brooch (pl. III, *d*) which are obviously Viking (compare, for example with the masks on the silver pendant from Birka, grave 800 Arbman (1940–3), pl. 70, 12) and are like no masks known in the Anglo-Saxon corpus. The ideas behind the ornament of the brooch are as much Carolingian as Anglo-Saxon and the filigree ornament compares well with such similar flimsy filigree as occurs on the brooches from Birka, graves 607 and 507 (*ibid.*, pls. 73, 5 and 83, 1) and from Sogge, Grytten, Møre, Norway (Petersen (1928), fig. 153). The central element of the brooch is essentially Norwegian and can be compared with the simpler centres of various Norwegian trefoil brooches (e.g. *ibid.*, figs. 109–11); while the interlace is again not without parallel in the Viking material.

Closely connected in technique are two discs found at Lilla Howe, Yorkshire (Dunning and Evison (1961), pl. xlv, a). These are technically very close to the Scandinavian examples just quoted. They would appear to be part of a Viking Age hoard, and not as Miss Evison alleges (*ibid.*, 150) part of a grave find: cf. *Transactions of the Historic Society of Lancashire and Cheshire*, xxiii (1870–1), 200.

[1] Zimmermann (1918), pl. 281.
[2] *Ibid.*, pls. 315, b and 316, a.
[3] *Ibid.*, pls. 321 and 322.
[4] *Ibid.*, pl. 286. a.
[5] Romilly Allen (1903), fig. 227, a.
[6] Stevenson (1956), pl. 9.
[7] E.g. Keary (1887), pl. iv, 9 and 10.

certain single whirling snakes in the same coin series.[1] These parallels provide a substantial body of the dating evidence for this object. Other than in a very general manner the displayed animal on the sword pommel cannot be paralleled elsewhere in Anglo-Saxon art: barbed animals are not known and, although displayed animals seen from above are not uncommon, this particular, distinctive, zoomorphic pattern is unknown. The spiral structure in the centre of the animal is quite common in Anglo-Saxon manuscripts of the late eighth and early ninth centuries. Similarly the foliate motif which fills the background of the object is of a very distinctive type: it occurs in its pure form, for example, on a small bronze object from Kaupang[2] and, in a slightly more elaborate form, on such objects as the Abingdon sword (pl. VI), the Beeston Tor brooches (nos. 2 and 3) and the Fuller brooch (no. 153).[3] Later in its development it can be seen combined with zoomorphic ornament on the second Trewhiddle horn mount (no. 95). Technically the closest parallel to the Fetter Lane hilt is the silver-gilt finger-ring in the Victoria and Albert Museum from the River Thames at Chelsea.[4] The quality of competent craftsmanship, the shallow carving and easy curve of the lines, make convincing comparisons with the Fetter Lane hilt. It would be dangerous to over-emphasise this parallel, but it is worth noticing that the animal heads of the ring are not unrelated to the animal heads of the Fetter Lane snakes, although they are, as Reginald Smith pointed out,[5] also related (as are the heads of the Fetter Lane snakes) to heads on such objects as the Whitby mounts (nos. 105–106), the Witham pins (no. 19) and the Ixworth brooch (no. 25). The use of silver-gilt is, as I have emphasised, rather an eighth-century feature and it is tempting to place both the ring and the hilt as representatives of a metropolitan workshop of the late eighth century.

It is naturally extremely difficult to date the Fetter Lane sword pommel on the basis of the very insubstantial body of comparative material which can be quoted. The remnants of Celtic ornament to be seen in this piece, together with the presumably correct dating by numismatists of the sceatta series to the end of the seventh and the first half of the eighth century,[6] and the dating, on general grounds, of most of the manuscripts of the Canterbury School of illumination (to which the Stockholm Codex Aureus belongs) to the late eighth and early ninth centuries, are reasonable indications of a late eighth-century date for the Fetter Lane sword. The general probability that this is the correct date is strengthened in the light of my dating of the ninth century metalwork (see below). Reginald Smith's dating of the object 'probably about A.D. 800'[7] is perhaps as close as one will ever get to the date of the object by modern art-historical methods.

(ii) *The ninth century*

A technical feature of the Fetter Lane sword fragment is the occurrence of niello on the object. Niello, the black sulphide of silver, was a very popular material in the sixth and

[1] *Ibid., loc. cit.*
[2] Blindheim (1960), fig. 6, centre, right.
[3] An interesting use of this leaf pattern in a possibly continental context is demonstrated by Miss Evison on the Palace of Westminster sword; Dunning and Evison (1961).
[4] Oman (1930), frontispiece, no. 225.
[5] Smith (1925), 247.
[6] E.g. Kent (1961), 11 ff.
[7] *BMASG*, 93.

seventh centuries, in the eighth century however it occurs rarely, but comes back into fashion during the ninth century. There are two key pieces of nielloed ninth-century metalwork—the rings of Æthelwulf, King of Wessex (reigned 839–58[1]), and Æthelswith, Queen of Mercia (853–88) (nos. 31 and 1). Both these rings are similar in style and technique and presumably date from the middle years of the ninth century. They can hardly have been the personal finger-rings of these members of the house of Wessex, rather they must be seen as the gifts of the king or queen concerned to some dependent— indeed it might be possible to see in these objects a survival into Christian times of the quality of generosity and gratitude, so popular in heroic literature, which resulted in the chieftain or king being known as 'ring-giver'. Whoever owned these pieces, unless they be considered as memorial rings (unlikely in view of the fact that mourning rings did not become general until after 1600[2]), they were undoubtedly made during the lifetime of the people whose names appear on them.

The ring of King Æthelwulf appears to be of poorer quality than that of his daughter, but this may be due to later damage and to no fault in the skill of the metalworker who made it. The inscription itself forms part of the design on the ring, so there can be no question that it is secondary. The ornament of the ring is important, for many of its features occur frequently in the metalwork of the ninth century. The speckled borders and ornament are presumably a development of the discreet dotting which can be seen on the Fetter Lane object (no. 41) and may be derived from the deliberate punching of the Witham pins (no. 19), but the beaded border at the base of the ring seems to be a full-blooded feature of ninth-century English metalwork, and one which apparently makes its first appearance on the Källby harness-mounts.[3] The small saltire with arrow-like terminals at the back of the ring is perhaps not unrelated to the equal-armed cross in the Q of fol. 43a of the manuscript British Museum, Royal 1.E.VI,[4] in the D of fol. 5b of the manuscript British Museum, Tiberius C.II[5] or on the strap-end from Cuerdale (no. 13). The birds which face each other on either side of the plant-like central element have heads (with prominent forehead, nick over the nostril and small punched circular eye, small mouth and rounded ear) and feet (simply represented by a swelling with a central nick to form a paw at the end of an unnaturalistic leg) of a general character similar to that of many animals which occur on Anglo-Saxon metalwork of the ninth century and, like a fair number of such animals (e.g. on the Strickland brooch (no. 152)), they are collared with a double incised line. The wings of the birds are difficult to parallel, as birds are rarely represented in the metalwork of this period; but there is a general resemblance to the wings of the *imago hominis* of the ninth-century Book of Cerne (University Library, Cambridge, L1.1.10).[6] The tails, again, are difficult to parallel but they are reasonably similar to one of the birds on one of the brooches from the Beeston Tor hoard (deposited *c.* 871) (no. 2) or on fol. 22r and 32r of the MS. L1.1.10 (Book of Cerne) in the University Library, Cambridge.

[1] But see below pp. 56 and 82.
[2] *B.M. Ring Cat.*, li.
[3] Wilson (1955a). These may well be Continental and not English objects.
[4] Zimmermann (1918), pl. 289.
[5] *Ibid.*, pl. 291, b.
[6] *Ibid.*, pl. 295, a.

The two confronted birds are presumably derived from the motif, taken into Early Christian art from Late Antique sources, which consists of two peacocks confronting each other on either side of a tree or cup. This motif had some symbolic meaning at an earlier date and it is possible that this meaning survived into the ninth century.[1] If there is any Christian symbolism behind this motif it is interesting in connection with the next object to be discussed, the ring of Queen Æthelswith (no. 1), which is ornamented with an *agnus dei*.

The ring of Queen Æthelswith is perhaps less useful for comparison with other metal-work: it could be argued, for example, that the inscription is secondary, added to an old ring for some specific purpose, and that the dating is consequently not so reliable as it might be. Secondly this is the only occurrence in the body of material with which I am dealing of a portrayal of an *agnus dei*; and, while this symbol has a certain interest,[2] its character as a definite religious symbol detracts greatly from its value in an art-historical context. However, if we accept the fact that the ring was indeed manufactured for Queen Æthelswith there is at least one feature, the double nick on the hindquarters of the lamb, that falls into a dated context. This double nick is an extremely common feature in ninth-century English metalwork, while its occurrence in the tenth century is a matter of some considerable importance. The animals on the shoulders of the ring are not easily paralleled in the metalwork but are rather similar to certain small animals in the manu-script art—particularly in the roundel at the head of the central column of the Canon Tables in British Museum MS., Royal 1.E.VI, fol. 4a (pl. *v*).

Closely related in style to these two rings, and also executed in gold and niello, are Ædred's ring (no. 30) and Alhstan's ring, the latter found at Llysfaen, Caernarvonshire in the eighteenth century and now in the Victoria and Albert Museum.[3] Although there is no reason to identify the Alhstan of the ring with Alhstan, Bishop of Sherborne from 817-67, there is no reason to deny the ninth-century date of this ring: the animal style and the general stylistic similarity to the rings of Æthelwuf and Æthelswith confirm this beyond question. Similarly, there can be little doubt that Ædred's ring (no. 30) belongs to the same group. To this group can probably be added the Kingmoor runic ring (no. 27), the ring of Buredruð (no. 85) (although the latter is not nielloed) and the ring with a nielloed, cryptic inscription set against a plain background (no. 145). A ring of different design but one which can be placed confidently in this period is the gold ring from Ebbesborne Wake (no. 16) with its speckled plastic animal heads (see below, pp. 27, 29 ff.).

Together with the rings of Æthelwulf and Æthelswith, which are dated by inscription, we must consider the group of objects which are found in ninth-century hoards, partic-ularly those from Beeston Tor, Trewhiddle (nos. 2–7 and 90–103) and Talnotrie (pl. IV, *d*: National Museum of Antiquities of Scotland). These hoards all contain objects of nielloed silver and are of the utmost importance to the art-historical sequence. The enormous Viking hoard from Cuerdale (dated *c*. 903) also contains one such object

---

[1] A short discussion of this motif with full references will be found in Lasko (1956), 347.

[2] It is of interest that the words *agnus dei* are inscribed on a contemporary Anglo-Saxon ring (now lost) from Driffield, Yorkshire (Fowler (1870)).

[3] Oman (1930), frontispiece, no. 227.

(no. 13), but this is completely out of context and need not detain us here. Similarly, the importance of the Anglo-Saxon nielloed finger-ring of gold in the richest of all Norwegian hoards, that from Hon[1] (dated *c.* 855), should not be over-emphasised here—although the date of deposition is not without interest.

The nodal hoard is that from Trewhiddle, St. Austell, Cornwall; it was deposited, as the associated coins show, *c.* 875. The hoard contains many undecorated objects, which will be treated below, and a number of decorated objects which must be thoroughly discussed here. The ornament of these objects can be divided into three groups: the first represented by the ornament of the two larger horn-mounts (nos. 94 and 95), the strap-ends (nos. 97 and 98) and the small box-like object with its lid (no. 93); the second represented by the ornament of the pinhead (no. 92), and the third group by the ornament of the small horn-mount (no. 96).

The first group is the most important, as it is perhaps most typical of the surviving art of this period. The motifs differ from object to object, depending on the scale of the surface under decoration; but certain ornamental features are evident in each piece. Every object is nielloed and ornamented with animals set in a series of small fields divided from each other by a beaded border: the motifs themselves are decorated with triangular specks, executed with the point of the engraver's tool. The mounts were attached to their base by means of dome-headed rivets; the head of which is allowed for by a plain space surrounding each rivet-hole on the decorative surface of the mount, this feature is responsible for a certain contortion of the ornament in some fields. The ornament is mostly zoomorphic, but interlace, leaves and scrolls also occur, while in some cases the animal ornament degenerates into leaf ornament. The animals vary, but are normally speckled, have a squared snout, a sub-triangular body, a shaped hip and a thin leg with three toes; the forehead is pronounced, or the nick, noticed between forehead and snout on the Æthelwulf ring, is here developed so that the eye is given more prominence, by its seeming attachment to the head by a short-string-like feature. At the terminals of each of the two large mounts are repoussé animal masks decorated, within triangular fields, with degenerate foliate ornament.

The ornament of the pinhead—my second group—is more angular, rigid and formalised —perhaps, at the same time, more skilful. The speckling is less coarse, closer to that on the Æthelwulf ring (no. 31) and the Fetter Lane hilt (no. 41); the heads of the animals are emphasised, the upper jaw runs into the forehead and the eye appears at the apex of the head, being given considerable prominence in the larger fields; the lower lip is curled, while the body is unimportant. The whirling leaf motif and the strangely treated cruciform pattern in two of the fields are unique and need not concern us here.

Finally the ornament of the small mount is distinguished by unspeckled ornament. The animal which occurs in one of the two fields is generally related to the animal ornament of the first group, but differs in some important respects. The other field contains a leaf pattern, with possible zoomorphic characteristics. The animal is collared and rather more degenerate than is usual in the first group of ornament, its lower jaw is produced to form a leaf pattern and the front leg penetrates the body at the neck. The most im-

[1] Brøgger (1920–1), fig. 8.

portant ornamental detail, however, is provided by the double nicks in the contour of the body of the animal—a feature which is repeated in the leaf ornament.

The two most important groups are the first and third. The style of the second group is peculiar to the Trewhiddle hoard: its main importance lying in its reminiscence of the technique of speckling used on the Fetter Lane hilt (no. 41) and the Æthelwulf ring (no. 31); it need not concern us further here.

The third group is important in that the plain body with the double nick at the contour is a feature which replaces the speckling on a number of objects decorated with animal ornament (occasionally it occurs together with the speckling, as on a small roundel from Whitby Abbey (no. 109)). It is interesting that the leaf ornament is decorated with similar nicks. The double nicks continue into a later period, occurring, for example, on the Canterbury disc brooch (no. 10) and the Sittingbourne scramasax (no. 80). These nicks occur on a number of ninth-century objects in the British Museum, on the Fuller brooch (no. 153), on one of the Beeston Tor brooches (no. 2), on the Scales Moor sword pommel (no. 65), on Æthelswith's ring (no. 1) and on a number of other minor objects. The first group is the most typical and forms the basis of any discussion of the style.

The most interesting comparison, outside metalwork, of the Trewhiddle hoard is with the Canterbury group of manuscripts, especially with the latest manuscript of the group, British Museum, Royal 1.E.VI. These parallels have been emphasised before, chiefly by Brøndsted[1] and Kendrick,[2] but, although both these scholars have emphasised that the Trewhiddle objects are later than the manuscript, it is an interesting and undeniable fact that the black and white treatment of the animals in British Museum MS. Royal 1.E.VI, with its speckling,[3] is so different from the treatment of the animals in any other manuscripts of the group, or indeed in most other insular manuscripts of an earlier date, that it would seem likely that the scribe was copying in these small panels in the canon tables a metal prototype—that his black and white are equivalent to the metalworker's niello and silver. If we consider the canon tables at fol. 4a (pl. V) of this manuscript many techniques of the metalworker will be seen translated into another medium. Some of these techniques, as for instance the speckled borders and the *pointillé* zoomorphic and interlace panels within the heads of the arches, are derived from metalwork, by way of other manuscripts.[4] The rectangular fields, the roundels and the square spacing panels, the key patterns, beaded borders, etc., while not without parallel in manuscript art, are all derived from metalwork sources. It would be foolish to over-elaborate a point which might seem very tenuous, but it is an undoubted fact that there are more elements of metalwork in Royal 1.E.VI than in any insular manuscript illuminated since the Book of Durrow. Allowing for the differences of technique, the animal ornament of the canon tables of Royal 1.E.VI and of the Trewhiddle horn-mounts has reached the same stage of degeneration: in both contexts we have small speckled animals, and animals degenerating into leaf ornament, of the type already noticed on the Fetter Lane hilt. At

[1] (1924), 127–8.
[2] (1938*a*), 185.
[3] Zimmermann (1918), pl. 290.
[4] Cf. for example, the Lindisfarne Gospels

fol. 95r Kendrick *et al.* (1960), and the two bowls from the St. Ninians' Isle treasure, O'Dell (1960), 21.

the same time the animal ornament is not very far removed from that of the Æthelwulf ring, which is firmly dated to the second quarter of the ninth century. Unfortunately, the date of the manuscript is by no means clear: the conventional art-historical dating is to the early ninth century, palaeographers tend to date it to the late eighth century (Lowe[1] cites it as 'Saec. VIII ex.'). There is no internal evidence to date it more accurately. Occasionally palaeographical hypothesis must give way to archaeological hypothesis and any dating of Royal 1.E.VI must be on a hypothetical basis. Royal 1.E.VI stands out from other members of the Canterbury School, it is much more competently executed and much more reminiscent of metalwork than the other manuscripts. Even the use of silver on the purple pages (e.g. fol. 43a)[2] reflects the popularity of silver in the ninth century.

Silver does not seem to have returned to popularity as the jeweller's chief medium until the end of the eighth century. Its return to favour as a metalworker's material may well have been influenced by the reform and standardisation of the coinage in the third quarter of the eighth century by Heaberht and Ecgberht of Kent and by Offa (757–96), when England finally reconciled itself to a silver-standard.[3] From then onwards there would be sufficient silver circulating in England to allow for the manufacture of a large amount of silver jewellery (that coins and brooches were often regarded as so much bullion is emphasised by the hoards of the ninth century, where scrap silver, coins and jewellery are mixed together). The Fetter Lane sword-hilt (no. 41) and the Chelsea ring belong to the early part of this silver-loving period; but, at a later stage, the market was suddenly flooded with large quantities of silver and as a result with silver jewellery, not gilt, but heavily inlaid with niello and decorated with a lively, mobile style which has completely lost the discipline of the carefully planned and executed carving of the earlier period. This is the quality that is seen in the Trewhiddle hoard and reflected in the manuscripts Royal 1.E.VI and Cotton Tiberius C.II.[4] The ornament of Royal 1.E.VI is, as I have stressed, so strongly reminiscent of metalwork that it must have been copied from metal objects of the type found at Trewhiddle. It seems hardly likely, although it is not impossible, that the objects found in the Trewhiddle hoard were seventy-five years old when they were buried. The destruction of Whitby Abbey in 867 gives us a slightly earlier final date for an object with many of the qualities of the first group at Trewhiddle (no. 114). There is a possibility that Æthelwulf's ring (no. 31) was manufactured at an early date in his reign. The deposition of the Norwegian Hon hoard, which contains a ring decorated with animals closely related to the Trewhiddle style, in 855 moves us twenty years nearer the beginning of the century, while there is a distinct hint in the series of objects from the Sevington jeweller's hoard (no. 71) of Trewhiddle animal forms —about 840, which is admittedly a *terminus ante quem*. The dating of the Tassilo chalice between 777 and 788 would suggest that chip carving was still quite popular in the last quarter of the eighth century in the English missionary areas on the Continent and presumably, therefore, in England. If this be so it would seem that the metalworker's art of the Trewhiddle style was developed during the first half of the ninth century and

[1] (1934–), ii 27 (no. 214).
[2] Zimmermann (1918), pl. 289.
[3] Cf. Blunt (1961).
[4] Zimmermann (1918), pl. 291, b.

that Royal 1.E.VI was painted in the same period, I would suggest that this manuscript was illuminated towards 840/50, when such late classical features, as the pages of the preface executed in large, almost monumental script, would be in keeping with Carolingian taste, with its striving for Ancient Rome. If a ninth-century date for Royal 1.E.VI is accepted by the palaeographers—as it must, I think, be accepted by the archaeologists—then the resurgence of artistic achievement in metalwork of the early ninth century can be understood: it rests basically on the thorough investigation and exploration of the possibilities of silver as a medium of artistic expression, for silver was now available in greater quantities than ever before in England.

The following objects in the British Museum's collection fall into a series which must be considered together with the Trewhiddle objects: the Æthelswith ring (no. 1), the two brooches from Beeston Tor (nos. 2 and 3), the strap-end from the Cuerdale hoard (no. 13), the Ebbesborne Wake ring (no. 16), the strap-end from Icklingham (no. 24), the Kingmoor ring (no. 27), the Ædred ring (no. 30), the Æthelwulf ring (no. 31), the Poslingford ring (no. 61), the Scales Moor sword pommel (no. 65), the Southwark knife (no. 81), the Buredruð ring (no. 85), a small roundel from Whitby Abbey (no. 109), the silver and niello strap-end from Whitby (no. 114) and at least five other strap-ends from the same site (nos. 115–17, 120 and 121), the bezel of a finger-ring (no. 130) also from Whitby, a strap-end with no provenance (no. 144), the ring with the meaningless inscription (no. 145), the Strickland brooch (no. 152) and the Fuller brooch (no. 153). All are of ninth-century date and apart from those already discussed above, the Æthelswith ring, the Æthelwulf ring, the Kingmoor ring, the Ædred ring, the Buredruð ring, the Ebbesborne Wake ring and the ring with the meaningless inscription, a number of these objects fit so exactly into the Trewhiddle style that they need only be listed here. The small silver roundel from Whitby (no. 109), for example, would certainly not be out of place in the Trewhiddle hoard. Five of the base metal strap-ends from Whitby (nos. 115–17, 120 and 121) bear Trewhiddle animal ornament in a more-or-less degenerate form, as does the Icklingham strap-end (no. 24), which is only remarkable because of its scalloped edges and the single nick on the chest of the animal. The ears of the animal at the terminal of this strap-end are comma-shaped and closely allied to the ears on a number of other strap-ends, e.g. Whitby (no. 122).[1] The form of the border and the proportions of the strap-end are closely comparable with similar features of one of the Youlgreave strap-ends (no. 138), which has a nielloed interlace design in place of the animal. The strap-end with no provenance (no. 144), bears two pairs of affronted animals interlacing with each other; the animals are without limbs and their bodies degenerate into interlace. This motif is a more elaborate version of the similar, single, affronting animals which are quite common in the manuscript art of the period,[2] with bodies interlacing in exactly the same way. Another strap-end which is closely related to this design is that from Østebø, Sandeid, Vikedal, Rogaland, Norway[3] and, in a less elaborate fashion, the same motif occurs on a strap-end from York.[4] The ears of the animal at the terminal (oval with a

[1] Similar ears can be seen on the animal-heads of the Reculver tweezers (no. 62).

[2] Cf. the springers of the arches in Royal

1.E.VI at fol. 4a (pl. v).

[3] Shetelig (1940), v, fig. 147.

[4] Waterman (1959), fig. 10, 2.

27

lunate incision) are a common feature on strap-ends of this period, occurring on two of the Youlgreave strap-ends (nos. 136–9), on the strap-ends from Stratton (no. 82), Lakenheath (no. 29) and on three from Whitby Abbey (nos. 115, 117 and 120). Ears of this form are uncommon on objects other than strap-ends, but they do occur on a prick spur in the Ashmolean Museum from Pakenham, Suffolk.[1] The leaves pendant between the two rivet-holes at the terminals are common and occur on well over half the recorded strap-ends of this type.

The strap-end from the Cuerdale hoard (no. 13) is ornamented with animals similar in many ways to those on the strap-end with no provenance (no. 144), save that the four animals do not interlace with each other, but are set between the arms of a cross. The animals bear double nicks in their contour, a feature of the third group of animal ornament in the Trewhiddle hoard. The beaded borders, the niello inlay, the shape of the animals' heads and the form of the leaves into which the animals degenerate, are all features of the Trewhiddle hoard. The closest parallel to these animals is provided by the small animals in the oval fields on the gold ring from the Hon hoard (deposited

FIG. 1. Ornament on a silver strap-end from Dymchurch, Kent. (*Sheffield: City Museum*). Scale ¾.

c. 855).[2] A design very similar to the central panel of this object occurs on a strap-end from Dymchurch, Kent[3] (fig. 1) (though the arrow-like terminals of the dividing cross are missing from this object) while the precise equivalent of the division of the fields and of the animal style can be seen in the initial d at fol. 56 of the Bede Manuscript, Tiberius C.II, in the British Museum.[4] Despite the fact that the Cuerdale hoard dates to the early tenth century, this strap-end must have been of some considerable age when it found its way into this otherwise typical Viking treasure. It is interesting that all the late Anglo-Saxon strap-ends of this form, found both in this country and abroad (and there are nearly a hundred of them),[5] where their ornament can be analysed, seem to belong to the ninth-century, all the parallels cited so far have been with ninth-century objects, while the two strap-ends in the Trewhiddle hoard (nos. 97 and 98), which are dated c. 872–5, the Talnotrie strap-end (pl. IV d), dated c. 875 and the series of strap-ends in various stages of manufacture in the Sevington hoard (nos. 71–8), which are dated to c. 840, give a well-founded basis for typological dating. Many of the strap-ends are decorated with debased ornament. While some of this debased ornament makes sense as a degenerate expression of the Trewhiddle style (e.g. on the Stratton strap-end, no. 82), many objects (e.g. a strap-end from Lakenheath (no. 29)) bear completely degenerate ninth-century ornament. The interlace decoration of one of the Youlgreave strap-ends (no. 136), can be paralleled by the similar interlace on one of the strap-ends from the firmly dated Sevington hoard (no. 71). Certain strap-ends are decorated with incised linear ornament, sometimes with a terminal recognisable as a formalised animal head; such a strap-end is that from Great Wakering (no. 21), which bears a general resemblance to a pair from Sutherlandshire in the Ashmolean Museum, Oxford. Another strap-end, one of two

[1] Baldwin Brown (1903–37), iv, 422 and fig. 16, c.
[2] Brøgger (1920–1), fig. 8.
[3] Sheffield City Museum.
[4] Brøndsted (1924), fig. 101.
[5] Listed: Wilson and Blunt (1961), 120–2.

from Icklingham (no. 23), belongs to the same general group, the treatment of the terminal is rather unusual and can best be compared with the similar treatment on the Dymchurch strap-end. The quality of the engraving is very similar to that on one of the three strap-ends possibly from Felixstowe, in the Castle Museum, Norwich.

Only one strap-end in the collection is of first-class quality—the well-known example from Whitby Abbey (no. 114). This is executed in silver and niello and is most closely paralleled, among strap-ends, by that from the Talnotrie hoard (pl. IV, *d*) (dated *c*. 875). The ornament of the Whitby example is more closely related to the third group at Trewhiddle.

A strap-end which is rather out of the ordinary run is that from York (no. 135). The long ears in openwork are without parallel in the Anglo-Saxon series, but their general form and the muddled interlace, inlaid with niello, of the main field of decoration is typical of the ninth-century strap-end series.

The strap-end from Coswick (no. 12), belongs to a different, but related series. The two chief parallels are a strap-end from Bledlow, Bucks[1] and an unpublished, but rather elaborate, example from St. Mary's Abbey, York.[2] The heads in relief, set back to back, are rather similar to the double heads on the Ebbesborne Wake ring (no. 16).

Of the group of objects listed above, the brooches from Beeston Tor (nos. 2 and 3) are of interest in that they were probably buried in the same year as the Trewhiddle hoard. The two brooches are distinctly different in style and quality, and are only related to the Trewhiddle style in a general way. The smaller of the two brooches (no. 2) is of finer quality—its appearance being enhanced by the extremely fine state of preservation of the niello. The bird-like creature in the panel to the right has a head similar to the Trewhiddle animals and a tail not unlike those on the Æthelwulf ring (no. 31). The beaded borders and the dome-headed rivets are likewise related to the Trewhiddle decoration, as is also the rather wispy leaf or scroll ornament associated with the animals. Three of the animals have the double nicks of the third group of Trewhiddle ornament. The heads of the other three animals are reminiscent of the head of the human figure on the Abingdon sword (pl. VI). Other features of the Abingdon sword are also of importance in relation to the small Beeston Tor brooch; the tail of the bird is treated in a similar way on both objects and the ornament is embellished with double nicks—but more important is the fact that the leaf ornament of the sword is faceted in exactly the same way as the *fleur-de-lys* pattern of the Beeston Tor brooch; such faceting does not normally occur in metalwork of this period and, although the Beeston Tor brooch is an openwork design and therefore more susceptible to faceted carving, one might hazard the guess that the two objects were made in the same workshop. At the same time I think it should be emphasised that the Abingdon sword is a little more developed in style.

The closest parallel to the leaf ornament of the Abingdon sword is provided on the disc brooch from Inedahlsgatan, Stockholm,[3] which was found with coins dating the deposition of the hoard to *c*. 1025. The leaf ornament of the brooch, however, is not faceted. This brooch is interesting in that in the division of its fields by curved beaded

[1] Head (1955), fig. 32.
[2] York: Yorkshire Museum.
[3] Bruce-Mitford (1956a), pl. xxxi.

borders terminating in dome-headed rivets, and in the devotion of its ornamental repertoire to leaf and interlace patterns, all set against a nielloed background, it is similar to
the larger Beeston Tor brooch (no. 3). Both these brooches and the smaller Beeston Tor
brooches are flat, unlike the rest of the surviving large disc brooches, which are dished.
It is easy to over-emphasise the similarity between the Stockholm brooch and the
Beeston Tor brooches, but the likelihood remains that the Stockholm brooch belongs to
the ninth century and was well over a hundred years old when it was buried. The leaf
ornament of one of the square fields of the larger Beeston Tor brooch, as has been pointed
out, bears some relationship to the leaf ornament of the Fetter Lane sword (no. 41),
but the clearest parallels are with the leaf ornament of the smallest mount at Trewhiddle
(no. 96), with the ornament of the box-like ornament of the Trewhiddle hoard (no. 93),
with the Abingdon sword (pl. VI) and with the swords from Grønneberg and Dolven
in Norway.[1] The beaded borders and the dome-headed rivets also relate it to the Trewhiddle hoard, while the billets which fill certain fields are related to the ornament of
the Trewhiddle pinhead. It is difficult to judge whether the degenerate quality of the
ornament is due to bad workmanship or to a devolution of the ornament, but it would
seem likely that the brooch is later in date than the classic Trewhiddle ornament of the
larger horn mounts (nos. 94–5).

Two other disc brooches should now be considered. Firstly the Fuller brooch (no. 153),
which is one of the finest objects of the period to survive. It has been treated at length by
Bruce-Mitford[2] and little can be added to his discussion. It is one of the few pieces of
metalwork in the field covered by this catalogue which can be interpreted iconographi-
cally and Mr. Bruce-Mitford's discussion of this matter is reprinted in appendix B
(p. 91f.). The human figures cannot be paralleled stylistically in the metalwork. The only
full-length human figures known to me in Anglo-Saxon metalwork of the period covered
by this catalogue are those which appear on the pommel guard of the Abingdon sword
(pl. VI), on the strap-end from Selsey, Sussex,[3] and on the much later and very different
mounts of the portable alter in the Cluny Museum, Paris,[4] and the crozier of St. Heribert
in the Cologne Cathedral Treasury, but these are by no means adequate parallels. Bruce-
Mitford[5] found approximate parallels in the manuscripts of the Canterbury group,
particularly in the Book of Cerne (Cambridge University Library, MS., Le.1.10),[6] but
quite rightly insisted that its stylistic parallels were best seen in the metalwork. The fine
quality of the craftsmanship makes such comparisons difficult. In its foliate details the
Fuller brooch is related to the Abingdon sword (pl. VI), the Beeston Tor brooches and
decorated objects from Trewhiddle, while the roundels can be compared, in some
respects, with the oval fields of the Ebbesborne Wake ring (no. 16). The animal and bird
motifs, on the other hand, are not easy to parallel in the metalwork because their fine
quality sets them apart from other objects, but such details as the collars and nicks on
the animals, together with their general stance, relate them to the animals etc., of the
Trewhiddle hoard. Perhaps the best parallel for the quality of the animal ornament of

[1] *Ibid.*, pl. xxiii.
[2] *Ibid.*, 173 ff.
[3] Salzmann (1912,) pl. 5.
[4] Wilson (1960), pl. 16.
[5] (1956*a*), 182–3.
[6] Zimmermann (1918), pl. 295.

the roundels of the Fuller brooch is provided by the ornament of the Anglo-Saxon finger-ring found in the River Reno at Bologna, Italy.[1] As well as the zoomorphic parallels one of the roundels of this ring has a floral motif not dissimilar in idea to the floral motifs in a number of the roundels of the Fuller brooch. There can be no doubt that the brooch is of ninth-century date and I am tempted to place it in the second or third quarter of the century.

The Strickland brooch (no. 152) is a splendid object. The technique of inlaying it with gold plates, as well as with niello and blue glass, together with the effect of depth achieved by carving it in a technique which occasionally pierces the metal, has given it a plasticity missing in the smooth surfaces of the Fuller and Beeston Tor brooches, even if it is perhaps crude in its finish and over-elaborate in its ornament. The technique of inlaying a silver surface with gold plates is rarely encountered in Anglo-Saxon contexts, but exact parallels are provided in two cases; the first at Kroken, Fjære, Aust Agder, Norway[2] where a fragmentary strap-end is inlaid in a similar manner (the gold plate of this object is speckled in the same way, even spreading off the gold-plate onto the silver, as on the Strickland brooch), the second example is provided by the sword pommel from Scales-Moor, Ingleton (no. 65), which is discussed below. A similar plate was obviously inlaid in a strap-end from Lansdown, nr. Bath, Somerset,[3] but all that is left is the empty rectangular setting. All these objects obviously belong to the same chronological horizon as the Strickland brooch. The blue glass eyes, already noticed in the eighth century on the Witham pins (no. 19) and the Thames mount (no. 45), re-appear here and are repeated fairly often in the metalwork of the Anglo-Saxon world, e.g. on the Hon ring,[4] and, though in a different colour, on the mount of Bishop Æthelwald's seal (no. 18), both of which are dated to the middle of the ninth century. The beaded borders which occur on this brooch have already been shown to be a familiar feature of ninth-century metalwork, but the main border, consisting of alternating pellets and lozenges, is not paralleled elsewhere in the metalwork, but the whole form of the ring of Alhstan[5] is, as Bruce-Mitford has pointed out,[6] the exact parallel of the form to the border of the Strickland brooch. The origins of this motif go back to classical sources. The dome-headed rivets, seen here, have been noticed already on the Stockholm[7] and Beeston Tor brooches (nos. 2–3), while their existence has been inferred on the Trewhiddle horn mounts. They occur as early as the seventh century (with similar beaded wire ring), on one of the Dover swords[8] and (without a beaded wire ring), as late as the eleventh century, on the Sutton, Isle of Ely, brooch (no. 83). The small regular dog-like animals are of typical Anglo-Saxon form, they are not so contorted as the Trewhiddle animals but can be more closely compared with the animals on one of the Whitby strap-ends (no. 115). They are collared in the same way as those on the smaller Beeston Tor brooch (no. 2), the Fuller brooch (no. 153) and on many other objects already noticed. The animal masks are rather more

[1] Bruce-Mitford (1956a), pl. xxii, B–D.
[2] Shetelig (1940), v, 179 and fig. 144.
[3] Gardner (1955).
[4] Shetelig (1940), v, fig. 142.
[5] Brøndsted (1924), fig. 111.
[6] Bruce-Mitford (1956a), 193.
[7] Ibid., pl. xxxi, A.
[8] Unpublished, excavated by Miss V. I. Evison for the Ministry of Works.

elaborate examples of the motifs which appear at the terminals of the two larger Trewhiddle horn-mounts (nos. 94–5), and, more especially, at the terminals of many strap-ends. Bruce-Mitford pointed to the similarity in position and form of the masks on a filigree pendant from the Hon hoard,[1] which he consequently identified as English. I have elsewhere doubted this attribution,[2] but the parallel is striking and, if the pendant is not English, its design is certainly based on an English prototype. Finally a feature clearly seen here, where the niello is missing, is the keying of the channels cut to receive the niello inlay, a feature which can often be seen on objects of the period covered by

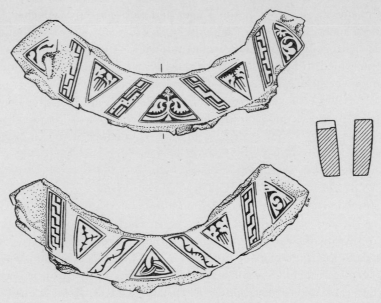

FIG. 2. Pommel guard from Knafhólar, Iceland. Scale $\frac{1}{1}$.
(*Reykjavík: National Museum.*)

this catalogue (e.g. on the two larger Trewhiddle horn-mounts, nos. 94–5). The Strickland brooch is a typical product of ninth-century Anglo-Saxon metalwork.

The Scales Moor, Ingleton, sword-pommel (no. 65), like the Strickland brooch, is decorated with inlaid plates of gold. The ornament of the gold panels is made up of a degenerate animal and leaf ornament, not unlike that of the Stratton strap-end (no. 82) or of the sword pommel guard from Knafhólar, Iceland (fig. 2), but more accomplished in execution and with more definite zoomorphic form in many of its details. The contorted character and the same high standard of craftsmanship as the animals on the Abingdon Sword (pl. VI), but they appear to be closer in form to those of the Witham sword,[3] which are of much less accomplished quality. The multiplicity of animal heads occurring in a single panel is more closely paralleled by the bronze strap-end from Goldsborough, Yorkshire,[4] by the ornament on the Coldingham Priory strap-end (fig. 3),

[1] Bruce-Mitford (1956a), pl. xxvii, D.
[2] Wilson (1960c), 25.
[3] Wilson (1960a), pl. 23.
[4] Collingwood (1915), 179.

on a strap-end from York[1] and, probably, by the ornament on the (now lost) ring from Malton, Yorkshire[2]. On this object, as on the Strickland brooch (no. 152), the animals are collared and, as on the small roundel from Whitby Abbey (no. 109), the animals are decorated both with speckling and double nicks. This again must be seen as a ninth-century object, but the degree of degeneration of the ornament might conceivably place it in the latter half of that century.

The Poslingford ring (no. 61) bears an interesting mixture of both animal and leaf ornament, related in many ways to the Abingdon sword and yet having a restraint in the design totally missing from that object. Like other rings of its type (e.g. the Ædred ring (no. 30)) it has a beaded border and, like a ring from Hexham in the possession of the Duke of Northumberland (fig. 4), it is divided up into rectangular fields. The animal ornament is more disciplined than the zoomorphic features of the Wallingford sword and is more nearly related to the animals of the smaller Beeston Tor brooch (no. 2), the Trewhiddle horn-mounts (nos. 94–5) and the roundel from Whitby Abbey (no. 109). The leaf ornament is, in part, faceted, as on the Abingdon sword, while the 'potted plant' motif, in fields 1, 3 and 5, is paralleled in the same place. Its origin must be found in the vine-scroll, as can be seen from the Vespasian psalter (British Museum MS., Vespasian A.1.), where a similar, if more elaborate, motif with grapes occurs on fol. 30b.[3] There are, on this ring, traces of the leaf ornament of the Fetter Lane sword pommel (no. 41), just as there are in the decoration of the Abingdon sword. This ring must be of ninth-century date.

The knife from Southwark (no. 81) is only related in the most general way to the Trewhiddle style. For many years it has been dated to the twelfth century,[4] but the original theory (of R. A. Smith) that it is of pre-Conquest date,[5] must I think, stand. The identification is based chiefly on the scrollwork, which can be closely compared to the

FIG. 3. Strap-end from Coldingham priory, Berwickshire. Scale ⅟₁.

(*Private possession.*)

FIG. 4. Ornament of a gold finger-ring from Hexham, Northumberland. Scale ⅟₁. (*Private possession.*)

very similar scrolls which occur, usually with zoomorphic features, in the Canterbury group of manuscripts, e.g. in the scroll in the letter 'd' at fol. 5b of the Bede manuscript, British Museum, Tiberius C.II.[6] Perhaps the closest parallel, but one that is useless except for the most general chronological purposes, is to be seen on one face of the cross-slab from Bakewell, Derbyshire.[7] The origins of the motif in the vine-scroll are to be seen, for example, on the crosses from Ilkley, Yorkshire.[8] An interesting parallel, but

[1] Waterman (1959), fig. 10, 3.
[2] Waterman (1951).
[3] Zimmermann (1918), pl. 286, a.
[4] Ward-Perkins (1940), 51.

[5] *The Antiquaries Journal*, xiv (1934), 61.
[6] Zimmermann (1918), pl. 291, b.
[7] Brøndsted (1924), fig. 57.
[8] Particularly Collingwood (1927), fig. 63.

one that is not easy to understand, is in inlaid ironwork on the folding stool from Pavia, which is also of ninth-century date. Two of the Pavia panels[1] have designs similar to that in one of the rectangular panels of the Southwark knife. Otherwise the panels contain ornament too ordinary to identify. This parallel is satisfying as the stool is taken to be of ninth-century date.[2] The Southwark knife probably belongs to this century.

The objects from the Sevington hoard (nos. 67–79), apart from the worn strap-end (no. 71), are either unfinished and undecorated or are decorated with a crude ornament that is hardly susceptible to analysis. The ornament of the spoons (interlace, a human mask, etc.), is scratched on the silver in a manner similar to that on the Gravesend Cross (no. 20) and may perhaps be considered as the sketch for a final design. Of some interest, however, are the moulded heads of the spoons, which can be compared with the head on one of the styli from St. Augustine's Abbey, Canterbury.[3] But any further comparison is useless.

Apart from one or two objects which are dealt with below and which, although they cannot be dated, may belong to the ninth century, only one object of ninth-century date remains to be discussed in this context: Æthelwald's seal (no. 18). The design of the seal-die itself can only be considered in a numismatic context. It clearly imitates coins of Æthelbert's 2nd type[4] which dates from *c.* 865. This dating would confirm the opinion expressed above that this is the seal-die of the Æthelwald who was Bishop of Dunwich in the middle of the ninth century.[5] The conical setting of the die has an interest of its own, being chiefly remarkable for the animal masks set in and between the arches. Originally, like the animal heads on the Strickland brooch, these animals had their eyes inlaid with glass, perhaps red, perhaps blue. The heads, however, are very similar to those on the Sevington spoon and, less certainly, to the heads on the terminals of the strap-ends. A close parallel to the animal masks is afforded by the Ebbesborne Wake ring (no. 16), which has similar eyes, ears, nostrils, etc. Any relationship between the heads of this object and the heads on the censer covers from Canterbury, London Bridge and Pershore (nos. 9, 44 and 56) is coincidental, but like these objects the setting of the seal is architectural form and the animal heads might be considered as label-stops like those in Deerhurst Church, Gloucestershire, which might well belong to the ninth century.[6]

With the exception of a certain provincialism in the poorer quality metalwork, the metalwork of the ninth century seems to have enjoyed favour over the whole of Anglo-Saxon England. No single motif appears to have been confined to any one particular area: the discovery of a metalworker's bone trial-piece with Trewhiddle style animals in York,[7] and the presumption that Æthelwulf's ring (no. 31) was manufactured in Wessex, demonstrate the remarkable uniformity of animal ornament in England in the ninth century. The geographical distribution of the objects can give no clue to the origin of the

---

[1] Schramm (1954), pl. 32, c.
[2] *Ibid.*, 331. Some of the ornament of this stool is very insular in flavour and deserves closer examination.
[3] Radford (1940), 507, second from left.
[4] Grueber and Keary (1893), pl. iv, 2.

[5] Cited by Powicke (1939), 144, as consecrated between 845 and 870, but see below, pp. 80–81.
[6] Gilbert (1954), fig.
[7] Wilson (1960*a*), pl. 67.

style, finds are scattered as far west as Cornwall and as far north as the Highlands: there is no apparent concentration in a major area.

(iii) *From the Trewhiddle hoard to* 1100.

Before turning our attention to the few major pieces of tenth-century Anglo-Saxon metalwork a group of small, base-metal, disc brooches should be discussed. Some may be of ninth-century date, but most of the available evidence seems to point to a tenth-century date for the series. The brooches have few artistic pretensions, but a fair number are known. The example from the River Thames (no. 88), the surface of which is divided in the same way as the larger brooch from Beeston Tor (no. 3), demonstrates that the design of these objects was based on that of the rich disc brooches of the more wealthy members of society. A few of these brooches are of bronze, but the majority are of white metal—pewter, lead or very base silver.

Some of these brooches are set with imitation coins and can be dated accordingly,[1] but there are certain obvious exceptions to such dating. For example, one brooch included in this catalogue (no. 142) has a centre which imitates a classical coin,[2] but there can be little doubt that it belongs to the late Saxon period, for the ladder-like border is of a familiar Anglo-Saxon pattern. Similarly a brooch (of Viking type) from Gärsnäs, Ö. Herrestad, Skåne, Sweden, which has a centre which imitates a late imperial coin, was found in a hoard which included coins of Canute.[3]

In the main, coin brooches found in England, except for nos. 142 and 39 and an example from York,[4] imitate tenth-century Anglo-Saxon coins. A brooch from Winchester[5] copies a Derby coin of Edward the Elder by the moneyer Heremod, the coin would be dated *c.* 920.[6] The famous coin brooch from Canterbury, inscribed WVDEMAN FECIÐ[7] has its parallel in a London coin of Eadgar, minted by Ælfnod.

This tendency towards a tenth-century date for this type of imitative coin-brooch confirms the Scandinavian evidence cited by Stenberger.[8] It is further borne out by the

[1] One omission must be explained here. The Boxmoor brooch (*VCH Hertfordshire*, i, p. 253, fig. 7) has not been included in this catalogue. It imitates a solidus of Louis the Pious (cf. Grierson (1951), pl. I, iv and viii) and has none of the typical features of the Anglo-Saxon series. It is much closer to the ninth-century Continental examples quoted by Dinklage (1955, fig. 4). It is completely out of series with the English brooches and there seems to be a strong likelihood that it is Frankish.

[2] This coin is a poor imitation of a fourth-century coin of Constantine (320–1). The trident-like features above the head are close in detail to the rather degenerate crest of the helmet on certain coins of Constantine, similarly the border of the cloak imitates the border of the cuirass on certain Constantinian coins, while the diadem-like feature is, in fact, a degeneration of the brow-guard of the helmets on these coins: cf. Maurice (1911), pl. II, 11. I am indebted to Dr. J. P. C. Kent of the Museum's Department of Coins and Medals for this identification.

[3] Stenberger (1947–58), i, 55 and fig. 81. The hoard has been dispersed.

[4] Baldwin Brown (1903–32), iii, pl. xlvi, 6, which imitates a coin of Valentinian.

[5] *The Numismatic Chronicle* (1908), 83–4.

[6] All the numismatic information used here has been kindly supplied by Mr. R. H. M. Dolley.

[7] *VCH Kent*, i, 382 and fig. 27.

[8] (1947–58), 53–64.

brooch from Rome (no. 64), which is set with a coin of Eadgar. There is little evidence to suggest that there is a continuous tradition of manufacture of these brooches from the classical period onwards and, as the York brooch and the British Museum example (no. 142) are so close in style to brooches found in an undeniable late context, there can be little doubt that they were manufactured in the Christian Saxon period, and probably in the tenth century. However, we must not lose sight of the fact that there is earlier evidence for such brooches on the Continent.[1]

It is difficult, from their style alone, to date brooches which do not imitate coins. A single example from York[2] is related to the tenth-century Anglo-Scandinavian Jellinge style, but it would be difficult to find a satisfactory parallel for it. But, although the division of the surface of the brooch from the Thames (no. 88) can be compared with the ninth-century Beeston Tor brooch (no. 3), this means little or nothing, for the same pattern can be seen on the eleventh-century Sutton brooch (no. 83). The same is true of another brooch from York[3] which can be compared, in the division of its field, to the centre of the Stockholm brooch.[4]

Some brooches are obviously imitative of filigree (e.g., nos. 47 and 151), but, while they can be generally compared with various Scandinavian objects on which true filigree occurs,[5] such a comparison is of little chronological use. Many are divided up into various linear, beaded and zig-zag patterns, a particularly common feature is the ladder-like border (seen, e.g., on nos. 51–4), which might well be a "negative" impression of the beaded border so common in the finer metalwork. The same feature can be seen on the border of the pendant (no. 149), but the feature cannot be dated.

There can be no doubt that these brooches were made in this country, as the large homogenous hoard from Cheapside, London[6] adequately proves. However, the silver and pewter objects in this hoard are of a better quality than most of the pewter brooches found in this country (e.g. no 11).

One of the Museum's pewter brooches is of slightly better quality than the others. It comes from Bird-in-Hand Court, Cheapside, London (no. 37) and is decorated with a backward-looking animal in the centre of an imitation filigree border. Although in certain of its tricks of billeting and panelling it can be compared with the brooch from York,[7] cited above, the comparison is so tenuous as to be practically valueless. This brooch may perhaps best be compared with a group of bronze brooches, of which one example is in the Museum (from Swaffham, Norfolk (no. 84)). The shaggy, backward-looking animal of this brooch is exactly paralleled on brooches from Barnham, Norfolk,[8] Ixworth,[9] near Bury St. Edmunds, Suffolk,[10] Burgh Castle and Branston, Suffolk,[11]

[1] Dinklage (1955), 43–4.
[2] Waterman (1959), fig. 10, 9.
[3] *Ibid.*, 10, 8.
[4] Bruce-Mitford (1956a), pl. xxxi, A.
[5] Cf. Arbman (1937), pl. 64; Arbman (1940–3), pl. 97, 21 and 22.
[6] *Catalogue of the Collection of London Antiquities in the Guildhall Museum*, London 1903, 120 and pl. LIV.
[7] Waterman (1959), fig. 10, 9.
[8] Cambridge University Museum of Archaeology and Ethnology.
[9] Cambridge University Museum of Archaeology and Ethnology.
[10] Private possession.
[11] Ipswich Museum.

Felixstowe[1] and a number of other sites. The rather similar brooch from Butley, Suffolk (no. 8), may well belong to the same series. The style of these objects is distinctive and unlike any other style of the period[2]: it appears to be confined to East Anglia. This style of jewellery was presumably worn by the poor man of the area and can be compared with the metropolitan style of the pewter jewellery from Cheapside. The comparison between this East Anglian series and the roundels from the Oseberg ship-burial, first postulated by Smith,[3] is hardly valid. The Norwegian objects[4] are carefully finished and well drawn —beyond the fact that they are backward-looking, none of the animals compares with the East Anglian Series.[5] If an origin for this series is to be found outside Britain it might best be seen in the series of Carolingian and enamelled objects of Kettlach type[6] which, although apparently originating on the Continent, are also found in this country, e.g. at Bedlington, Northumberland in a Viking grave.[7]

A group of bronze brooches, of which no. 15 is a typical example, have certain tenth-century characteristics and will be discussed in their appropriate context below.[8] Apart from this small group none of the small base metal disc brooches (with the possible exception of some of those which imitate coins) can be satisfactorily dated to within two centuries. A different chronological picture begins to emerge when the major pieces of metalwork of the post Trewhiddle period are considered.

The state of learning in England towards the end of the ninth century, according to King Alfred,[9] was in a parlous state and, if we are to judge from the surviving material, the country was producing no great works of art. England was divided politically, and the division is reflected in the surviving metalwork. In the north, contact[10] between the Viking Kingdom of York and the Viking Kingdom of Dublin had produced a new, Viking phase of Hiberno-Saxon art. During the latter half of the ninth century and the first thirty years of the tenth century a new phase of Hiberno-Saxon art was developed, common to Ireland and the North of England. This art is most clearly seen in the metal-work—especially in the thistle brooches and the large, silver, penannular brooches with expanded terminals. The thistle brooches must have flourished before the end of the ninth century, for fragments are found in the great treasure from Cuerdale,[11] which was deposited in 903.[12] The penannular brooches with expanded terminals were developed under very strong English influence at about the same time. The dome-headed rivets

[1] Brøndsted (1924), fig. 122.

[2] There is a singular comparison between these animals and those on the, presumably rather earlier, Werden casket (Baum (1937), pl. xxxiii, 109); but the meaning of this German parallel is obscure.

[3] *VCH Suffolk*, I, 348.

[4] Brøndsted (1924), fig. 123.

[5] Although the Oseberg roundel might be generally compared with the brooch from Bird-in-Hand Court (no. 37).

[6] E.g. Riegl (1923), pl. xxviii, 6.

[7] *BMASG*, fig. 121, *cf.* also below p. 47 f.

[8] P. 48 f.

[9] Introduction to his translation of Gregory's *Cura Pastoralis*.

[10] For these contacts see e.g. Wilson (1955c), 171–2.

[11] Hawkins (1847), figs. 62–4.

[12] Before 950, when the Skaill hoard was deposited, thistle brooches were being decorated with a fully developed Jellinge style (Anderson, 1883, figs. 71–7).

4

and the billeted divisions of the fields of these brooches[1] reflect very strongly the design of the disc brooches and other objects of the ninth century. The craftsmen who manufactured these brooches were extremely skilful and it is with some sense of shock that one compares their competent productions with the clumsy decoration of objects made in the South of England at this period, as represented by the King's School, Canterbury, disc brooch (no. 10) and the two casket plates (nos. 154–55).

At the same time, however, it is probably unfair to judge the quality of the metalwork of the South of England in the tenth century by the few examples that have survived. For in quantity the surviving pieces of the late ninth, tenth and eleventh centuries is but a handful compared to the amount of early ninth-century material; partly because of an absence of hoards of the period.

The key object of the immediately post-Trewhiddle period is the Sittingbourne scramasax (no. 80). The panels of this object demonstrate many facets of late ninth-century art. Panel *d*, for instance, is very closely related to the leaf scroll panel of the smallest horn mount from Trewhiddle (no. 96), even down to such details as the double nicks in the contour. Panel *a* is extremely close in design and execution to the panel containing a bird-like creature on the pommel guard of the Abingdon sword-hilt (pl. VI). The ornament in panel *b*, however, more nearly approximates to the style of the inter-spacing ornament of the stole of St. Cuthbert,[2] which is dated 909–16, and which, says Kendrick, 'foreshadow[s] the later Winchester style'.[3] The fourth purely ornamental panel (*h*) contains an extremely degenerate animal ornament, undoubtedly immediately derived from the Trewhiddle ornament, but closely related to the ornament of the King's School, Canterbury disc brooch (no. 10), which will be discussed below. It can be seen, therefore, that the ornamental repertoire of this scramasax should be assigned to the period after the manufacture of the Trewhiddle hoard, to a period when the Anglo-Saxon artist was beginning to take notice of the Continental acanthus ornament and was trying, unsuccessfully, to break away from the native animal art. The first and most easily distinguishable example of this stage can be seen on the Abingdon sword (pl. VI), which is undoubtedly later, or at least more devolved, than the Trewhiddle style.[4] With the Sittingbourne scramasax this object must be dated to the end of the ninth or the beginning of the tenth century.

The billeted lines and the twisted wire which, with the inscription, make up the remaining ornament of the Sittingbourne scramasax are paralleled on the scramasax from the River Thames at Battersea (no. 36), where a runic inscription takes the place of the inscription in Latin characters on the Sittingbourne example. The same mixture of metals is used in the same linear technique, while the pendant triangles and small billets on the Battersea scramasax can be compared with the inlaid plates of the Sittingbourne example. The Battersea and Sittingbourne scramasaxes are so close in the technical detail of their ornament that one is tempted to consider them both as objects from the same

---

[1] I have discussed the date and origin of these brooches in Wilson (1958*a*). The earliest datable context is in the Cuerdale treasure (*c*. 905), cf. Hawkins (1847), figs. 91 and 94.

[2] Battiscombe (1956), pl. xxiv.
[3] (1949), 3.
[4] Brøndsted (1924), 129.

workshop. It is incidentally of interest, in view of the find-place of the object, that one of the names inscribed on the Sittingbourne scramasax (*Biorhtelm*) is Kentish (see below, p. 86).

A series of other scramasaxes with similar, but less elaborate, inlay may also be considered in this context. Two in the museum are those from Hurbuck (no. 22) and London (no. 50): the former was found in a hoard of iron tools and weapons, but neither is susceptible, either by association, art-historical considerations or typology, to any close dating. A tenth-century date would seem reasonable for both objects. The scramasax from Honey Lane in the City of London (no. 43) may possibly be associated with a coin hoard (see below, p. 150 f.), dated *c.* 1003, so again this object may well belong to the tenth century. Another scramasax, or knife, in the British Museum which also has an inlaid blade is that from Southwark (no. 81), but this, as we have seen,[1] may be considerably earlier than the series discussed here. Inlaid scramasaxes are, of course, known outside the British Museum—an interesting specimen was published by Lethbridge from the River Cam at *The Pike and Eel*[2]—while another example comes from the River Ouse[3] and a number of other examples are known. Another object with related decoration is the sword from the River Witham at Lincoln (no. 32); the lozenges on the hilt of this object are inlaid by hatching the area to be decorated with a graver and hammering into these fine grooves short lengths of wire to make up the required pattern.[4] The pattern produced on the hilt of the Witham sword is very similar to that on a sword from the Thames at Westminster[5], which is executed in the same technique. A similar technique can be seen on the sword found just above Tenfoot Bridge, Shifford, Oxfordshire, now in the Reading Museum.[6] This technique may have been derived from the ninth-century practice of inlaying sheets of silver in the iron hilt of a sword, as for example on the Abingdon sword (pl. VI), where it is seen at its most elaborate. There are, however, many examples of much poorer swords with simpler inlaid patterns, e.g. on the sword fragment from Knafhólar (fig. 2), on the sword from Kaupang (pl. VIII, *c*) and on two unpublished swords, one from Gooderstone, Norfolk[7] and the other possibly from Yorkshire (*ex* Strickland Collection).[8] This technique is also practised in the tenth century on objects other than weapons, occurring for example on the Canterbury censer cover (no. 9).

Closely related, because of their technical parallel with the Witham sword, are a series of stirrup-irons. Three are in the Museum's collections: from near Battersea, London (no. 35), from the River Thames (no. 89) and from the bed of the River Witham, near Lincoln (no. 33). The scroll-work on these objects (which is executed in the same technique as the Witham sword) is not really capable of art-historical analysis. A number of these objects are found in Britain: a striking parallel to the examples from the British Museum is that from the Thames near the Tower of London.[9] Further interesting

[1] Pp. 33–34.
[2] *VCH Cambridgeshire*, i, pl. IV, b.
[3] Cambridge University Museum of Archaeology and Ethnology.
[4] Kendrick (1934), fig. 2.
[5] *VCH London*, i, fig. 10. Private possession.
[6] Grove (1938), fig. 4.
[7] Castle Museum, Norwich, inv. no. 11, 958.
[8] Private possession.
[9] Wheeler (1927), fig. 17.

parallels are afforded by the ornament of the pommel of the 'Ingelri' sword from the Thames at Battersea (pl. VII) and a spur from Canning Town, London.[1] Objects with this form of decoration are rarely found outside England.

Plenty of inlaid ironwork is, of course, found in Continental contexts. Techniques exactly similar to those of the Sittingbourne scramasax can be seen on Viking objects; a particularly fine example being provided by an axe from Sweden, which Strömberg is probably right in assigning to central Europe.[2] The well-known spearhead from the River Thames is, however, omitted from this catalogue,[3] although Kendrick thought it was of English manufacture,[4] for it is so closely paralleled by a large number of Viking spearheads.[5]

Panel *h* of the Sittingbourne scramasax (no. 80) can be used to introduce one of the most remarkable tenth-century finds of recent years—the King's School, Canterbury, disc brooch (no. 10). Many of the ornamental details of this brooch are derived directly from its ninth-century predecessors. The collared, dome-headed rivets can be paralleled, in less elaborate form, on the ninth-century disc brooches; the small rivets are best paralleled on the Fuller brooch, while the beaded wire collars are found, if not in exactly the same form, on the Strickland brooch. The main division of the field into a quartrefoil is paralleled on the Strickland brooch (no. 152), while the billeted lines of division are closely paralleled, in a rather less coarse form, on the similar Stockholm disc brooch[6] and on the large disc brooch from Beeston Tor (no. 3). The use of silver and niello is a typical feature of ninth-century metalwork. Certain technical details, the gold rivet-head in the centre of the brooch and the gold beaded wire collars and gold plates around and beneath the rivet-heads, are unique to this object. The major ornamental elements of the brooch set this object apart from the rest of the series.[7]

The filigree ornament is similar to, but much finer than, the serrated band technique which occurs on the much earlier Kirkoswald brooch (no. 28). Its closest parallel in the Anglo-Saxon corpus is to be found on the Seine sword pommel (no. 66), which is probably of ninth-century date. Not only is the filigree wire of this object of similar form and gauge to that on the Canterbury brooch, but the actual structure of the plate itself is similar to that of the central plates on the brooch (see description, p. 167). Generally speaking, however, this type of fine-gauge, serrated-band filigree is found on the Continent in late Carolingian and Ottonian contexts; it can be seen, for example, on the early eleventh-century reliquary of the Nail at Essen,[8] on the Lothar cross at Aachen[9] (which dates from about 1000), on the cross of Duke Otto at Essen[10] (which can be dated to between 973 and 982) and on the cross of Victory at Oviedo[11] (dated to 908). The character

[1] *Ibid.*, fig. 19.

[2] Strömberg (1953).

[3] Arbman and Stenberger (1935), 73 and, for inlay only, Kendrick (1934), fig. 5.

[4] *Ibid.*, 398.

[5] Cf. Arbman (1940–3), pl. 9, 3 and 4 and Petersen (1919), 31–3.

[6] Bruce-Mitford (1956a), pl. xxxi, A.

[7] I have discussed this object in greater detail elsewhere, cf. Wilson (1960c), the following is merely a summary of my arguments there.

[8] Schnitzler (1957), pls. 134–5.

[9] Jantzen (1947), pls. 151–3.

[10] Elbern (1956), pl. 49.

[11] Schlunk (1950), fig. 18.

of the filigree on these examples is very close to that on the King's School, Canterbury, brooch. Similar filigree also occurs in Scandinavia,[1] where it is presumably derived from the Continent. The designs of the filigree panels are fairly simple and typical of much Continental filigree work. They have little relation to motifs in the art of the period, save that the rich elaborate panels of the border might be compared in a general way with the tight vine-scroll of the Corpus Christi, *Vita Cuthberti* (Corpus Christi College, Cambridge MS. 183, fol. 1b),[2] which probably dates from the first third of the tenth century. The dating of the brooch and its main interest really lie in the incised and nielloed designs to which attention must now be turned.

The parallel between the dividing lines of the face of the brooch and those of the ninth-century disc brooch series has already been drawn. It is further interesting to note the distinct parallel with the dividing lines of the Trewhiddle horn mounts (nos. 94–5) and the group of Hiberno-Saxon, penannular brooches mentioned above (p. 37 f.), as well as with the casket plate (no. 155), which will be discussed below. The smaller fields of ornament are filled with a motif consisting of a four-element interlaced knot, the centre of which is surrounded by a ring; although this motif occurs only once in Anglo-Saxon metalwork of the period,[3] it is found in sculpture[4] and in the Continental manuscript art.[5] It is of no chronological significance, but it is perhaps worth mentioning the fact that the interlaced ring is a typical feature of Anglo-Viking Jellinge and Ringerike art.[6] The clumsy incoherence of the animal ornament which fills the larger fields is closely allied to the ornament of panel *h* of the Sittingbourne scramasax (no. 80). The amorphous, interlacing bodies are nicked at the contour and are related to the Trewhiddle animals by way of that on the Sittingbourne scramasax. An added embellishment is the spiral hook at the hip, a feature which can be traced in insular animal ornament as far back as the seventh century[7] and which is also a particularly marked feature of the Jellinge and Ringerike styles in both Scandinavia and England.[8] In a general manner the animals on this brooch can be compared with animals on the Viking sculptures of northern England, for instance on the Sinnington cross shaft[9] and on certain Scandinavian objects, the decoration of which apparently imitates Anglo-Saxon art, e.g. the Stenåsa stirrup[10] and the Austris brooch.[11]

The Canterbury brooch must be considered in relation to the pair of casket plates (nos. 154–5) of unknown provenance. I have discussed these objects elsewhere,[12] here I must merely summarise my arguments and consider them in connection with the King's School, Canterbury, brooch (no. 10), which had not been found when I wrote my

[1] E.g. Arbman (1937), pls. 62, 17 and 61, 2.

[2] Kendrick (1938c), pl. lxxii, 1.

[3] On the sword from Nedre Store-Var; Petersen (1919), fig. 95.

[4] Cf. Kendrick (1949), pl. 49, 2 (in a rather developed form).

[5] Cf. MS., Rome, Vatican, reg. lat. 482, fol. 13 (Rand (1929), ii pl. 74, 1).

[6] Cf. Kendrick (1949), pls. 58, 61, 1 and 48, 1.

[7] Cf. the Lindisfarne Gospels, *passim*.

[8] Cf. Kendrick (1949), pls. 49, 2, 59 and 67 and Lindqvist (1931), fig. 24.

[9] Collingwood (1927), fig. 143.

[10] Holmqvist (1951), fig. 40.

[11] Stenberger (1947–58), ii, fig. 140, a.

[12] Wilson (1956c).

paper. The lower, rectangular, plate (no. 154) is of less importance from an art-historical point of view than the roof plate (no. 155). Originally there were repoussé bosses in the centre of each roundel and this feature is paralleled on the silver disc from Igelösa, Skåne, Sweden.[1] The four triquetra knots within an equal-armed cross are paralleled, in a more or less contemporary context, on a large thistle-headed penannular brooch from Penrith,[2] although here the equal-armed cross, which separates the triquetras on the casket plate, is missing. In many of its details the roof plate reflects the art of the Trewhiddle horn mounts (nos. 94–5). The triangular fields, the billeted borders, the use of niello, the use of dome-headed rivets (now missing), the speckling of the ornament and the sub-triangular bodies, all stem from the Trewhiddle style. The scratched human mask is paralleled on one of the Sevington spoons (no. 67), but the rest of the ornament has features of the Viking Jellinge style. The double contour of the bodies of the animals, the ring interlacing with the neck and one of the limbs and the leaf-like quality of the head, are all features of the Jellinge style in its homeland.[3] The muddled interlace surrounding the body of the animal is typical of the Jellinge style as it appears on the Anglo-Saxon sculptured crosses of the North of England.[4] The same interlace occurs, together with the typical Jellinge hipformed of a spiral hook, on the disc brooch from the King's School, Canterbury (no. 10). Both these objects must have been manufactured at a time when the tradition of the Trewhiddle style was still alive and I would be tempted to place these objects, together with the Sittingbourne scramasax (no. 80), at the end of the ninth or the beginning of the tenth century, in a period, say, some fifty years later than the date of the manufacture of the Trewhiddle horn mounts.

The casket plate and the brooch would seem to be the result of an attempt by an Anglo-Saxon artist to achieve a foreign style—the Jellinge style. Anglo-Saxon craftsmen were never really at home in the florid Viking style, they were led into clumsy over-elaboration: this applies to both metalwork and sculpture and in only a few pieces, such as the Skaill brooches[5] and the carvings of the eleventh century, such as the famous stone from St. Paul's churchyard,[6] did the insular craftsman achieve a complete mastery over this alien style. I would further deny that the Jellinge style had its roots in England, as Shetelig[7] and many others have suggested: the Jellinge style is an indigenous Scandinavian style and was never really at home on English soil. The Anglo-Saxon artist of the tenth century was developing his own style and most of its inspiration came from France, Germany and the Mediterranean world. This is not to deny that Anglo-Saxon art of the tenth century influenced the art of the Viking homeland; the Austris brooch and the Stenåsa stirrup, which have already been quoted,[8] are adequate evidence for this, but these are not classic examples of Jellinge ornament.

The art of the tenth-century manuscripts reflects little of the contemporary Viking

[1] Bruce-Mitford (1956*a*), fig. 39, *bis*.

[2] *Proceedings of the Society of Antiquaries of London*, 2nd series, xxi, 68 and fig. 2.

[3] Parallels are cited in Wilson (1956*c*), 36–7.

[4] Cf. the cross-shaft from Otley, Yorkshire and the grave slab from Levisham, Yorkshire:

Wilson (1956*c*) fig. 5 and pl. V, b.

[5] Anderson (1883), figs. 71–7.

[6] Kendrick (1949), fig. LXVII.

[7] (1948).

[8] See p. 41.

styles, it is not until the latter part of the century that Scandinavian influences begin to appear in the manuscript art. The style, which above every other style, revealed the true genius of the Anglo-Saxon artist in the last two centuries of the Anglo-Saxon era is the Winchester style. An early aspect of the florid Winchester art can be seen in a restrained manner in the Bede manuscript from Corpus Christi College, Cambridge (MS. 183)[1] which, it is alleged, was presented by King Æthelstan to the shrine of St. Cuthbert at Chester-le-Street[2]; this attribution may be too precise, but there can be no doubt that this manuscript belongs to the first half of the tenth century. To the same group belong a number of other manuscripts (e.g., British Museum MS., Cotton Galba A XVIII; Bodleian Library, Oxford, MSS. Tanner 10 and Junius 27 and the Durham Rituale, Durham Cathedral Library MS. A IV.19) and the stole and maniple of St. Cuthbert[3] which is, as we have seen, well dated. Panel *b* of the Sittingbourne scramasax (no. 80) has already been related to this early group, but this is practically the only metal object decorated in the style of the group.

The back of the matrix of the seal of Ælfric (no. 104) is one of the few metal objects decorated in the classic Winchester acanthus style of the late tenth century. The only other major objects of metalwork decorated in the true Winchester style are a portable altar in the Musée de Cluny, Paris (the frame of which is decorated with human figures in the style of the Winchester school[4]) the mounts of a crozier in the treasury of Cologne Cathedral,[5] and a bronze, enamelled roundel, from Oxford, which is discussed below[6]. The ornament of the seal is floriate and is probably best compared with the acanthus decoration at the corner of certain frames to illuminations in the major Winchester manuscripts, e.g. in the Benedictional of St. Æthelwold, which can be dated between 971 and 984.[7] But there is a certain restrained and spindly quality to the ornament of the seal which is not present in the Benedictional, it might loosely be compared with the acanthus of the rather later Charter of the New Minster.[8] The extremely close connection between seal-dies and coins in the Anglo-Saxon period indicates that the die makers were very conscious of coin design and this enables us to date the seal-die, for the spray in front of the bust of the seal face is only found on English coins struck between March 978 and Michaelmas 979. It would seem unlikely that an old coin was used as a model by the die-maker because coins were frequently and regularly re-minted at this period and had a comparatively short life in circulation. If this dating is correct, it was made within a few years of the painting of the Benedictional of St. Æthelwold, an hypothesis which might have some far-reaching effects on the dating of the Winchester manuscripts.

What seems to have been one of the equivalents in metalwork of the Winchester style is a group of bronzes, of which four are in the British Museum: the censer covers from Canterbury and London Bridge (nos. 9 and 44), an unprovenanced strap-end (no. 148) and a small jug or 'cruet' which also has no provenance (no. 147); to these can probably

[1] Kendrick (1949), pl. XXXIII.
[2] James (1912), 441, following Plummer.
[3] Battiscombe (1956), 375–432.
[4] Wilson (1960), pl. 16.
[5] Goldschmidt (1926), pl. II, 10.
[6] P. 45 f.
[7] Cf. fol. 90b. Wormald (1959), pl. 6.
[8] Kendrick (1949), pl. II.

be added the Pershore censer cover (no. 56) and the silver disc from Cuxton (no. 14). These display few traces of Viking art, but, in the grotesque creatures which embellish them (although they may not have been derived from ninth-century sources), can be seen the inherent love of the Anglo-Saxons for contorted animal ornament. Kendrick, who first drew attention to this group of objects,[1] suggested that the ultimate origin of the animals was to be found in the Carolingian vine scroll, which makes its first appearance in England in the Corpus Christi Bede.[2] The pairs of birds on the cruet are very similar to those which appear in this manuscript, and it would be tempting to say that the object, which is distinguished from the other objects of this group by the small feet of the birds, belongs to the earliest phase of this ornamental style. Although this may be true it cannot be stated too positively, in the face of the occurrence of small birds' feet in the late tenth-century Lambeth Aldhelm manuscript[3] and as it is difficult to date the spiral animal hips on the spout of the object, which are executed in a Viking manner. Kendrick's skilful comparison of this hip with an initial from the Durham Rituale[4] is perhaps even more significant than was at the time realised. The initial is of Viking inspiration, the mask at the base of the initial is a typical feature of the Jellinge style[5] and the spiral hip is undoubtedly derived from the same source. But this early manuscript parallel (the Durham Rituale is usually dated to the early tenth century) is of no significance in fixing the chronological position of the 'cruet', for the ornament could quite as easily be compared with late tenth- and eleventh-century details in Viking art.[6]

The engraved ornament on the foot of the 'cruet' is of little significance. The technique of reserving an ornament against a pointillé background occurs frequently in the surviving tenth-century metalwork, as on the Velds stirrup-plates (pl. IX, a).

The closely related censer covers are equally difficult to date satisfactorily. They bear no traces of the Viking influence present on the 'cruet'. On the other hand there is a greater variety of motifs on these objects. The relationship of the 'cruet' to the Canterbury censer cover can clearly be seen in two of the lower panels, where similar adorsed birds, separated by a foliate element, occur. The birds in the gables of both the London Bridge and Canterbury censer covers are but one of many features which relate these two bronzes. This relationship is extremely interesting when we consider the parallel these birds afford to similar birds with similar stances in the Winchester group of manuscripts, particularly in Trinity College, Cambridge, MS., B.10.4. On fol. 13b of this manuscript (pl. VIII, a) these single birds can be seen in similar contorted positions, and in the same place can be seen the typical animal of the period, a lion-like creature, *passant regardant*, with its tail passing between its hind legs and crossing its body. Another manuscript, perhaps of slightly earlier date,[7] an *Arator*, also in Trinity College, Cambridge (B.14.3), shows a bird on fol. 5a with wings displayed in a contorted manner similar to that which appears in the lozenge-shaped fields and on one of the rectangular

[1] Kendrick (1938c), 378.

[2] Corpus Christi College, Cambridge, manuscript 183; Kendrick (1949), pl. 33, 1.

[3] *Ibid.*, pl. 33, 2.

[4] Kendrick (1938c), 381 and fig. 2.

[5] E.g. Christiansson (1959), pl. 149.

[6] Cf., for example, the animal on a brooch from Hurva, which is found in a mid-eleventh-century hoard, Holmqvist (1951), fig. 38.

[7] Wormald (1945), 135, dates it to *c*. 1000.

panels of the Canterbury censer (pl. VIII, *b*). The inlaid silver panels at the base of the Canterbury censer cover, decorated with a linear representation of degenerate acanthus ornament, are closely paralleled in the Sherborne Pontifical (Paris: Bibilothèque nationale, fonds latins, 943) where they occur in the borders of fols. 4b and 6b[1]—this manuscript is firmly dated to 992–5.

In fact, most of the ornamental details of this group of objects can be paralleled in those manuscripts which are loosely classified under the heading, 'The Winchester School'. It would be stretching the evidence, however, to say that they should be dated to the end of the tenth century just because there are a large number of parallels in manuscripts of that period. The bird in the initial on fol. 12b of the early tenth-century manuscript, Bodleian Library, Oxford, Tanner 10, with its contorted form and strangely displayed wings,[2] is as close a parallel to the Canterbury censer cover as any that can be provided nearly a century later in the same medium.

If it were possible to date the phases of the Viking 'Ringerike' style more exactly, it might be possible to gain an approximate date for this relief style, by comparing it with a comb in the British Museum, which is decorated on one face with a Ringerike design and on the other with a pair of small contorted animals with masks not unlike those on the London Bridge censer cover.[3]

Outside England interesting parallels have been drawn between this group of objects and the swords from Vrångabäck and Dybäck in Sweden.[4] The different opinions concerning these swords are adequately summarised by Dr. Strömberg[5]:

'Brøndsted betrachtet das Schwert von Dybäck als skandinavische Arbeit nach südenglischem Muster. M. Rydbeck hält es für nicht ausgeschlossen, dass die Griffe der beiden Schwerter in Schonen gemacht worden sein können. Arbman schreibt 1935 über die Waffe aus Dybäck: "Wahrscheinlich ist es ein schonischer Meister, der sie herstellte, wobei er fast sklavisch südenglischen Vorbildern gefolgt ist". Paulsen schliesslich meint, dass einige Züge in der Ausführung der Schwertgriffe unzweifelhaft nordisch seien; doch sind nach ihm die südenglischen Kennzeichen so auffällig, das die Griffe in Südengland, allerdings unter wikingischem Einfluss, enstanden sein müssen. Die Ansichten gehen also auseinander, doch ist man sich darin einig, dass hier neben gewissen unmissverständlich nordischen Stilelementen sehr starke englische Züge vorliegen. Mir [Strömberg] will es so scheinen, als ob diese Schwerter mit ihrem doch nicht so auffällig nordischen Gepräge, aber so zahlreichen englischen Charakteristika in England hergestellt und nach Schonen exportiert wurden, denn zwischen beiden Ländern bestanden im 11 Jh. enge Beziehungen.'

I do not consider these swords to be English objects; the animals on the Vrångabäck hilt particularly[6] are in many respects different from the animals on the censer covers and other objects in this group; further the use of the surface of the two hilts is unparalleled in England, while the scabbard mount of the Dybäck sword is in no way English. The

[1] Wormald (1952), pl. 5a.
[2] Kendrick (1949), pl. XXVIII, 1.
[3] Wilson (1960*b*).
[4] Rydbeck (1931/2).
[5] (1961), i, 140.
[6] *Ibid.*, i, fig. 15.

snake on the Vrångabäck sword is only found in English contexts where the design is purely Viking (as on the bone comb cited above). I see these swords as a product of a South Scandinavian craftsman working under strong English influence, in much the same way as the master of the Austris brooch was working under strong English influence a few years earlier (see above, p. 42).

Another interesting parallel is provided by a group of objects of which the Kremsmünster candlesticks are the leading examples.[1] These objects are mentioned in an inventory of the Abbot Sigmar (1012-40) (*duo candelabra auro et argento parata*) and may well have been of some age when the list was drawn up. The incised silver bands which spiral up the stems of these objects cannot be related to the English material, but the ornament of the foot and the cast zoomorphic decoration of the stem are quite closely comparable with the English material. The large animals at the foot of the candlestick can be compared, as Arbman has pointed out,[2] with the lion above the spout of the 'cruet' (no. 147), while the inlaid panels on the bodies of these animals[3] can be compared with the similar feature on the Canterbury censer cover (no. 9). The animals on the stems of the candlesticks are of a very individual form: the tail of one animal curling round the neck of the animal below it. They bear a resemblance—although only a very superficial one—to the animals on the censer covers. They are more closely to be associated with a number of Continental objects, such as a candlestick in the Landesmuseum at Bonn[4] and an enamelled disc brooch in the British Museum.[5] The former has birds treated in a manner similar to that of the animals on the Kremsmünster candlesticks, while the latter has a frieze of very similar animals. Another interesting parallel is afforded by a book box from Seitz a.d. Lahn, Germany (pl. IX, *b*) which has many features closely comparable to the English bronzes, as has a gold finger-ring in the British Museum from the Castellani collection[6] which was almost certainly found in Italy. It is unfortunately impossible to date any of these objects closely, but it is surely significant that a monastic foundation with as many English contacts as Kremsmünster should have produced these remarkable objects. I would suggest that here again the Anglo-Saxon artist was influencing his Continental colleagues.

Neither of these two groups is of any great assistance in the study of the Anglo-Saxon objects under consideration here. While there can be little doubt that the swords from Sweden were copied from Anglo-Saxon prototypes, it is possible that the style of the English objects was derived from a Continental source, but the geographical position of this style, in an area much influenced by Anglo-Saxon culture,[7] is perhaps indicative of a stylistic traffic from England to the Continent and to Scandinavia. Whatever the real situation, there can be little doubt concerning the popularity of this style in England: as many carvings in bone and ivory,[8] as well as in stone, witness. It would be a bold man who would attempt to argue against the accepted dating of the Breedon-on-the-Hill

[1] Arbman (1958).
[2] *Ibid.*, 190.
[3] *Ibid.*, figs. 3–6.
[4] Falke and Meyer (1935), pl. 6, 14.
[5] Wilson (1957*a*).

[6] *B M Ring Cat.*, pl II, 207.
[7] Cf. Haseloff (1951), 66 f.
[8] E.g. Kendrick (1949), pl. XXXVI, 1, Wilson (1960*b*) and Brøndsted (1924), fig. 132.

carvings (put forward by Clapham[1] and Kendrick[2]), but one might suggest that not all the sculpture at Breedon is of the same date and that some of it may reflect the art of the censer covers and 'cruet', and may belong to the tenth or eleventh centuries.[3]

As well as the unprovenanced strap-end (no. 148), which belongs to this group of bronzes, one other object must be considered—the Pershore censer cover (no. 56). This object stands on its own: typologically it is very close to the Canterbury and London Bridge censer covers (nos. 9 and 44), the form of the roof and the gargoyle-like animal heads are very close parallels. Unfortunately it is not possible to relate the ornament to the rest of the group of bronzes, other than in a very general sense. The small duck-like creatures in the lozenge-shaped panels of the roof, although they are unlike any other birds in Anglo-Saxon art, have a few features of the Winchester style—particularly the large, spread feet to which I have already drawn attention.

I have, with some hesitation, omitted from this catalogue an object which Kendrick considered to be of twelfth-century date—the sword pommel said to be from East Anglia.[4] Although there are many features which might associate it with this group of objects, Kendrick is surely right in placing it where he does; for the general flacidity and flatness are features which cannot be paralleled in the available corpus of pre-1100 material.

FIG. 5. Detail of ornament from an enamelled brooch from Oxford. Scale c. $\frac{2}{1}$. (*Ashmolean Museum, Oxford.*)

An object which also belongs to this group is the disc from Cuxton (no. 14), this has birds which might roughly be compared to those on the censer covers, etc. The large foot, the displayed wings and the contorted position of the lower bird are all paralleled in this group. The motif itself was a popular one in Germanic art from an early period, occurring for example on the Sutton Hoo purse-lid.[5]

The small piece of sheet-bronze of no provenance (no. 143) may be considered here. It has acanthus scrolls which show Winchester influence, but so little survives that it is difficult to be too precise in attribution, although in the manner and technique of decoration it might well be compared with the later Viking style panel from Winchester (pl. X, *a*). The slightly ragged leaves are not dissimilar to those on the Velds stirrup plates (pl. IX, *a*).

A much more complicated problem is raised by an object from Oxford, in the Ashmolean Museum. It is a bronze enamelled disc of the familiar Kettlach type[6] and is decorated with birds (fig. 5), which are distinctly comparable to the art of such Winchester style manuscripts as Bodleian Library, Oxford MS. Tanner 10.[7] There can be little doubt that this object is English, indeed it is one of the very few pieces of metalwork

[1] (1928).

[2] (1938*a*), 171 ff.

[3] E.g. the panel, Kendrick (1938*a*), pl. lxxiii, top right.

[4] Kendrick (1938*c*), pl. lxxiv, 5.

[5] [Bruce-Mitford] (1956*b*), pl. 18.

[6] See above, p. 37.

[7] Cf., for example, fol. 12b; Kendrick (1949), pl. 28, 1.

that imitate closely the art of the manuscripts. The question then arises whether another object—and possibly more—in the Museum's collections could not be considered as English, one of these is a brooch from a Viking grave at Cambois, Bedlington, Northumberland,[1] which Reginald Smith refused to attribute to any particular country. The Museum has a number of other examples of this type of brooch, one comes from Temesvar, Hungary,[2] and two are of no provenance.[3] These three objects are undoubtedly foreign and may be associated with the Kettlach series, known in Austria, Hungary and Germany. But the Bedlington example, of the English provenance and the fact that an example from Hyde Abbey (in the Winchester Museum) may come from the same mould, might lead us to consider that it, like the Oxford example, is English. There is no inherent quality in this brooch which would associate it with an English art style and, for the moment, there is not sufficient evidence to include it in this catalogue.[4]

The post-Jellinge phase of Viking-influenced art in England is difficult to set in order. There is undoubtedly a distinct difference between the pure Viking styles of eleventh-century Scandinavia and the amalgam of styles appearing at the same period in English metalwork. Such objects as the Pitney brooch (no. 60) fit comparatively easily into the sequence and can be seen in a clear relation to their Scandinavian ornamental prototypes; but other objects are less easy to analyse. The following objects listed in this catalogue are of post-Jellinge Viking style: a brooch from Dunwich, Suffolk (no. 15), the Hammersmith plaque (no. 42), the Kemsley Downs mount (no. 26), the Lincoln mount (no. 33), the Barnes buckle loop (no. 34), the Oxshott Wood mount (no. 55), the Pitney brooch (no. 60), the Sutton, Isle of Ely brooch (no. 83), the Peterborough mount (no. 58), and an unprovenanced mount (no. 141) and disc brooch (no. 151).

The style usually described as Ringerike is well recognised in England; the finest monument is undoubtedly the well-known gravestone from St. Paul's churchyard, London,[5] which is carved in a flat relief and was painted in various colours, and may well have been carved in the first quarter of the eleventh century, when Viking kings occupied the English throne. There are a number of other stone carvings which give a very clear idea of the competence of the English craftsmen in this medium, but the style is poorly represented in metalwork. The brooches (and mounts) from Dunwich (no. 15) and Oxshott Wood (no. 55), and the example without provenance (no. 151), are decorated in a style which is roughly related to the Ringerike style. Other examples have been published by Miss Evison[6] and come from Threxton, Bottisham Lode, and the (?) Leicester district.[7] I have elsewhere[8] compared the Oxshott Wood mount with the pendants from Saffron Walden, Essex,[9] which had been dated by Brøndsted[10] to the tenth

[1] *BMASG*, 101 and fig. 121.
[2] Reg. no. 1930, 10–24, 23.
[3] Reg. no. 80, 8–20, 28 and Wilson (1957).
[4] The brooch should be compared with Dinklage (1955), colour plate.
[5] Kendrick (1949), pl. 67.
[6] (1957): the Dunwich example is missing from her inventory, but backs up her arguments.
[7] The brooch from London (no. 48), which is too corroded to interpret, may be a more elaborate example of this group.
[8] Wilson (1956a), 70.
[9] Kendrick (1949), pl. 83, 2.
[10] (1924), 255.

century and by Kendrick[1] to the eleventh century. The Oxshott mount shows a very marked broken back to the lower contour of the curve of the loop, a feature which is to be seen in the Winchester/Ringerike ornament of the late tenth and eleventh centuries in England.[2] These would seem to be the best comparisons—and with the Oxshott mount must go the other objects. The Saffron Walden pendants I take to be slightly earlier, exhibiting traces of the more rounded and florid Winchester style of the tenth century. The pellets in the Oxshott mount may tentatively be interpreted as eyes, but it would be impossible to insist on this zoomorphic characteristic. The objects have, as Miss Evison has pointed out, certain Scandinavian characteristics and their immediate precursors may be such brooches as that from Allmänninge, Valbo, Gästrikland, Sweden,[3] which has a similar, but more developed, pattern executed in silver filigree, which was deposited in a hoard dated 1100 and has a design whose history goes back to the early Viking period. The bronze brooches are, however, undoubtedly of English workmanship. Their typological resemblance to the brooches decorated with shaggy animals[4] and their distribution in the East of England, may indicate that they too were made in East Anglia.

The nearest approach to a pure Ringerike style in the Anglo-Saxon metalwork in the British Museum is to be found on the brooch from Sutton, Isle of Ely (no. 83). As Bruce-Mitford said '. . . it remains difficult to claim anything more specific for the art of the Sutton brooch than that it is an English equivalent of late Viking style'.[5] It is extremely difficult to estimate the different components of the style of this piece. Its very sketchy technique is difficult to parallel in the English series. The parallels with the metal mounts of the Cammin casket drawn by Bruce-Mitford[6] are fair, but there is perhaps a firmness in the execution of the Cammin casket mounts that is not present on the Sutton brooch. The techniques of the two objects are undoubtedly the same, but the ornament of the Sutton brooch is more developed—or more degenerate—than that of the Cammin casket. There is a sense of that movement in the figures of the Sutton brooch which is so typical of the art of the Ringerike style; while the trilobate ornament, in the corners of certain fields, is surely a freer expression of the rather stiffer motif seen on such Ringerike objects as the bronze strip from Winchester (pl. X, *a*), the St. Paul's gravestone in the British Museum[7] and the Hammersmith plaque (no. 42). The ring round the interlacing portions of the snakes, although a typical Ringerike feature, also occurs in Jellinge art, as on the casket plate (no. 155). The cross-hatching round the borders of the field and the treatment of the edge of the brooch are without parallel. The two-faced head of one of the animals on the brooch is not unknown in Viking art, but the best parallel to the form of the head is provided by the Jellinge style on an antler sleeve from

[1] (1949), 38.

[2] Cf. particularly the capital of Bodleian Library, Oxford, MS., Junius II, fol. 57. (Kendrick, 1949, pl. 73, 2). The ears of the animal in the initial of Cambridge, University Library, MS., Ff. 1. 23, fol. 37 v. (*ibid.*, pl. 73, 1) and fol. 17b of the Lambeth Palace MS., 200 (*Ibid.*, pl. 32, 2).

[3] Stenberger (1947–48), i, fig. 1, 1.

[4] See above, p. 36 f.

[5] (1956*a*), 197.

[6] *Loc. cit.*

[7] *Ibid.*, pl. 68.

Køge Strand, Denmark.[1] The closest parallel in style, if not in ornamental detail, is to be found on the Velds stirrup plates (pl. IX, *a*), which are undoubtedly English objects (with Winchester style birds and the speckled background of the Winchester plate cited above). If one begins to analyse the Velds ornament certain similarities emerge which, although they cannot be defined too closely, give a similar impression to the eye: these are the lively freehand quality of the drawing, the bits of loose foliage (perhaps better paralleled on the bronze plate of no provenance, (no. 143)) and the formalised treatment of at least two of the birds portrayed, which can be roughly equated with the semi-zoomorphic motifs in the outermost fields of the Sutton brooch. I am aware that this parallel is subjective, but it may well be valid and may explain the English quality of the pseudo-Viking Sutton brooch. There are, of course, English elements in the ornament: the backward-looking animal is presumably derived from Anglo-Saxon sources, the division of the surface of the brooch and the bosses at the points where the borders of the field join are typical features of the English disc brooch, added to this is the fact that there is a rhyming Anglo-Saxon inscription on the back. But the Viking influence is strong; the lentoid fields with their spirals, for example, are derived from the hips of Viking animals. We have already seen one on the cruet (no. 147) and they are frequent in Ringerike contexts in the Viking homeland; as on the Söderala weather vane[2] and, in England, on one of the Smithfield plates[3] (where they are divorced from its zoomorphic context). It must be recognised, however, that the Sutton brooch is decorated in a unique manner and that, until further parallels are produced, it is of little use to fix it too closely in an artistic context. It has a *terminus ante quem* supplied by its deposition with coins of William the Conqueror, so it is safe to date it to the late tenth or early eleventh century.

The bronze plaque from Hammersmith (no. 42) must be considered next. There is no doubt as to its Ringerike characteristics, the trilobate head is, as has been pointed out, a typical feature of Ringerike art, as are the long tendril-like scrolls. This style is best paralleled by the Winchester plate (pl. X, *a*), which Kendrick has no hesitation in ascribing to a pure Viking tradition with no English element in it.[4] This is of course true, but the Hammersmith bronze and the Winchester fragment must be considered to fall within the context of this catalogue as they were, like the St. Paul's slab in the Guildhall Museum,[5] made in England under the Viking kings of the early eleventh century and demonstrate the development, from the straggly Winchester acanthus, of the ornamental motifs that in Scandinavia would be classed as Ringerike. The similarity between the Winchester piece (pl. X, *a*) and the fragment with no provenance (no. 143), which shows only a very few traces of Viking elements and a more considerable amount of Winchester influence, is interesting as, technically, they are very close. The latter piece shows perhaps the beginning of the break-away from the Winchester style towards the Ringerike, which matures in this country in the Winchester plate and the Hammersmith bronze. The two styles, Winchester and Ringerike, were very close, and Kendrick[6] has demon-

[1] Brøndsted (1924), fig. 208.
[2] Lindqvist (1931), fig. 24.
[3] Wheeler (1927), fig. 21.

[4] Kendrick (1949), 100 and fig. 13.
[5] Kendrick (1949), pl. 67.
[6] (1941*b*), 139–40.

strated that there was 'a general sympathy' between them, which expressed itself in such manuscripts as Cambridge University Library Ff. 1.23, where the two styles appear both side-by-side and merged. It is further of interest that at Winchester itself, one of the centres of the English style, more than one object decorated in the Ringerike style should be found.

The bronze buckle loop from the Thames at Barnes (no. 34), which is decorated with Ringerike ornament of a very degenerate form, is obviously an unfinished piece of casting and was, therefore, presumably made in this country. It is completely without parallel.

The Pitney brooch (no. 60), the mounts from Lincoln and Peterborough (nos. 33 and 58) and the mount with no provenance (no. 141), together possibly with the mount from Kemsley Downs (no. 26), are all representative of the final phase of Viking art in this country—the late eleventh-century Urnes style. The ultimate Scandinavian-influenced style, represented by the crozier 'of Bishop Flambard'[1] and the sculpture of such objects as the famous Norwich capital,[2] is unrepresented in the Museum's collection of metal-work (and in any case may go beyond the limits of the dates of this catalogue). The Pitney brooch (no. 60) is the best expression in this country of the Urnes style—depicting the typical combat motif familiar in the Scandinavian homeland. The openwork treatment of the ornament is presumably derived from the Urnes style openwork brooches which occur in some quantities in Scandinavia.[3] Another openwork disc is that from Wisbech (pl. X, e), which is very similar to the Pitney brooch in design, save that there is no interlacing snake with the animal. The prototype of the ornament of the Peterborough, Lincoln and the unprovenanced mounts (nos. 58, 33 and 141), and more especially of the Kemsley Downs mount (no. 26), is demonstrated by such objects as the strap-distributor from Gotland, illustrated in pl. X, d. All these objects are totally unlike any Urnes objects found in Scandinavia and form such a homogeneous group that there can be little doubt that they represent an English facet of the same style.

As a footnote to this discussion it may be added that the mount from Kemsley Downs (no. 26) may be presumed to be a degenerate form of the same ornament. A further stage of this degeneration can be seen on a mount from Ixworth in the Cambridge Museum (pl. X, b). It can be also compared with the style of the sword-guard from Sherborne Lane, London.[4]

[1] Kendrick (1938b).
[2] Zarnecki (1951), pl. 76.
[3] Shetelig (1909), figs. 24 and 26 and

Brøndsted (1924), fig. 202.
[4] Wheeler (1935), fig. 43.

CHAPTER III

THE CLASSIFICATION OF THE OBJECTS

The notes that follow attempt to set out the catalogued objects in a typological sequence. Statistically there are too few objects to be treated in great typological detail—even when the whole corpus of material, both inside and outside the Museum, is considered. Only when an object is of especial typological significance, or when typology can fundamentally aid the dating of an object, or a group of objects, are any detailed arguments put forward; otherwise the entry is treated merely as a convenient place for listing all the objects of a single type in the Museum's collections and discussing their use. The objects are discussed alphabetically under types. Objects at present unidentifiable are listed at the end of the chapter.

Belt-slides: Two objects from the Trewhiddle hoard (nos. 101 and 102) are presumably belt-slides and were obviously used in conjunction with the pair of cast strap-ends from the same hoard (nos. 99 and 100). They are unique in Anglo-Saxon contexts.

Book-mount: See *Mount*.

Box-mount: See *Mount*.

Brooch: All the brooches included in the catalogue are circular. The disc brooch seems to have been as ubiquitous in the South of England as the penannular brooch was in the Hiberno-Saxon area. Brooches of other shapes are practically unknown and, apart from a rectangular, pewter brooch from York,[1] the quatrefoil from Hauge, Norway (pl. III, *e*) and the possibility that the trefoil object from Kirkoswald (no. 28) was originally a brooch (it has traces of some sort of fastening attachment on the back), there is little evidence of other forms in the surviving archaeological material of the period. Such objects are hardly susceptible to typological division—it is only possible to draw a distinction between the richer type of brooches made of precious metal (nos. 2, 3, 10, 83, 152 and 153) and the poorer type of brooch made of base metal (nos. 8, 11, 15, 37, 39, 47, 51–54, 84, 88, 134 and 142). The larger brooches are occasionally dished, as are the Sutton (no. 83), Canterbury (no. 10), Strickland (no. 152) and Fuller (no. 153) brooches, but the rest are flat. The close relationship between the two groups is amply demonstrated by the division of the fields on the Thames pewter brooch (no. 88), which is imitative of the same feature on the larger, richer brooches, e.g. Beeston Tor (no. 3). Certain, rather richer, brooches, e.g. Pitney (no. 60), Ixworth (no. 25) and Rome (no. 64), seem to bridge the gap between the two groups.

Certain discs (e.g. no. 55, from Oxshott) are probably brooches, as they are paralleled ornamentally with known brooches. But other discs, such as that from Sevington (no. 70), are almost certainly not brooches and are listed below under the *Unclassified* heading.

---

[1] Richardson (1959), fig. 18, 3.

The object, no. 15, which is without pin or catch-plate and merely has two lugs on the back (fig. 16), presumably fulfilled the function of a brooch.

Bruce-Mitford has clearly shown[1] that the form of the large disc brooches is derived from that of the circular brooches found in pagan Anglo-Saxon contexts. Brooches of this form do not occur at all on the Continent. The smaller brooches are probably to be derived, to some extent, from the same source; but the universal prevalence of coin brooches on the Continent and the presence of enamelled, base-metal brooches there,[2] should caution us not to make too hasty a judgement in this matter. A circular brooch is such an obvious thing that typological judgements concerning it can only be used with great caution.

It would appear from the manuscript illustrations that, in the later part of the period at least, round brooches were worn on the shoulder, fastening the outer garment (cloak) of a man[3]; occasionally, however, the brooch occurs on the breast.[4] Women are rarely, if ever shown wearing a brooch.

Buckle and *buckle plate:* Despite the apparent similarity between the Sevington buckle plate (no. 79) and the Trewhiddle buckle (no. 103), little typological sense can be made from the four buckles or buckle-plates included in this catalogue (nos. 34, 49, 79 and 103).

Casket: The two plates (nos. 154 and 155), which decorated a casket, may well have belonged to a house-shaped shrine of Hiberno-Saxon type. Such shrines are fairly common in the Celtic world[5] and on the Continent.[6] The Gandersheim casket[7] is an English example of this type of object. It is interesting, in the case of these plates, to see that the type persisted in England until the tenth century.

Censer cover: All the three known Anglo-Saxon censer covers are in the British Museum (nos. 9, 44 and 56). The form of each cover is architectural. Censers with covers of this type are apparently not represented in the manuscripts of the period; the normal form of a censer depicted in these sources is spherical.[8] Censer covers of architectural form are hinted at as early as the seventh century in Eastern Europe, where a censer of architectural form was found in the Early Christian basilica at Clapavice, near Salona, which was destroyed in 624.[9] This has a cover of slightly pyramidal form, pierced with arches and crowned by a small bird. Fleury[10] records another architectural example from Metz, which is of similar date. In the Romanesque period architecturally-shaped censer covers were very popular in Western Europe, and it must be presumed that there was a continuous tradition of this form from the end of the Early Christian period onwards.

There are no parallels, either in England or abroad, to the tower-shaped form of the

---

[1] (1956a), 171–3.

[2] Cf. Dinklage (1955).

[3] Cf. Wormald (1952), pls. 13, *b*, 20 and 30 and Millar (1926), pls. 3–5, 12, etc.

[4] *Ibid.*, pls. 23 and 39.

[5] Listed by G. Swarzenski (1954). Another example has since been found; it is in the Trondhjem Museum and comes from Setnes, Grytten, Romsdal, Norway.

[6] Some listed by Conway, *Proceedings of the Society of Antiquaries of London*, 2nd series, xxxi (1918–19), 221 ff.

[7] Scherer (1931), pl. 1.

[8] Cf. for example, Millar (1926), pls. 4 and 8 and Fleury (1883–9), v, pl. CDXXIV.

[9] Braun (1932), fig. 502.

[10] (1883–9), v, 160.

Anglo-Saxon censer-covers and, in view of this lack of evidence, it is impossible to discuss them typologically—particularly as art-historically they all seem to belong to the same period. It is useless to speculate concerning the form of the bowl.

Chalice: There is only one chalice included in this catalogue—no. 90, from the Trewhiddle hoard. The only other surviving Anglo-Saxon chalice comes from Hexham Abbey,[1] while a possible Anglo-Saxon chalice is that from Hazleton, Gloucestershire.[2] Both these latter are funerary chalices, but, although smaller, are fairly close in form to the Trewhiddle cup.

The Trewhiddle chalice, as it survives to-day, is not complete. A small silver collar was found in the hoard, but is now missing. It consisted of a circular plate, pierced by three holes, on which was placed a collar surrounded by a twisted silver wire. This was apparently part of the stem of the chalice. The correspondence of the holes in the base of the chalice to the holes in the missing piece was pointed out by the original owner of the hoard, who reproduced a picture of it.[3] There is little room to doubt that this piece

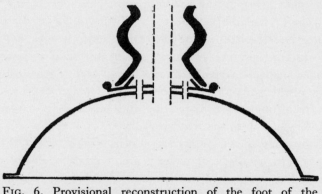

FIG. 6. Provisional reconstruction of the foot of the Trewhiddle chalice (no. 90). Scale $\frac{1}{1}$.

was attached between the base and the knop of the chalice and it is possible that a similar piece was attached between the bowl and the knop, but this can never be proved as the bottom of the bowl is missing. A provisional reconstruction of the foot of the bowl is illustrated in fig. 6. In this reconstruction it is presumed that the base was riveted to the collar through the two side holes and that a central bar passed through the knop and central hole, to be riveted beneath the foot. The two holes flanking the one in the centre must have been used to attach the collar to the foot, for the constriction in the knop is too narrow to allow lateral rivets to pass from the bowl to the foot.

The Hexham chalice has a similar collar above the knop. Many continental chalices have a similar feature above, below, or both above and below, the knop[4] and such a feature would not be out of place on the Trewhiddle chalice.

[1] Wilson and Blunt (1961), 90, 91 and pl. xxviii, a.

[2] Unpublished—exhibited to the Society of Antiquaries in 1942.

[3] Rashleigh (1794).

[4] Cf. The Kremsmünster (Tassilo) chalice, Haseloff (1951); the St. Chrodegand chalice, *The Dumbarton Oaks Collection Handbook*, Washington D.C., 1955, 64, the Skara chalice, Wideen (1955), fig. 158, and many others.

The bowl of the Trewhiddle chalice has been pierced at the rim at irregular intervals. In the holes are the shanks of rivets, set in two lines, one just above the rough top edge of the gilded band which encircles the rim, and the other within the gilded band (fig. 7, *a*). The gilded band is a little way below the rim. It would seem that a narrow silver strip was fastened with rivets below the rim and that this strip, the band, the flange and the interior of the bowl were all gilt. The rivets within the gilded band and the inscribed line some distance below the band are less easy to explain. My tentative reconstruction is that a further applied band, soldered to the bowl, could have been reinforced by dome-

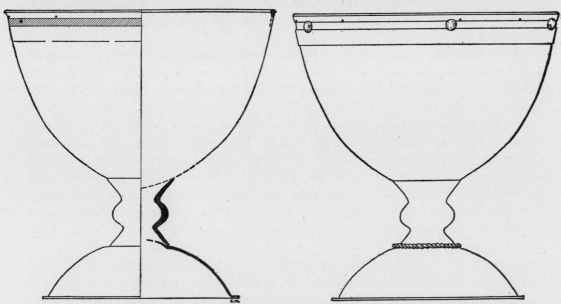

FIG. 7. (*a, left*) Section through the Trewhiddle chalice. (*b, right*) suggested reconstruction of chalice. Scale ½.

headed rivets which acted as flanges (fig. 7, *b*). Such a band could have been inscribed (the St. Martin des Champs,[1] Skara,[2] Ludger[3] and Chrodegand de Seez chalices,[4] have inscriptions on the bowl below the rim).

There is a general similarity of form between the Trewhiddle chalice and the early Continental chalices. The form of the foot, however, is different, but this may be an accidental feature, for, unlike Continental chalices which are usually made up of two pieces (foot and bowl) the English chalices consist of three pieces—foot, knop and bowl. But with so few chalices available it is difficult to say whether this is a typical or an atypical piece.

Cross: The small sheet-metal cross (no. 113) from Whitby Abbey was presumably mounted on a base and used in the monastery or by a member of the community. See also *Pendant.*

Cruet: See *Jug.*

[1] Stollenmeyer (1949), 54–5.
[2] Wideen (1955), fig. 158.
[3] Fleury (1883–9), iv, ccxcv.
[4] Stollenmeyer (1949), 54–5.

Finger-ring: The commonest type of finger-ring of this period is apparently made up of a flat gold band, decorated with an inscription (nos. 27, 30, 85 and 145), or with panels of ornament (no. 61). The shape appears to be an English one, but the form is so simple that it would be difficult to uphold such a statement with any authority.[1] The fragment of a ring with an oval bezel (e.g. no. 130 from Whitby) is paralleled in form by the Chelsea ring,[2] while the ring of Queen Æthelswith (no. 1), although more substantial, must be related to it. The Æthelwulf ring (no. 31) is without parallel in form, while the ring with no provenance (no. 146), may be related to the Continental series.[3] The Ebbesborne Wake ring (no. 16) is without parallel. The finger-rings of this period seem to bear little relationship to the pagan Anglo-Saxon finger-rings and provide little opportunity for typological division.

There is no evidence as to the use of the finger-rings, although they may have inherited some of the symbolic significance of the heroic 'ring', which was the main gift of a chieftain. They may have already become significant as symbols of marriage. The rings bearing the names of King Æthelwulf and Queen Æthelswith (nos. 31 and 1) must be seen not as the personal rings of the monarch whose name is inscribed on them, but rather as gifts of that monarch to a person or institution. It would be too much of a coincidence to have the personal rings of two Anglo-Saxon monarchs, and possibly a third,[4] in a period when inscribed rings are in any case rare. The personal ring of a king would presumably be buried with him. The only certain example of the royal ring is that of the Merovingian King Childeric I, found in his tomb at Tournai; but this was a signet ring and had a specific use—unique to one person.[5] The recent find in the church of St. Denis, of the finger-ring inscribed with the name of Queen Arnegunde, the mother of Chilperic, is of interest,[6] for this is not a signet ring and, on the analogy of the rings of Æthelwulf and Æthelswith, this need not necessarily be the personal ring of a queen.

We have no evidence of memorial rings being used earlier than the sixteenth century, so it seems unlikely that the rings of Queen Æthelswith and King Æthelwulf could have fulfilled this function.

The ring from the River Nene at Peterborough (no. 57) is of unique form, but in the three granules of gold at either side of the bezel can be seen traces of a very typical feature of finger-rings of the Merovingian period.[7]

Fork: See *Spoon.*

Horn-mount: The three mounts from the Trewhiddle hoard (nos. 94-6) come, apparently, from drinking horns. I have discussed this identification elsewhere,[8] but my arguments can be summarised shortly. The two larger mounts form a suite and it is difficult to imagine any object of diminishing, half-round, form to which they could be attached

---

[1] Other examples are known from Hexham (fig. 4), Bramham Moor (Wilson (1960b)) and elsewhere.

[2] Brøndsted (1924), fig. 130.

[3] E.g. Wilson (1958b), pl. xxvi.

[4] *VCH Suffolk*, i, 349.

[5] Cochet (1859), 363. Certain doubts con-

cerning the genuineness of this ring have been raised from time to time and are mentioned by Cochet, 364 ff and Schramm (1954), 213 ff.

[6] Fleury and France-Lanorde (1961), fig. 3.

[7] Cf. *B.M. Ring Cat.*, pl. I, 158.

[8] Wilson and Blunt (1961), 86–8, to which the reader is referred for detailed arguments.

other than a horn; the tags beyond the terminals may have been hidden by the suspensory mechanism. A close parallel is afforded by an object which is undoubtedly the mount of a cup or horn, from Burghead, Elginshire,[1] which is of the same date as, and related in style to, the Trewhiddle mounts. The rim-binding of this object is of a form known on drinking-horns and cups throughout north-western Europe. The sub-triangular panels which appear both on the Burghead and Trewhiddle mounts may be typologically derived from the pendant triangular fields round the rims of the Sutton Hoo[2] and Taplow[3] horns. With these two mounts must go the smaller mount (no. 96), which is of the same basic form. Although it is flat and decorated in a different style, it may have been an addition to the horn which was mounted with nos. 94 and 95, or it may have belonged to another object.

Jug: The spouted vessel with no provenance (no. 147) has been distinguished as a cruet by Kendrick.[4] There is no evidence for this, nor of any other purpose for which it could be used. It is unique and bears no resemblance to any surviving object in any other material—pottery, glass, wood, etc. It originally had a hinged lid.

Key: Five keys are included in this catalogue (nos. 38, 40, 46, 132 and 140), a number of keys which are undecorated, or which are of unknown date, are omitted. The Anglo-Saxon keys have one peculiarity which, unfortunately, is not universal: they have occasionally a suspension loop at right-angles to the bow. Of all the hundreds of early medieval keys from the continent of Europe only one, from Kastell Saalburg, Germany, has such a feature,[5] while Almgren records eight with this feature from England.[6] Keys are notoriously difficult things to set in a chronological and typological sequence and it is useless to attempt to do so on the slender evidence available in England.[7]

Knife: The Southwark knife (no. 81) is the only object of its type in this catalogue: it is impossible to parallel it in the English material. Its chronological identification, controversial though it may be, is based purely on art-historical arguments.

Linked pins: The Witham pins (no. 19) are the sole representative of this class in the Museum's collections. In form they are not unique, although the survival of a complete set of pins of this type, size and quality is unique. The form of the pins perhaps stems from the pair of pins, linked by a chain, which are well known in seventh-century pagan contexts.[8] The closest parallel in form is an hitherto unpublished pin from Kegworth, Leicestershire (pl. III, *a*),[9] which has a circular head decorated with an expanded-arm cross, within the arms of which are crude interlace motifs. Attached to the circular head, by means of a loop of wire, is a bar of sub-lozenge shape, similar in form to the links of the Witham pins. This pin almost exactly duplicates in design that of another pin from Roos, Yorkshire, in the Hull Municipal Museum,[10] which is pierced at one side to take a loop

[1] *Ibid.*, pl. XXIX, b.
[2] Bruce-Mitford (1956*b*), 28.
[3] *BMASG*, fig. 71.
[4] 1938*c*.
[5] Almgren (1955), Tabell I, no. R.37.
[6] *Ibid.*, Tabell II.
[7] Cf. *ibid.*, 70–6.

[8] Cf. the pins from Cowlow, Derbyshire; Howarth (1899), 221 and Leeds (1936), fig. 23.
[9] Leicester City Museum, reg. no. 95,71,11.
[10] Kitson Clark (1941) pl. opp. p. 333. This pin has a dotted border similar to that on the Witham pins.

of wire, as is a fragment of a pin-head from South Ferriby.[1] A pin from Meols[2] probably belongs to this group, although it is very fragmentary, as does a pin from Birdoswald, Cumberland,[3] while a pin from Hitchin (pl. II, *a*),[4] which has a loop at the top, can be compared closely to the Witham pins, both because of the competence of its execution and because of the similarity of the glass settings with their beaded wire collars. The type continues into the eighth century, as is shown by the pins from the Talnotrie hoard (dated *c*. 900) (pl. IV, *d*), which are pierced on one side so that they can be linked together. Whether the link in some of these cases was of metal or of a more perishable material is uncertain. Two pins of this sort may have supported, for example, a festoon of beads.

Kendrick's suggestion that they 'were probably converted by a Viking robber into the trio of pins, having been filched originally, with their connecting plates, from costly English shrines; for the three discs are not a set, that on the right, the smallest, being of different workmanship',[5] probably contains no more than an element of truth. The right-hand pin was obviously made by a different hand to that of the other two pins. At the same time there is no evidence for the pins having been mounted in a different manner on a book or shrine. The large, pierced, circular and lentoid holes obviously have no functional purpose and the only hole which cannot be explained is the left-hand hole on the left-hand pin. The careful decoration of the border of the pin-heads and the lack of solder, or any other trace of fixative, on the back of the pin-heads is reasonably convincing evidence that these heads were not mounted on a book, shrine or other object. It is perhaps worth drawing attention, in this context, to the fact that the heads of the central and right-hand pins are broken at the point where the pin joins the head. There is an obvious weakness of structure here and it may well be that the right-hand pin-head was a replacement to the set, the original having been broken beyond repair. Certainly Kendrick's suggestion, that the connecting plates came from a shrine, seems to be denied by the fact that no such plates are known on contemporary insular shrines and by the even more convincing fact that a link of substantially similar form was found attached to the pin-head from Kegworth (pl. III, *a*). An added argument is that the burr-like border to the hole at the back and front appears on the left-hand and central pins only—an argument both for the secondary nature of the left-hand pin and against Kendrick's theory that the heads were originally applied to a base, for it would not fit flush in such a condition. At the same time one of the closest parallels in form to the right-hand pin-head comes from Støle, Etne, Hordaland, Norway,[6] which was certainly adapted secondarily as a brooch and may originally have been an applied plaque.

Mount: book or box: The four mounts nos. 26, 33, 58 and 141 are presumably from books. In form they are paralleled by the early mounts of rather different structure on the Fulda bookbinding,[7] and have further parallels, unattached to their bases, from among other places, Cambridge, Fordham,[8] Northampton[9] and Ixworth, Suffolk (pl. X, *b*). A number

[1] *Ibid., loc. cit.*
[2] *Ibid.*, 335. Grosvenor Museum, Chester.
[3] Tullie House Museum, Carlisle.
[4] Hitchin Museum.
[5] Kendrick (1938*a*), 170.

[6] Shetelig (1940), v, fig. 47.
[7] Wilson (1961).
[8] *VCH Cambridgeshire*, i, 323 and pl. XII, g and i.
[9] Northampton: Central Museum.

of other objects discussed by Dr. Roes probably belong to the same class.[1] The tendency of these objects to have their rivet holes in the angle of the object would indicate that they were attached to something thin and flat, like a book board, rather than to something deeper, like a box.

Other mounts may well have been removed from books or boxes (e.g. nos 105–7), but the exact use of these mounts can never be finally settled.

Pendant: Only one purely ornamental pendant is included in this catalogue (no. 149). Its sub-rectangular shape is unique. Although other pendants are known from the period covered by this catalogue, they are all of different shape.[2]

Another pendant, but one with symbolic significance, is that from the Gravesend hoard, dated *c.* 875 (no. 20). It takes the form of a cross and, both in form and size, is comparable to the Canterbury Cross[3] and the cross of St. Cuthbert.[4] It is distantly related to the Wilton and Ixworth Crosses,[5] both of which are of seventh-century date.

Pin: See also *Linked pins.* Only one pin is included in this catalogue—no. 92, from the Trewhiddle hoard. This is the only Anglo-Saxon specimen extant of the class of objects designated by Reginald Smith as 'hand pins'[6]—a type of object more commonly found in the Celtic areas.

It is quite possible that a number of smaller pins in the Museums' collections are of Anglo-Saxon origin,[7] but there are no stylistic or typological reasons to confirm or deny it.

Pommel: See *Sword.*

Ring: Two plain rings of bronze wire and one of gold, of lozenge-shaped cross-section, from Beeston Tor (nos. 5–7) defy typological discussion. See also *Finger-ring.*

Scourge. The Trewhiddle scourge (no. 91) is the only object of its kind known from Early Christian Europe. The fact that it was made of silver and was found in association with a chalice suggests a ceremonial, ecclesiastical use for the object.[8]

The chain from which it is made is of a type popular in Southern Europe from the first millennium B.C. It is not common in Northern Europe but is by no means unknown: examples occur, for example, at Isenbüttel in Lower Saxony,[9] on the Tara brooch[10] and in the Cuerdale hoard.[11]

There is no evidence that there was a handle to the scourge—the glass bead may well have served as a grip.

Scramasax: The scramasax may in origin be a Frankish weapon; it is common in Frankish

[1] Roes (1958), pl. xvii, 1–5.

[2] E.g., the Saffron Walden pendants: *VCH Essex,* i, 329f.

[3] Jessup (1950), pl. 31, 2.

[4] Battiscombe (1956), pl. xv.

[5] *Ibid., loc. cit.*

[6] Smith (1913).

[7] E.g. some of those from Whitby—Peers and Radford (1943), fig. 14.

[8] A Romano-British bronze scourge was found at Great Chesterford, *The Archaeological Journal,* vi (1849), 197, and another is known from London, *Catalogue of the Collection of London Antiquities in the Guildhall Museum,* London 1903, 55 and pl. xxviii, 19. Scourges of similar form are illustrated by Perret, *Les catacombes de Rome,* v, pl. ix, 18.

[9] Portratz (1943–8).

[10] Mahr (1932), 15.

[11] Hawkins (1847), 129.

graves and attested in the literature: Gregory of Tours, for example, tells how two servants of Fredegund used scramasaxes to murder Sigibert at Vitry.[1] The blades of the scramasaxes were poisoned on this occasion, but this need not have been a general practice. Scramasaxes first appear in Anglo-Saxon contexts late in the pagan period— perhaps not until the seventh century. These early types have a curved back,[2] which later developed into an object with a straight back and a slightly upturned point.[3] The later type, of which five examples are included in this catalogue (nos. 22, 36, 43, 50 and 80), is distinguished by a sharp angled break in the back. There appear to be two of these later types, one with its cutting edge almost parallel with the back (as on the Battersea scramasax (no. 36) and possibly on the Hurbuck scramasax (no. 22)). The second type has a much broader blade and the back tends to rise out of parallel with the cutting edge to the angle from which the point emerges (nos. 43 and 50). Whether there is any chronological or utilitarian significance in this typological division is not clear, although it is possible that the second type is later for there is some, rather intangible, evidence that the Honey Lane scramasax (no. 43) may have been buried with tenth-century coins,[4] while on general grounds the ornament of the Sittingbourne scramasax (no. 80) may be somewhat later than that of the Battersea example (no. 36). It would, however, be profitless to pursue this discussion.[5]

The Southwark knife (no. 81) might also be considered as a scramasax, but is treated here under *knife*, as, (a) it is rather short and broad, and (b) it seems to be the wrong shape for an offensive weapon.

Seal-die: Only two seal-dies are included in this catalogue (nos. 18 and 104). Æthelwald's seal-die (no. 18) is mounted with an openwork grip and it is probable that Ælfric's seal-die (no. 104) had a simple grip attached to the reverse in the two places on the back where the decoration is broken. The only other seal-die of the Anglo-Saxon period known to exist, that of Godwin and Godgytha,[6] is of ivory.

Shrine: See *Casket.*

Spatula: See *Spoon.*

Spoon: Although the spoon from Pevensey (no. 59) has in the past been considered to be of twelfth-century date it is probably slightly earlier. There is no other spoon from England of this period, and only one from the Celtic area—from the eighth-century St. Ninian's Isle treasure.[7] The form of the bowl of the St. Ninian's spoon is the same as that of the Pevensey spoon and, similarly, there is an animal head at the joint of the bowl and stem; but as Bruce-Mitford has pointed out, 'the bowl does not develop, as is regular in all medieval spoons, out of the mouth of a flattened animal head modelled at its junction with the stem; the animal head is in this case a separate casting mounted

<hr>

[1] *History*, iv, 36 (51).

[2] Cf. Baldwin Brown (1903–37), iii, pl. XXVIII, 19 and 20.

[3] *Ibid.*, XXVIII, 1.

[4] See below, p. 150 f.

[5] I cannot take seriously the argument of Nerman (1959), concerning the Battersea

scramasax. On grounds of typology, size, geography and runology, it would be difficult to accept his comparison. The parallel of ornament is slight and incidental.

[6] Tonnochy (1952), 1 f.

[7] O'Dell (1960), pls. 34 and 35.

above the bowl and is fully in the round with its tongue licking the interior of the bowl'.[1] The Pevensey spoon conforms to the familiar 'medieval' pattern with regard to the head at the junction of the stem and the bowl, but it should be noticed that a head similar to that on the Pevensey object can be seen on the 'spoon' from Sevington (no. 67), which is firmly dated by coins to *c.* 840. The twisted top of the Pevensey spoon is closely paralleled on the Coronation spoon.[2] The Coronation spoon is of late twelfth-century date—although it was reworked in the seventeenth century—but its ornament, while consistent with this date, has many features which seem to be old-fashioned and there seems no reason to suppose that the twisted terminal should not be a feature, like the animal-head, with a long tradition behind it.

In the past the main reasons for considering the Pevensey spoon to be of twelfth-century date have been archaeological and typological. Simms in his original article said: 'the decoration has a strong Anglo-Saxon feeling, but from the position in which the spoon was found it must be Norman'.[3] In fact all that can be deduced from its archaeological context is that the spoon was used in the Norman period; it may well have been of some age when it was lost. The typological decision as regards the spoon rests on the fact that when it was found the earliest early medieval spoons known (other than the Sevington objects, nos. 67 and 68) were the Coronation spoon, the Iona spoons,[4] the Taunton Castle spoon[5] and a series of spoons from Scandinavia,[6] and these were reasonably close in form to the Pevensey spoon. No spoon of later date than the seventh century, or of earlier date than the twelfth century, was known. The discovery of the St. Ninian's Treasure has provided a spoon with certain typological features of the Pevensey spoon at an earlier date.

Two objects which have for a long time been called spoons—from Sevington (nos. 67 and 68)—must be considered here. Their bowls are spatulate and, even if they had been completed, they could hardly have been used at table. One has a double-pronged fork at one end, but the other has a spatulate feature at both ends. They are closely related to a group of bone and ivory spoons, of which four are known from London,[7] and one from Winchester.[8] The Winchester example is decorated with a Winchester/Ringerike motif and must be dated to the late tenth or early eleventh century, but the others bear no datable decoration. Another closely related example was found in excavating a church in Rotterdam, it is of bronze and is undecorated.[9] I know of no other examples and all those I have quoted are single-ended. Double-ended spoons are rare, the earliest example known after the Sevington spoons is that found in a hoard at Ribe, Denmark, dated to 1247.[10] This is a very much more elaborate object, more related to the Pevensey, Iona and Coronation Spoon series. At the same time a spoon, of the Romano-British or pagan Anglo-Saxon period, from Desborough, Northamptonshire,[11] may show the origin of the double-ended type, for it has a pierced spatula-like terminal.

[1] O'Dell *et al.* (1959), 259.
[2] How and How (1952), pl. 1.
[3] (1932), 74.
[4] Curle, (1923/4).
[5] How and How (1952), pl. 4.
[6] Nørlund (1935).

[7] Ward Perkins (1939), pl. LXIV.
[8] Bennet-Clark (1954), pl. III.
[9] Unpublished: Historisch Museum der Stad Rotterdam.
[10] Nørlund (1935).
[11] Baldwin Brown (1913–14), fig. 5.

The use of this type of spoon is a matter for conjecture—but it would not be un-reasonable to suppose, in view of the bone and ivory examples that are found, that they were not intended for ritual use during Mass, but were domestic implements.

Stirrup-iron. Three stirrup-irons (nos. 35, 89 and 133) are included in this catalogue and are of a well-known type. Other decorated examples comes from the Avon, near Chippen-ham, Wiltshire,[1] from Oxford[2], Reffley Spring, Norfolk and the Thames[3]: Seaby records fourteen stirrup-irons of this form in England[4] and goes on to say that they are closely related to the Norwegian type, Rygh 590.[5] In fact Petersen's later variant of this type[6] is very much closer in form to the English stirrup-iron. It may well be that Seaby's suggestion that these stirrup-irons are a product of the Danelaw (and their distribution in the Midlands and East Anglia supports such a statement) is right.[7] It is at least prob-able that this form was introduced from that area, particularly when one considers the prevalence of the inlaying technique on the stirrup-irons from Denmark.[8] It is not with-out interest that many of the English stirrup-irons were found in rivers.

Strap-distributor: The Rome strap-distributor (no. 63) is the only object of its type of Anglo-Saxon origin. More-or-less contemporary examples are known from the Conti-nent,[9] but are of little use in identifying the nationality of this object.

Strap-end: The Anglo-Saxon strap-end is a ubiquitous and stereotyped object. Only four (nos. 12, 99, 100 and 148) out of the 42 (nos. 12, 13, 21, 23, 24, 29, 71–78, 82, 97–100, 114–29, 135–9, 144 and 148) strap-ends included in this catalogue are not easily classified with their fellows: two of them, those from Trewhiddle (nos. 99 and 100), are plain, undecorated and unique, while the third (no. 12), which is cast in relief, is only paralleled by a few objects from Bledlow,[10] York[11] and Cheddar[12]. The fourth (no. 148) is of tenth-century date and of a completely different form.

The typical strap-end first occurs in seventh-century pagan Saxon graves, as at Malton Farm, Barrington, Cambridgeshire,[13] but is chiefly found in later Anglo-Saxon contexts and can most usually be dated on art-historical grounds to the ninth century (see above p. 22 ff). The more elaborate examples have a terminal in the form of an animal's head seen from above, but this is sometimes replaced, before the middle of the ninth century if we are to judge from the Whitby examples (nos. 121, 122 and 124–6), by a small bar or by a featureless terminal. But these features apparently have no chronological significance, for late ninth- and early tenth-century hoards contain strap-ends with animal-head terminals (e.g. Trewhiddle, nos. 98 and 99, Cuerdale, no. 13, and Talnotrie, pl. IV, *d*). In the tenth century they seem to have been replaced by the heavier strap-ends, of which no. 148 is an example. Other examples are known from Thetford, Norfolk,[14] Suffolk[15] and

[1] Coventry Museum.
[2] Seaby (1950), fig. 14.
[3] Wheeler (1927), fig. 17.
[4] Seaby (1950), 38.
[5] Rygh (1885), fig. 590.
[6] Petersen (1951), fig. 32.
[7] Seaby (1950), 39.
[8] Cf. Brøndsted (1936), pls. II–IX and

Lavrsen (1960), figs. 7 and 8.
[9] Werner (1959), pl. 24, 8.
[10] Head (1955), fig. 32.
[11] Unpublished: Yorkshire Museum, York.
[12] Unpublished: Taunton Castle Museum.
[13] Unpublished: British Museum.
[14] Kendrick (1938c), pl. LXXIV, 2.
[15] *Ibid.*, pl. LXXIV, 3.

Wilbury Hill, Hertfordshire,[1] while examples in bone and ivory are known from Leicester[2] and London.[3]

Peers and Radford discuss the use of the ordinary type of strap-end of eighth/ninth century date and say that it should be 'disassociated from the normal type of strap-end which forms part of the costume'; they further suggest that it may have been used as the terminal of a silk book-marker.[4] There is no evidence for the use of such book-markers before the end of the Middle Ages and I have suggested elsewhere that the strap-ends may have had a more common application as girdle ends,[5] the narrow openings at the split ends being paralleled by the narrow openings of the buckles of the period. In Scandinavia similar tags were certainly worn on belts and occur in many graves in association with buckles.[6] This suggestion as to the use of strap-ends is supported to some extent by the undecorated strap-ends from Trewhiddle (nos. 99–100), which have a pair of matching slides (nos. 101–102) which undoubtedly belong to a belt of some sort.

The series of strap-ends from Sevington show the process of manufacture of this type of object, from an ingot with a split-end (no. 76) to the finished object (no. 71). The Sevington hoard must be one of the very few jeweller's hoards known from early medieval Europe.

Stylus: Styluses are uncommon objects in Anglo-Saxon contexts, occurring at two sites only, Whitby (no. 131) and St. Augustine's Abbey, Canterbury[7]—both places being monasteries. They occur occasionally in early medieval contexts on the Continent.[8] Anglo-Saxon styluses were probably derived directly from Roman sources,[9] but their use in the Anglo-Saxon period is well attested by the bone writing-tablet from Blythburgh, Suffolk,[10] which presumably formed half of a diptych and is decorated with eighth-century interlace ornament. Such tablets and styluses were used for notes of an ephemeral nature. I have only included one stylus in this catalogue as it is the only example from Whitby which is certainly Anglo-Saxon.[11]

Sword and Sword Mount: Swords and sword mounts lend themselves to typological discussion based on the form of the hilt; unfortunately apart from the well-known Petersen type L,[12] of which fairly large numbers are known, English swords of other forms are difficult to affix in a typological series. The type L sword, of which the Scales Moor pommel (no. 65) may be an aberrant representative, appears to be fairly well dated by archaeological and art-historical methods. The Grønneberg,[13] Dolven[14] and Hoven[15]

[1] *Ibid.*, pl. LXXIV, 4.
[2] Brøndsted (1924), fig. 132.
[3] *Ibid.*, fig. 133.
[4] No. 121, Peers and Radford (1943), 56 from Whitby has been adapted for use as a *book clasp*, by the addition of a bored hole, cf. Meyer (1929), fig. 5.
[5] Wilson and Hunt (1961), 97.
[6] Arbman (1940–3), pls. 86 and 87.
[7] Radford (1940), 507.
[8] E.g., Wincklemann (1953), fig. 139.

[9] *British Museum: Guide to the Antiquities of Roman Britain*, 2nd ed., London 1958, 48 and fig. 22, 3 and 4.
[10] *BMASG*, fig. 138.
[11] For the others see Peers and Radford (1943), fig. 15, 1–4 and 6.
[12] Petersen (1919), 112–16.
[13] Bruce-Mitford (1956a), pl. XXI, A–B.
[14] Petersen (1919), fig. 94.
[15] Brøndsted (1924), fig. 124.

swords are all decorated with ornament closely related to the Trewhiddle style and occur in ninth-century Viking graves, the slightly more developed form of the Abingdon sword (pl. VI) is also consistent with an art-historical dating towards the beginning of the tenth century. After this period the dating evidence is less easy to use. Although large numbers of swords are depicted in manuscripts of the tenth and eleventh centuries, they are of a very diverse type and are of little use for fine typological dating as they are not illustrated on a sufficiently large scale and may, in any case, have been drawn from earlier proto-types. It seems reasonably clear, however, that, towards the beginning of the tenth century, the hilts of the Anglo-Saxon swords became more substantial, although retaining roughly the same form as the Abingdon sword with curved pommel and guard. The Lincoln sword (no. 32), the Exeter pommel guard (no. 17) and the Seine pommel (no. 66), all belong to this group. It should be emphasised however that the typological dating of swords after the end of the ninth century in Europe is so vague that it can only be used where all other methods fail. Art-historical dating is much more useful, and in all the examples quoted above, with the possible exception of the Lincoln sword (no. 32), a better date is obtainable from art-history than typology. I doubt if it is possible to date an undecorated Anglo-Saxon sword, of the period 900–1100, within a hundred and fifty years, even on the basis of the decorated examples which survive.

One example remains to be considered—the Fetter Lane sword-hilt fragment (no. 41)—this object has been dated by means of its decoration art-historically to the eighth century. It is interesting, therefore, that the type of sword-hilt is much closer to the pagan Saxon type, than to Petersen's type L. The form of the pommel guard on this sword with its accompanying rivets is very closely allied to that on the pommel of the sword from Crundale Down, Kent,[1] which was found in a pagan Anglo-Saxon grave-field and which is undoubtedly of seventh-century date. The pommel itself, however, is of an unfamiliar form, but is perhaps distantly related to a Norwegian sword of unknown provenance[2] or to the similar sword from Termonde.[3] Although these parallels are somewhat far-fetched, they are perhaps less far-fetched than the parallels quoted by Reginald Smith[4] and Miss Evison.[5] Typology, in fact, is of little use in this context.

Tag: The two tags from the Tetney hoard (nos. 86 and 87) are paralleled by a similar hook-like object from Whitby,[6] which I have not included in this catalogue as there is no evidence for its date. The use of this type of object is unknown but it is reasonable to suppose that they formed the terminals of a strap or ribbon. It is unlikely that they were book-clasps as the common book-clasp of this period has a central hole to engage with a peg in the edge of the board.[7]

Tweezers: The tweezers from Reculver (no. 62) are the only known example of tweezers which definitely belong to the period covered by this catalogue, apart from an unpublished example from Cheddar. Originally they must have had a handle, but this is now

[1] *BMASG*, fig. 6.
[2] Petersen (1919), fig. 84.
[3] Dunning and Evison (1961), pl. xxxix, 6.
[4] *Proceedings of the Society of Antiquaries of London*, xxiii (1910), 303 and fig. 1.
[5] Dunning and Evison (1961), 142 and 145.
[6] Peers and Radford (1943), fig. 12, 10.
[7] Cf. the Enger Gospels binding, Meyer (1929), fig. 5.

missing. The normal type of pagan Anglo-Saxon tweezers take entirely different forms.[1]

The tweezers were presumably used for toilet purposes.

Weight: A single weight is included in this catalogue (no. 150). It is without provenance. A fair number of Celtic weights of this period are known,[2] but this is apparently the only example of late Anglo-Saxon origin, other than an example from Mildenhall.[3] It weighs 68·7 gm. or 1061 grains. Based on the Anglo-Saxon unit of 3·1 gm.,[4] this is just a little more than 22 units and weighs within two grains of the largest weight in the group of nineteen, found in a pagan Anglo-Saxon grave at Sarre, Kent.[5] It weighs the equivalent of 40 silver pennies of a period when the standard was rather high, as for example during the currency of Æthelred II's long cross type[6]; at 240 pennies to the pound, this is a sixth of a pound.[7]

UNCLASSIFIED OBJECTS

In most cases it would be unprofitable to do more than draw attention to objects which cannot be classified. They are listed here in order of their catalogue numbers and, in certain cases, attention is drawn to their possible identity.

No. 4. This object may be a tag-end of unusual form, it was apparently riveted to a fairly thin base—? leather.

No. 14. This object might have been a brooch from which all traces of the catch plate and hinge have been removed, or it might have been sewn, glued or otherwise fastened to a base.

No. 28. There is a strong probability that this object is a brooch, but there is no proof of this; there are traces of catches on two of the arms, but the original form of these is unknown. Trefoil brooches were popular in Scandinavia[8] and are not unknown in Carolingian contexts.[9]

No. 42. Unclassifiable.

No. 45. Unclassifiable. It is a binding strip of some description, but apart from the head, which must have protruded gargoyle-wise, it was designed to be looked at from one side only. The back of this strip, behind the inscription, is plain.

No. 48. Unclassifiable.

No. 55. Unclassifiable.

No. 69. Unclassifiable.

No. 70. Unclassifiable.

No. 93. Unclassifiable, but might have been one terminal of a wand.[10]

[1] Cf. Baldwin Brown (1903–37), iv, pl. LXXXVII, 4–6 and 10.

[2] Brøgger (1921), figs. 19–35 and 38.

[3] *VCH Suffolk*, i, fig. 12.

[4] Smith (1923).

[5] *Ibid.*, 123.

[6] The most prevalent weight of this is 26·5–26·99 grains (Butler (1961), 203). This weight would measure 40 of these coins at 26·5 grains.

[7] This is not the place to enter into a discussion of Anglo-Saxon mensuration; the reader is referred to the following: Brøgger (1921), Smith (1923), Skinner and Bruce-Mitford (1940) and Jankuhn (1943), 187–202.

[8] Petersen (1928), figs. 99–115.

[9] Arbman (1937), pl. 48.

[10] Wilson and Blunt (1961), 96–7.

No. 108. Collar for rivet or for setting of semi-precious stone.

No. 109. Unclassifiable.

No. 110. Unclassifiable, but it was certainly not circular in its original condition.

No. 111. Unclassifiable.

No. 112. Unclassifiable, but perhaps from a book-binding, box or similar object.

No. 143. Unclassifiable, but it can be compared with the Winchester panel (pl. X, *a*). It was presumably attached to a casket, book-binding, or other similar object.

APPENDIX A

THE INSCRIPTIONS

by R. I. Page

This appendix deals with the inscriptions wholly or mainly in Old English. These can be divided into two groups, those in runes, and those in Roman characters.

1. The Runic Inscriptions. It is usually assumed that runic script came to England with the Anglo-Saxon invasions. There is no direct evidence for this in the form of English inscriptions certainly contemporary with these invasions. However, the runes ᚨ ('a') and ᚩ ('o')[1] appear only in English and Frisian inscriptions, and their creation seems connected with Anglo-Frisian sound-changes. It is reasonable to suppose that these distinctive rune-forms were developed in the 'period of Anglo-Frisian unity' and passed to this country with West Germanic tribes invading from the Low Countries.[2]

How long runes continued in epigraphical use in Anglo-Saxon England is impossible to determine. Presumably the period of use varied from district to district. From Wessex there survive virtually no runic inscriptions, and it is unlikely the script ever flourished there, except possibly in early times. Inscriptions survive in numbers from the south-east, East Anglia, Mercia and Northumbria. Here coin evidence supplies dates. The runic sceattas circulated mainly in the south-east and East Anglia and date 'from the late seventh to the third quarter of the eighth century'.[3] Kentish regal coinages in the eighth and early ninth centuries and coins of the Archbishops of Canterbury up to the early tenth use only Roman script. If the coins reading BEOnna REX and BEnna REss, and +EÐIIBERH/T 'lul' are to be ascribed to Beorna and Æthelberht of East Anglia, runes were in official use in that kingdom in the eighth century. Later East Anglian coins show only occasional runes in predominantly Roman texts. The earliest Mercian coins, those of Offa, commonly use Roman characters, but occasional runes are intermingled with them, and some moneyers' names, those of Wihtred and Botred for example, are

---

[1] Runes are transcribed according to the system described in Dickins (1932) and further in Dickins and Ross (1940). Note that runes are transliterated by lower-case characters, and that these are placed between single inverted commas, save in mixed runic and Roman texts, where such a convention would be inconvenient.

[2] The rune-inscribed astragalus of Caistor-by-Norwich was found in a fifth-century urn (Clarke (1960), 137, 230). The pottery of this find is related to that of Schleswig-Holstein, and the single-barred 'h' of the Caistor in-

scription suggests that it should be treated as a NGerm rather than a WGerm text. Other OE runic inscriptions, that of the Sandwich stone for example, have been dated very early. I am not aware of any convincing argument that would place them as early as the fifth century.

[3] Grierson (1958), plate VII. See also on this subject Kent (1961). Sutherland (1948), 54–5 gives an earlier date for some of these coins, but this depends on a doubtful identification of the 'pada' and 'æþiliræd' of the legends.

found completely or mainly in runes. Runes continue to appear in the name Wihtred in the reigns of Cenwulf and Ceolwulf I, but later Mercian coin legends are in Roman lettering. The few early Northumbrian coins—from the late seventh and eighth centuries —have only occasional runes. The plentiful coinage of Eanred, from the first half of the ninth, uses mainly Roman script, but some moneyers, Broþer and Wihtred for example, have their names also in runes. On the coins of later Northumbrian kings runes are rare.

The evidence summarised suggests that runes could be used for official purposes in the late seventh and early eighth centuries, but that from the late eighth century onwards official inscriptions were commonly in Roman characters. Runes were still acceptable, though not common, for official texts up to the late eighth century in East Anglia, and the early ninth in Mercia and Northumbria. The script certainly continued in use longer for less official purposes, for memorial texts on stones, owner's or artist's signatures on jewellery, and so on. Unfortunately, apart from coins and the coffin of St. Cuthbert (which is too early to be of value to the present discussion) none of the English rune-inscribed objects can be dated closely by reference to people or events known from historical sources. We are obliged to rely on datings suggested by linguists or art historians. With our present knowledge linguistic dating can only be approximate. We know little about the dates of sound changes in the local dialects of OE, and nothing of the spelling tradition within which the rune-masters worked. Inscriptions are often short and offer few distinctive features. The opinions of art historians on the dates of rune-inscribed objects may differ considerably. In many cases the material has not been adequately examined—we still lack, for example, an authoritative modern account of the Anglo-Saxon sculptured stones. It follows that any deduction made from available publications is tentative, but a few examples may be noted here. W. G. Collingwood placed the rune-stones of Whithorn and St. Ninian's Cave not earlier than the tenth century.[1] The Ministry of Works' guide-book agrees, putting the first in the late tenth or eleventh century, the second in the eleventh.[2] The only piece of linguistic evidence is the form of the personal name element -ferþ on the Whithorn stone, which suggests a date after 800. Collingwood placed the Alnmouth cross in the tenth century, Kendrick apparently agreeing.[3] The Alnmouth personal name Myredah (Old Irish Muiredach, Muredach, Muridach) is not recorded elsewhere in OE sources, but is found in Domesday Book[4] and also in early ME place-name forms, being 'current in the north in the 11th and 12th centuries'.[5] The Alnmouth pronominal form meh has been ascribed to the tenth century, though there is little to show that it could not be a century earlier.

If, as seems likely, the dates given here to the Whithorn, St. Ninian's Cave and Alnmouth crosses are accurate, runes were used on memorial stones as late as the tenth and eleventh centuries. I know of no OE rune-stones later than these.[6] Memorial inscriptions

[1] Collingwood (1927), 63.
[2] Radford and Donaldson (1957), 41, 45.
[3] Collingwood (1927), 62, Kendrick (1949), 58.
[4] Feilitzen (1937), 331.
[5] Armstrong et al. (1950–2), ii, 434. See

also Dickins and Ross (1940) on this inscription.

[6] It is perhaps significant that the twelfth-century runic font at Bridekirk uses Scandinavian rather than OE runes, even though the text is in English.

are often in old-fashioned language and the runes of these late stones may be archaistic, the script having otherwise fallen out of epigraphical use. On the other hand tenth-century runes are found in OE manuscripts. The Exeter Book, its manuscript ascribed to the second half of the tenth century,[1] uses runes as a cryptic script in its riddles. The lost manuscript of the Runic Poem 'can hardly have been written earlier than the end of the tenth century'.[2] The first hand responsible for the runes and values in MS. Cotton Domitian A IX has been variously dated between the mid-tenth and twelfth centuries.[3] Runic inscriptions deriving from manuscript tradition could be as late as the end of the tenth century, perhaps later.

From this brief summary it is clear that there is little evidence to enable us to give a useful date for the last appearance of runes in metalwork inscriptions: that an object is rune-inscribed does not in itself give much help in dating it within the four centuries covered by this catalogue. The following generalisation can be made. The script could certainly be used on metalwork of the eighth and ninth centuries, probably too in the tenth. The eleventh is the least likely. If there were other grounds for holding an object to be pre-eleventh-century, the fact that it had a runic inscription might be held to support them.

This catalogue lists four objects with runic or partly runic inscriptions, the Thames or Battersea scramasax (no. 36), the Greymoor Hill ring (no. 27), the Thames mount (no. 45) and the Lancashire gold ring (no. 30). This list excludes inscriptions in Roman lettering which have the rune *wynn* for W. This letter was adopted into bookhand as early as the seventh century and remained in use into the ME period. There is no reason to believe it was regarded as a rune when in an otherwise Roman context. On the so-called runic inscription of the Sutton brooch (no. 83), see below, pp. 88–9.

(a) The Thames scramasax (no. 36) runes are:

I 'f u þ o r c g w h n i j ʒ p x ʃ t b e ŋ d l m œ a æ y êa'
       5   10   15   20   25
II 'b êa g n o þ'
   1 2 3 4 5 6

I is the OE *fuþorc*, II the masculine personal name *Beagnoþ*, presumably that of the owner of the sword.[4]

The *fuþorc* of the Thames scramasax is the only known epigraphical one. It can be compared with the manuscript *fuþorcs* which survive from Anglo-Saxon times,[5] and with epigraphical *fuþarks* from North and Continental West Germanic sources. Two points arise from such comparison.

(i) the letter order of the Thames *fuþorc* is unique. Runes 1–19 preserve the traditional

[1] Ker (1957), 153.
[2] Dobbie (1942), xlix.
[3] Derolez (1954), 7.
[4] On the evidence of the charters Professor Dickins suggests that a name element *Beag-* was particularly common in Kent. See in this connection Dickins (1938), 83.
[5] For this manuscript material see Derolez (1954). Derolez's book is the source of most of the comments on manuscript runes given in the present work.

order with OE substitution of 'o' for the *a*-rune which originally occupied fourth place. 25-28 are the old *a*-rune ('æ') and three additional OE or Anglo-Frisian characters, their order 'a æ y êa' confirmed by most manuscript *fuþorcs*. In the case of runes 20–24 of the Thames inscription the traditional letter order is disturbed. It is certain that 20–22 of both *fuþorc* and *fuþark* were 'm l ŋ'. 23 and 24 of the *fuþorc* were either 'd œ' or 'œ d'. The order 'd œ' is the one commonly attested, but 'œ d' was that of the Runic Poem, if Hickes's transcript of MS. Cotton Otho B X is accurate in this respect. An equivalent confusion can be seen in the *fuþarks*, where 'd o' on the Kylver stone contrasts with 'o d' on the Grumpan bracteate.[1]

(ii) The Thames *fuþorc* has a number of unusual letter forms. 's' is the rare OE variant ᛉ, perhaps a borrowing of a bookhand character, perhaps a simplification of earlier ᚺ. The only other certain epigraphical examples are in the runic texts of St. Cuthbert's coffin,[2] and on the Greymoor Hill amulet ring,[3] though the Chessel Down scabbard plate inscription may provide a further one.[4] ᛉ appears in the *fuþorcs* of MSS. Cotton Domitian A IX and Oxford, St. John's College 17, in each case accompanied by one of the more common types of 's'. The Thames 'œ' is ᚥ. A similar form is found with a presumed value 'ŋ' in a small number of Scandinavian and Continental inscriptions. There is only one other OE epigraphical example of the form, that on the newly found Orpington (Kent) stone, where the value cannot be established.[5] 'œ' runes of this form are given in MSS. Cotton Domitian A IX, Oxford, St. John's College 17, and (ᚥ) Cotton Galba A II, while similar characters have the value *o* in MSS. Berne, Stadt- und Hochschulbibliothek 207, Leyden, Universiteitsbibliotheek, Cod. Vossianus lat. F 12 δ. The Thames 'j' is +, otherwise only found in connection with OE runes on the Rome fragment,[6] though there is a form with the same value on the Danish Sjælland 2 bracteate.[7] 'y' has the form ᚤ, not found elsewhere in inscriptions, but evidenced in runes scored on the final text page of the Leningrad Gospels.[8]

The Thames 'd', ᛞ, is unique. The form could be explained as a chance variant created by the difficulty the craftsman found in producing the standard 'd' form in his medium, but this is unlikely. Some of the inlaid patterns of the Thames scramasax are more complex than the standard 'd', while the inlayer found no difficulty in producing

[1] Friesen (1933), 34–5.

[2] Dickins (1956).

[3] See below, p. 73.

[4] Elliott (1959*a*), 79–80.

[5] This stone, a fragment of a sundial, has two damaged texts. The first, in two parts, reads -ELTELLAN7H/EALDAN+ '... to tell (or to count) and to hold', and -/ECÐÐANÐESECANCAN/HV '... for him who knows how to seek out how.' The second is OR[......]VM, presumably a form of Latin (*h*)*orologium*, preceded by three runes, 'o', the ᚥ form in question, and ? 'æ', in a combination meaningless to me.

[6] I have not seen this inscription. I rely on the drawing in Buck (1919–20). Though the inscription has the distinctive OE 'a', it has also a Scandinavian form of 'c'. + may then be of Scandinavian, rather than OE, provenance.

[7] Jacobsen and Moltke (1941–2), text, col. 959.

[8] These runes were discovered by Dr. D. Wright, and brought to my notice by Mr. D. M. Wilson. They read +ᛗᚦᛗᛉᚱᚤᚦ+ possibly a combination of the names Eþelstan, Eþeldryþ.

'm', which so closely resembles the usual 'd' form. Moreover, his variant 'y' must have been harder to produce than the common form of that rune. The Thames 'd' is probably either a genuine variant, no other example of which has survived, or an erroneous form produced by a craftsman with only a limited knowledge of runes. In connection with the first alternative it should be mentioned that, before the Leningrad Gospels runes were noticed, there was no known parallel to the Thames 'y', which could thus have been regarded as a decorative variant created by the scramasax smith. In favour of the second alternative is the confusion in letter order, presumably erroneous, in the Thames *fuþorc*.

The rare Thames runes could be explained as variants in common use in the south-east, the rune-masters of that area using certain distinctive forms as those of the north-west certainly did. However, the evidence of the few runic texts from south-east England does not support this suggestion. Y is not used in the Thames mount inscription[1] nor in the Dover stone '*jȝslhêard*',[2] whereas it is found on St. Cuthbert's coffin, made at Lindisfarne, and on the Greymoor Hill (Cumberland) amulet ring. Dover 'j' is X, found also on the Thornhill (W. R. Yorkshire) iii stone.[3] A more likely explanation is that the unusual Thames runes derive, not from the epigraphical tradition, but from a rather different manuscript one. Y, ϕ are quite common in manuscripts. D is only paralleled in a manuscript form. Thames 'j' does not appear in manuscript accounts of runes, but there is a formal difference between manuscript 'j' (ϕ) and its epigraphical equivalent. It seems likely, then, that the Thames scramasax was produced by a craftsman who was not a rune-master but who derived an imperfect knowledge of that script from a manuscript account. This would explain the curious 'd' and the unique letter order.

It has commonly been argued—recently for example by W. Krause and R. W. V. Elliott[4]—that the Thames *fuþorc* served a magical purpose, giving protection or success to the wielder of the scramasax. As evidence of a widespread use of runes in this way are quoted the early *fuþarks* of the Kylver stone, the Vadstena and Grumpan bracteates, the Breza pillar and the Charnay brooch, a connection being suggested between *fuþark* magic and late Classical alphabet magic. It is pointed out that runes were used for certainly magical inscriptions at some periods of their history, and magical use of the characters themselves is described in quite early Norse literary sources, in, for example, the Eddic poem *Sigrdrifumál*.[5] Further, the question is asked if the early *fuþarks* and the Thames *fuþorc* had no magic power, why were they cut? This is not the place for a long discussion of rune-magic, but it should be noted that the theory cited is not without its opponents. In an important book *Målruner og Troldruner* the Danish runologist A. Bæksted attacked the idea of an essential connection between runes and magic, arguing that there was insufficient evidence to prove an early belief that magical qualities existed in the characters of the *fuþark* themselves, and suggesting other reasons why the early *fuþarks* should have been inscribed on bracteates, stones, etc. In my opinion

[1] See below, p. 77.
[2] Elliott (1959*a*), 82–3.
[3] Elliott (1959*a*), 88–9.
[4] Krause (1937), 17, Elliott (1959*a*), 68, 72.

[5] For an enthusiastic acceptance of the theory of rune-magic see Elliott (1959*a*), particularly Chapter VI.

Bæksted's book gives a salutary warning against a too ready assumption of magical content in runic inscriptions. On the other hand some of his alternative reasons for the appearance of the early *fuþarks* are unconvincing.[1] The bracteate *fuþarks* may be, as he suggests, meaningless inscriptions in imitation of the legends of the Roman coins on which the bracteates were modelled. The Breza *fuþark*, found in proximity to a Roman alphabet, may be an attempt by a member of one of the Germanic peoples to indicate his literacy. But it is unlikely that the *fuþark* of the Kylver stone, which had some connection—though of what sort is not known—with a grave, was simply a pattern for or a copy of a bracteate text. The Charnay *fuþark* is unlikely to have been intended, as Bæksted tentatively suggests, as a key to the second inscription on the brooch. It is not clear how such a key could be used, while moreover the *fuþark* is incomplete, omitting the rune 'd' which occurs in the second text.[2] Bæksted regards the Thames scramasax *fuþorc* as purely decorative. It is curious that, if the inlayer thought of making a pattern of runes, he did not produce a meaningful text, particularly since the second inscription 'bêagnoþ' shows him using runes as a practical script. A legend like that of the non-runic Sittingbourne scramasax[3] would have been decorative and also meaningful.

On the whole it seems unlikely that the Thames *fuþorc* is not connected with rune-magic, but the connection may be less close than such runologists as Krause and Elliott believe. Bæksted bases his specific objection to magic content in the Thames *fuþorc* on two points, (i) even if the twenty-four letter *fuþark* were used as a magic formula there is no reason to believe that the same power would be ascribed to the later, twenty-eight rune, OE *fuþorc*, and (ii) magic power would not be thought to remain in a formula the letter order of which was disturbed. (i) may not be a tenable objection for we know little of the relationship between magical and practical uses of runes in early times. It is not certain that the magic power of the *fuþark* would not be considered to reside in the later, enlarged, *fuþorc*. (ii) is more important, but still not decisive, for there are examples of magic formulae with disturbed letter order in runic inscriptions. To take two examples of widely differing date from Denmark: the Nydam arrow has *lua*, read as a form of the common magic word *alu*, the well-known medieval magic word *agla* appears on the Revninge ring as *agla gala laga*.[4] Certainly the disturbance of the letter order of the Thames *fuþorc* seems more casual or accidental than that in these cases, yet the Nydam and Revninge examples show that a confused letter order in a magic formula would not necessarily be thought to affect its power. However, if we accept the suggestion made above that the letter order of the Thames *fuþorc* arises from the smith's ignorance of runes, we can hardly consider this *fuþorc* a genuine magic text. A more likely explanation is that it is a late survival of an earlier practice.

Perhaps the Thames *fuþorc* was cut when there was no longer a current knowledge of

---

[1] Bæksted (1952), 139–40.

[2] In a letter to the present writer, dated 27 February 1961, Dr. Bæksted has clarified his position. He writes (my translation), 'Naturally I did not think that the *fuþark* could be exactly a "key" to the interpretation of the inscription. That would be . . . meaningless. But something on the lines of: "This inscription is in this sort of runes." '

[3] See below, p. 86.

[4] Jacobsen and Moltke (1941–2), text, cols. 627, 629.

runes or belief in their magic power. The practice of inscribing runes, even *fuþorcs*, on weapons was an archaic one, known perhaps from earlier objects which had survived or from descriptions of such weapons. The smith who ornamented the Thames scramasax or the warrior who commissioned it wished the practice to be followed, and so the *fuþorc* was copied—inaccurately—possibly from a manuscript.

Such a theory—and it is only a theory—would explain the difficulties of the Thames *fuþorc*. It would also allow the acceptance of a date as late as *c.* 900. There is one objection to it. The name 'bêagnoþ' employs rune 'êa' correctly. A man ignorant of runes would be more likely to transliterate *ea* by the two runes 'e', 'a'. Since, however, the last rune he had cut in the *fuþorc* was 'êa', this character may have remained in his mind when he came to add the personal name to the scramasax.

(b) The Greymoor Hill ring (no. 27) runes are:

'+ æ r k r i u f l t k r i u r i þ o n g l æ ʃ t æ p o n|t o l'
     5   10   15   20   25   30

The inscription of the Greymoor Hill ring cannot be considered without reference to two related texts.[1] A gold ring now in the National Museum, Copenhagen, probably found at Bramham Moor and certainly found in Yorkshire, has the almost identical legend 'ærkriuflt|kriuriþon|glæstæpon/tol'. Divergencies are the use of 's' for 'ʃ', of the bind-rune 'n/t' for 'nt', the setting of all thirty runes outside the hoop of the ring and their division into three groups. The reading of runes 7–9 of the Bramham Moor ring as 'flt' derives from the Greymoor Hill legend. For the Bramham Moor text alternative readings are possible. The arm of 8 runs into that of 9. This could be accidental, but it is equally possible that we have here, not 'lt', but 'e' bound to a following 'l' or 't' (not ᛚ + ᛏ, but ᛗ + ᛚ or ᛏ).[2] Runes 7–9 would then read 'fe/l' or, less likely, 'fe/t'. In favour of such readings is the fact that *fel, fet* can be pronounced (as can the rest of the inscription), *flt* cannot. Greymoor Hill 'flt' could then be a miscopying of 'fe/l', 'fe/t'. Alternatively Bramham Moor 'fe/l', 'fe/t' could be a rationalisation of an unpronounceable 'flt'.

The third legend relevant to the discussion is that of an agate ring, now in the British Museum, of unknown provenance, but early recorded in a Bristol collection. This reads 'ᚸ ᛠ ery.ri.uf.dol.yri.uri.þol.wles.te.pote.nol'. The use of 'e' rather than 'æ' in 'ery', 'wles', 'te' is probably of phonological rather than semantic importance. If in fact this ring is from the south-west or west Midlands it could be from a 'second fronting' dialect area. In such an area the name of the rune 'æ' was probably not *æsc* but *esc*, so that for practical purposes 'æ', 'e' could be interchanged.[3] 'y' rather than 'k' in 'ery', 'yri' can be explained on runological grounds. The rune 'k' is a late creation, found only in the north-west of Anglo-Saxon England. The southernmost finds evidencing this character are the stones of Great Urswick (Lancashire, north of the sands)[4] and

---

[1] See in this connection Wilson (1959*b*) and refs.

[2] Cf. the binds 'e/l' in the Leningrad Gospels text, 'h/e/l' on the Whitby comb

(Stephens (1866–1901), iii, 180–2).

[3] For a fuller discussion of this point see below, p. 77 and Page (1962*b*) 486 ff.

[4] Collingwood (1911).

Thornhill (W.R. Yorkshire). 'k' was probably not in use very far south of this line, so that a southern or Midland rune-master copying a text containing it might well substitute the similar form of the known rune 'y'.

Other differences between the texts of the agate and the gold rings can be accounted for in different ways. 'þol' could have been substituted for 'þon' to make a rhyme with final 'ol' and this may also be the explanation of 'dol' for the uncertain complex of runes 8–10. Alternatively, 'þon' could have replaced 'þol' to form a rhyme with a penultimate syllable 'pon'. 'pote.nol' could derive from an earlier *potnol*, *e* being possibly a glide vowel, possibly added to form a rhyming syllable with preceding *wle*, *ste*. The variant forms *pontol*, *potnol* could arise from Bramham Moor 'pon/tol', where 'n/t' are bound and there is no means of telling what order they are to be taken in. The reading 'wles' is not certain, for the first rune is obscure and could well be 'ſ'. Possibly here is a form copied from a damaged 'g'.

The three inscriptions are amuletic. They contain no non-magic OE words, but some forms and rhyming patterns in them can be paralleled in the OE manuscript charms. Professor Dickins has pointed out that 'ærkriu' appears, as *ærcrio* and *aer crio*, in two versions of a charm for stanching blood.[1] H. Meroney has identified here Old Irish *ar* 'against', *cró* 'gore',[2] but it is likely that the words soon lost their specific meaning in Anglo-Saxon magic, for similar forms are found in charms used for quite different purposes—*acre arcre, acre earcre, arcre encrcre, arcu arcua, acræ ærcræ*.[3] The charms for stanching blood contain further forms resembling those of the ring legends: *thon(n)* (? Old Irish *tonn* 'skin') 'þon'; *ffil, fil* (cf. *fel delf fel* in a charm against theft; ? Old Irish *fil* 'it is', Old Irish *fuil* 'blood') 'fl', 'fe/l'; *leno* (? Old Irish acc. pl. *léunu* 'hurt') 'e.nol'.[4] Common in OE magic formulae is the repetition or rhyming of syllables, in such sequences as *caio laio quaque uoaque, audies maudies*.[5] The pattern of 'kriuriþonglæstæpon', two syllables rhyming together followed by a third rhyming with a corresponding syllable of the next word, is quite common: so, for example, *geneon genetron . . . catalon, beðegunda breðegunda elecunda*.[6]

In the cases of the two gold rings it is likely that the number of runes used has magic significance. The Greymoor Hill example has thirty runes, twenty-seven outside and three inside the hoop. The Bramham Moor ring has thirty runes in three groups of nine, nine and twelve. Three and its multiples are common magic numbers, and there is evidence from Anglo-Saxon charms of the magic significance of three, nine, twenty-seven and thirty.[7]

Finally, there is the question of rune-magic. Many scholars believe that magic powers were attributed to the runic characters themselves. The amulet ring legends have occasionally been cited as evidence for this intimate connection between runes and magic,

[1] Dickins (1935).
[2] Meroney (1945), 176, 179.
[3] Storms (1948), 236, 301–2, 306. It is interesting to note that one of these charms is described in the manuscript table of contents as *oþer scyttisc gecost gealdor* (Cockayne (1864-

6), ii, 10, 113.
[4] Storms (1948), 304–5.
[5] Storms (1948), 298.
[6] Storms (1948), 304, 308.
[7] Storms (1948), 96–100.

but in fact they tell us nothing about it. The ring legends contain words or syllables common in Anglo-Saxon charms. The texts were therefore magical whether in runes or Roman characters. Perhaps runes were used with the intention of strengthening the power of the magic words. Perhaps, however, the use of runes on amulet rings is not different from that on other Anglo-Saxon rings where there is no need to assume magic intent. There are, for example, mixed runic and Roman texts on the Lancashire gold ring,[1] with its maker and owner formula, and the Llysfaen (Caernarvonshire) gold ring, now in the Victoria and Albert Museum, which has the owner's name +ALHSTAn.[2] It is unlikely that here the runes have a significance different from that of the corresponding Roman letters, and the same may apply to the amulet ring legends. Runes occasionally appear in manuscript charms, but they are not prominent enough to suggest a specific connection between them and Anglo-Saxon charm literature.

(c) The Lancashire ring (no. 30) inscription is:

+ æ D R E D M E C A H E A n R E D M E C a g R O f
+ *Ædred mec ah. Eanred mec agrof.* '+Ædred owns me. Eanred engraved me.'

Owner and maker formulae are not found together on any other Anglo-Saxon ring. The most common type of ring inscription seems to have been a name alone, or name and rank. Examples are the legends of the Alhstan ring, and the Æthelwulf (no. 31) and Æthelswith (no. 1) rings.[3] Religious formulae added to the name appear on the Bvredrvð ring[4] and in the text NOMENEHLLAFIDINXPO on a gold ring from Bossington, Hampshire, now in the Ashmolean Museum, Oxford.[5] Owner formulae like that of the Lancashire ring are occasionally found on other pieces of Anglo-Saxon jewellery, as for example on the Cuxton (no. 14) and Sutton (no. 83) brooches,[6] in the case of the latter followed by a prayer for protection. There are no other maker formulae on Anglo-Saxon rings, except for a possible example on the Cramond ring in the National Museum of Antiquities, Edinburgh.[7] The ring's runic text is damaged and only partly legible, but it may contain a form of the word *worhte* 'made'. Maker formulae are frequent elsewhere. A coin brooch from Canterbury has the inscription ÞVDEMANFECIÐ.[8] OE examples are the texts of the Alnmouth and Kirkheaton[9] rune-stones, the Pershore censer-cover,[10] the Mortain shrine[11] and the Derbyshire bone plate,[12] the last two accompanied by a request for or statement of God's help for the writer. Closest to the Lancashire ring inscription is that of the Sittingbourne scramasax.

The Lancashire ring inscription uses five runes, 'æ', 'n', 'a', 'g', 'f', the rest being in Roman characters. Such a mixture of the two scripts is not unusual. It is found commonly

---

[1] See below.

[2] Oman (1930), 63.

[3] See below, p. 82.

[4] See below, p. 83.

[5] Baldwin Brown (1903–37), iii, 311 and plate 53, 5. FIDINXPO is to be read *fidem* (or *fides*) *in Christo*.

[6] See below, pp. 84, 86 *ff*.

[7] Stephens (1866–1901), iii, 216.

[8] Jessup (1950), 112 and plate xx, 2.

[9] Stephens (1866–1901), iv, 51.

[10] See below, p. 84.

[11] Cahen, Olsen and Osieczkowska (1930), 24.

[12] Stephens (1866–1901), iv. 47.

in coin legends of certain periods, and occasionally elsewhere. 'n' is frequently used in otherwise predominantly Roman texts. The Llysfaen ring has ALHSTAn, the Chester-le-Street stone EADmVnD.[1] lEOFDEGn, CVNEMVnD are forms of moneyers' names on stycas of Æthelred II of Northumbria,[2] and BEOnna REX, BEnna REss appear on coins uncertainly attributed to Beorna of East Anglia.[3] In the Latin text of the Lindisfarne Gospels 'n' takes the place of the usual written form in SECU/nDUS on fo. 13a.[4] 'g' and 'a' also appear quite often in Roman texts. Stycas of Eanred and Æthelred II of Northumbria have the moneyers' name forms LEOFDEgN, DAEgBERCT,[5] while a penny of Offa has the name BEAgHEARD.[6] 'a' is found on the BEOnna, BEnna coins and in the Alnmouth cross name MYREDaH. 'æ' and 'f' do not seem to be used elsewhere in non-runic contexts. In the case of 'f' the formal similarity of rune and Roman letter may have caused confusion.

The only linguistic form to offer a dating point is the personal name æDRED. The initial vowel may be the reflex of Germ au^i, and the name element may derive from Germ *audi-, cognate with *auda- which gives OE $\bar{E}ad$-. Alternatively, the form Æd- may have arisen first in such names as Ædwini, Ædgils, mutation being produced by the vowel of the second element.[7] Ædred would then be an analogical form. æ is not a common Anglian result of the i-mutation of Germ au. Much more usual—almost universal in later texts— is $\bar{e}$. æ is thought to be an early and intermediate stage.[8] The only text with considerable numbers of examples of it is the Moore manuscript of Bede's Historia Ecclesiastica.[9] Other early texts of this work commonly have e with only occasional examples of æ, as in Aeduini, Ænheri in the Leningrad Bede, Aedgild (for -gils) in the Namur text. After the eighth century æ forms are very rare, though there are a few cases in Anglian texts. For example, the Lindisfarne Gospels Gloss, with an overwhelming number of e forms, has the occasional form in æ[10]; the OE Life of St. Chad has æg ('island'), lægetas side by side with forms in e.[11]

On this evidence a form Ædred is most likely to date from the first half of the eighth century or before, though a later date is not completely excluded. Much depends on our interpretation of the evidence of the Moore Bede. Its use of both æ and e for the reflex of Germ au^i could derive from its exemplar, or could indicate partial modernisation by the Moore scribe of an original consistent æ. The fairly consistent use of e in the Leningrad Bede then suggests a more complete modernisation.[12] Under these circumstances the æ spellings in both texts would be archaic, and the change to e perhaps already completed. On the other hand the original text of the Historia Ecclesiastica may have had e

[1] Stephens (1866–1901), iii, 461.
[2] Keary (1887), 161, 172.
[3] Keary (1887), 83.
[4] See the facsimile of this page in Kendrick et al. (1960).
[5] Keary (1887), 148, 171.
[6] Keary (1887), 30.
[7] Ström (1939), 113.
[8] Chadwick (1899), 4, but cf. Luick (1914–), 180, where æ is described as 'bloss eine graphische Erscheinung'.
[9] Ström (1939), 100.
[10] Stolz (1908), 73.
[11] Vleeskruyer (1953), 92.
[12] Note, however, the suggestion in Lowe (1958) that this is an early text of the Ecclesiastical History, produced under Bede's supervision at Jarrow.

in nearly every case, and the Moore *æ* forms may be replacements by the scribe of that manuscript of old-fashioned forms perhaps persisting in his own local dialect. In that case *ǣ* (< Germ *auⁱ*) could have been a dialectal feature within Anglian for a long time, and this may account for the occasional Lindisfarne and St. Chad *æ* spellings.

So far the argument has been built up on the assumption that the vowel of *Æd-* is the reflex of Germ *auⁱ*. Towards the end of the tenth century another explanation of the form becomes possible. From that time onwards OE *ēa* (< Germ *au*) is smoothed to *ǣ*, the change first recorded in Mercian and completed *c.* 1000.[1] The unmutated element *Ēad-* then becomes *Æd-*, commonly found in the eleventh century.

On the evidence given above a form *Ædred* is likely to be pre-800 or post-1000. In the case of the Lancashire ring form, however, we cannot be sure how relevant this evidence is. æDRED is not *Ædred*, for the initial vowel is represented by the rune '*æ*'. The transliteration is a formal one only, and it is better to think of the phonetic value of the rune in terms of the initial sound of its rune-name. This is usually recorded as *æsc*, a word which is also an OE common noun meaning 'ash-tree'. As a common noun, and presumably as a rune-name too, the word would have local dialectal variants. In the 'second-fronting' dialects it would be *esc*, and there the phonetic value of the rune would perhaps be more accurately represented by *e* than by *æ*. In such a dialect æDRED might be a form for *Edred*, and the argument given above for dating the form would collapse.

It is clearly important to find out if the Lancashire ring came from a 'second-fronting' dialect area or not. Unfortunately this is difficult since (a) there is no evidence within the inscription itself, (b) we do not know the extent of the 'second-fronting' area of the West Midlands, (c) little is known of the OE dialectal characteristics of Lancashire, (d) we do not know if the ring was found in the north or south of Lancashire, (e) in the case of a portable object like a ring the place of manufacture may be distant from the place of discovery. There is no need to amplify these points here, for it is clearly impossible, with our present knowledge, to determine whether Lancashire æDRED should be treated as *Ædred* or *Edred*. The date of the ring must therefore be left undecided.

(d) The Thames mount (no. 45) runes are:

'sbe/rædht₃bcai | e/rh/ad/æbs'
     5   10 | 15   20

The Thames mount inscription remains a mystery. The runes are clearly cut and well preserved, and are unambiguous save in one case. The character transliterated above as 'e' (two examples) is not the usual form ᛗ, but 𝝡. This is probably a decorative variant of the rune; majuscule M is sometimes ᛗ in coin legends and manuscripts. It is, however, conceivable that ᛗ is a bind-rune 'e/i' (ᛗ + |) or 'e/u', 'u/e' (ᛗ + ᚢ), or perhaps even a new rune preserved only here. Another variant 'e' has been identified, though not with any certainty; this is the form ᛘ on the Gilton (Kent) sword-hilt.[2] Perhaps there was some reshaping of the runes in south-east England, though the paucity of examples from that area makes it impossible to be certain. Some early scholars read rune 11 as

[1] Luick (1914–), 332. Cf., however, Campbell (1959), 135, which dates the first   indications of the change 'soon after 1000'.   [2] Elliott (1959*b*), 141.

'u', though there are no other cases of such a form of the letter. The rune is clearly 'c' (cf. the same form in the personal name element '-lac' on one of the Lindisfarne stones[1]).

The difficulty of the Thames mount inscription is not the identification of the runes, but the interpretation of the text. Early scholars read it as plain language. G. Stephens and S. Bugge saw a reference to a carving of the biblical Jonah on the object to which the mount was attached. Stephens read ' ? (Her Jonas) SBERÆDH TyO BUA I ERHA DÆBS', interpreted as ' ? (Here Jonah) SPEIRETH (*asks*) TO BO (*bide, be cast*) IN *the*-ARG (*waves, trough*) *of-the*-DEEP'.[2] Bugge read '[fisc iona]s beraedh ti bua i erha dæbs', meaning *fisken bærer jonas at bo i dypets vand*.[3] Grienberger divided the text *sberædh tib-uai Erhad æbs*, which he translated *Erhadus episcopus assequitur viam caniculae*, postulating a reference to a carving of an otherwise unknown bishop Erhad.[4] These attempts require little consideration. A few of the more obvious objections to them can be listed. All depend on reading a 'u' rather than 'c' for rune 11. Stephens would further represent 'ʒ' as yO, to give TyO for the preposition *to*. Bugge reads a possible *i* at the expense of an improbable preposition *ti*. 'sb' for *sp* in Stephens's and Grienberger's *sberædh* remains unexplained and unparalleled in OE, nor is there any adequate example of the use of 'dh' for þ, which all three versions require. Stephens and Bugge assume *i* (not found in OE) for the preposition *in*, while *dæbs* for *deopes* is hard to explain. Grienberger postulates an unusual abbreviation *æbs* for *episcopus*,[5] and a word *tib-uai* (a dialectal form of *tib-weg*) not found in OE at all. All three readings require the existence of carvings —for which there is no evidence—to make the texts meaningful.

It is easy to criticise earlier readings, but hard to suggest an alternative. The following may be noted, (i) Grienberger observed that the first seven letters of the extant inscription are repeated, in a different order and with added 'a', at the end. He rejected the idea of an anagram incorporated in the text—'Es wäre nicht einzusehen, auf welche art von anagramm man da raten sollte'.[6] Yet the repetition is something of a coincidence, particularly in consideration of the way in which the letter order is varied. If runes 'sberædh' are numbered 1–7, the last eight repeat these in the order

'e r h a d æ b s'

3 4 7 . 6 5 2 1

which suggests deliberate interchange of letters. The addition of 'a' as fourth rune of the last eight is puzzling. However, the inscription as it now stands may be incomplete, for the left-hand edge of the mount is broken away. If 'a' formerly preceded the first extant rune there would be a group

'a s b e r æ d h',

1 2 3 4 5 6 7 8

---

[1] Peers (1923–4), 261–2, the rune is wrongly identified as 's'.

[2] Stephens (1884), 147.

[3] Bugge and Olsen (1891–1924), i, 120–1.

[4] Grienberger (1913), 50 ff.

[5] Cf., however, 'ebs' for *episcopus* in MS. Munich, Hauptstaatsarchiv, Hochstift Freising, Lit. 3a (Derolez (1954), 413).

[6] Grienberger (1913), 49.

the final eight letters repeating this group in the order

'e r h a d æ b s'.

4 5 8 1 7 6 3 2

A repetition in this order could scarcely be coincidental.[1] It is likely that there is here an anagram involving the eight runes *erhadæbs*, perhaps the whole group *tȝbcaierhadæbs*. (ii) If the Roman equivalents of the extant runes are put into alphabetical order the following letter groups appear: *abcde, hi, rst*. Two runes 'æ', 'ȝ' do not readily fit into the alphabet. Manuscript runic alphabets commonly give 'æ' the value *a*, sometimes *e*, while 'ȝ' appears as *i*, *k*, or occasionally *h*. The letter groups represented are then *abcde, hi(k), rst*. Again, this grouping is unlikely to be coincidental.

It is possible that the Thames mount text is amuletic, based on alphabet magic.[2] Such magic is believed to have flourished in late Classical times, and perhaps into the Middle Ages, though opinions differ as to that.[3] I know of no certain evidence for the existence of alphabet magic in Anglo-Saxon times, though there are some indications. One may note the common use of *alpha omega* formulae in OE charms—*Alpha et O, initium et finis, A et O, ōĀ, A + + + + + + Ω*, and so on.[4] In a gibberish charm for obtaining favours occurs *A.x.Box*, which suggests the beginning of an alphabetic series,[5] which however is not carried further, while later on are the words *A.B.et alfa tibi reddit vota fructu*.[6] This evidence is too slight to confirm the suggestion that the Thames mount inscription is an alphabetic charm, though in the absence of an alternative that suggestion is a likely one.

Finally, in connection with the group *erhad* which begins the last section of this inscription it should be noted that *er, h, d* occur in close proximity on an OE charm pattern for detecting theft.[7]

2. The Inscriptions in Roman Characters. In this section are OE or largely OE texts on eleven objects. To these may be added the Continental Germanic name, presumably that of the smith, welded into the blade of the Lincoln sword (no. 32). Few of these inscriptions provide evidence for close dating of the objects on which they occur.

The OE inscriptions can be divided into: (i) those of the Æthelwald (no. 18) and Ælfric (no. 104) seal dies, (ii) the legends consisting of name, or name and rank, of the Æthelwulf (no. 31), Æthelswith (no. 1) and Bvredrvð (no. 85) rings, (iii) the owner formula of the Cuxton brooch (no. 14), (iv) the maker formula of the Pershore censer-cover (no. 56) and probably of the Exeter sword-pommel guard (no. 17), (v) the owner and maker

[1] Similar rearrangements of letters occur in other OE cryptic texts; see, for example, *bprckpfbn* for *bckprfbn* (a code form of *aciorfan*), *weliogarn* for *wiolegran* in the Kentish Glosses (Zupitza (1877), 26, 44, Williams (1905), 137), and 'g', 'æro', 'hi' for *higoræ*, the answer to Riddle 24 of the Exeter Book (Krapp and Dobbie (1936), 193).

[2] Cf. the meaningless texts involving all the letters of the alphabet in confused order quoted in Dornseiff (1922), 69.

[3] See, for example, Jacobsen and Moltke (1941–2), text, cols. 773–4, Bæksted (1952), 118 ff. and refs.

[4] Storms (1948), 258, 272, 282, 284. See also nos. 85, 104 in this catalogue.

[5] Cf. the type of syllabary noted in Dornseiff (1922), 67–8.

[6] Storms (1948), 300–1.

[7] Storms (1948), 311.

formula of the Sittingbourne scramasax (no. 80), (vi) the owner, protection and Christian curse formula of the Sutton, Isle of Ely, brooch (no. 83), and (vii) the cryptic texts of the Sutton brooch and the *Eawen* ring (no. 145). Only those under (ii) need comment here. Owner formulae are common on jewellery, and it is therefore reasonable to take the names on these rings as those of the owners. The objection to this is a statistical one; it is surprising to find two royal owners of the three rings in this section. The possibility must therefore be considered that the Æthelwulf and Æthelswith rings record, not the owners', but the donors' names.[1]

(a) The Æthelwald seal-die (no. 18) has the text:

$$+ S \overline{II} E Ð I L V V A L D I : E P.^{-}$$

The final letter of S$\overline{II}$ (for *sigillum*) is either capital *gamma* or a square form of G badly cut with its base missing.

The owner of the seal has been identified with the ninth-century bishop Æthelwald of Dunwich.[2] Though there were several Anglo-Saxon bishops of the name, the Dunwich attribution is the most likely in view of the provenance of the die. The ninth-century history of the see is obscure, and the dates of Æthelwald's consecration and death are unknown. He is known only from the record of his profession as bishop of Dunwich, made to archbishop Ceolnoth.[3] According to the Anglo-Saxon Chronicle Ceolnoth was consecrated to the see of Canterbury in 830[4] and died in 870. Florence of Worcester's list of the early bishops of Dunwich does not include the name of Æthelwald, and concludes with a certain Wilred.[5] A document of 825 lists a Willred *electus* among the bishops,[6] one of 839 has *Signum manus Uuillredi episcopi*,[7] while Willred *episcopus* was witness to a charter of 845.[8] These are assumed to be the same man, identified as bishop of Dunwich on the evidence of Florence of Worcester. Willred was therefore bishop of that see when Ceolnoth was consecrated and at least until 845. Æthelwald's appointment to the see cannot then have been earlier than 845 or later than Ceolnoth's death in 870.

The identification of the Willred of the documents with Florence's Wilred is probably justified for the name is rare in OE and no other bishop Willred is known. However, we have only Florence's authority for the fact that he was bishop of Dunwich, not Elmham.[9] The OE lists of *Nomina episcoporum orientalium anglorum* of MSS. Cotton Vespasian

[1] See above, pp. 22, 56.

[2] *BMASG*, 110.

[3] Birch (1885–93), no. 528.

[4] Two or three years later according to some authorities; see Haddan and Stubbs (1869–73), iii, 610–11.

[5] Petrie and Sharpe (1848), 618.

[6] Birch (1885–93), no. 384.

[7] Birch (1885–93), no. 421.

[8] Birch (1885–93), no. 448. Robertson (1956), 266, 268 takes the *Wilfred episc* of a writ of 825 (?824) as Wilred of Dunwich, but

gives no reason for the identification.

[9] A detailed study of Florence's lists is needed. The MSS. used in Petrie and Sharpe (1848), 618 give the name of the see at the head of each list of East Anglian bishops. These headings are not found in all MSS. of Florence's *Chronicon*; in MS. Corpus Christi College, Cambridge, 92, for example, the lists are untitled. One would like to know which MSS. of Florence's work these rubrics appear in, and whether they are by Florence or derive from an exemplar.

B VI, Corpus Christi College, Cambridge, 183, and Cotton Tiberius B V show the division of East Anglia into two sees, without indicating which list applies to Dunwich, which to Elmham. The position of Willred's name in the lists varies. In CCCC 183 and Tiberius B V it appears in the list beginning *aecce*. In Vespasian B VI *uuilred* is added in a second hand to the list beginning *beadpine*.[1] M. R. James assumed that scribe 2 of Vespasian B VI added Uuilred's name to the wrong list, but the mistake could have been made in a text from which CCCC 183 and Tiberius B V (which are not independent at this point)[2] derive. The same tradition must then be recorded in Florence of Worcester. This argument suggests the possibility that Willred was bishop of Elmham, not Dunwich. If this were so the beginning of Æthelwald's episcopate could be placed before 845.

An early date fits the one small piece of linguistic evidence in the inscription. The element *Eðil-* retains PrOE unstressed *i* which later became *e*. The date of this change from *i* to *e* is hard to establish with precision because of the paucity of early OE texts. For the area outside Northumbria there are few manuscripts from before 800, and the more extensive of these are copies of earlier works. From East Anglia there survives almost no OE material at all. I. Dahl's study of early OE substantival inflexion led him to the following generalisation. The change from unstressed *i* to *e* began towards the end of the seventh century in England outside Northumbria; *i* was still commonly employed about the middle of the following century, but thereafter fell rapidly out of use. 'In the early 9th century -*i* was in any case on the way to being completely ousted by -*e*'.[3] The East Anglian coin legends support this generalisation. The element *Æþil-/Eþil-* preserves *i* forms only on the EÐIlBERH/T 'lul' coin, ascribed to the Æthelberht who died in 794, and on occasional coins of Æthelstan I (*c.* 827–37). Most coins of the latter king have *e* spellings, and *e* is invariably on those of Æthelward and subsequent kings. The coins of these early East Anglian kings are not plentiful, and legend evidence is notoriously hard to evaluate. Yet it does seem likely that *i* forms died out in the reign of Æthelstan I. This would suggest a date *c.* 830 for the seal die.

(b) The Ælfric seal-die (no. 104) inscription reads:

+ S I G I L L V M Æ L F R I C I $\overline{\text{X}}$

The final symbol is presumably a form of *alpha omega*.

This seal has been attributed to aldorman Ælfric of Hampshire who was killed at the

---

[1] CCCC 183 is given in James (1912), i, 433–4. James collates Vespasian B VI, which is given in Sweet (1885), 168. Tiberius B V is only available in Wright and Halliwell (1841–3), ii, 170. Sweet's edition of the lists of Vespasian B VI is misleading. He gives the name *uuilred* in italics, indicating that he believes it to have been written in the first hand, but overwritten at a later date. At the same time he quotes (p. 167) an opinion that the date of the first hand was 'between the years 811 and 814'. This would indicate a Wilred bishop of East Anglia before 825. There is, however, a confusion here. If all the names quoted by Sweet in italics were in the first hand, it could not be as early as 812—they include, for example, Ceolnoth of Canterbury. The British Museum catalogue regards Sweet's italicised names as addition of a later hand, which is certainly true in the case of *uuilred*.

[2] Sisam (1953), 291.

[3] Dahl (1938), 191.

81

battle of Ashingdon in 1016.[1] Linguistically there is no objection to such an identification, though there is little to confirm it, save perhaps the find-place of the die. Ælfric is a common OE name.

(c) Æthelwulf's gold finger-ring (no. 31) has the inscription:

+ E T H/E L V V L F R/X

The name form is consistent with the identification of the owner/donor with the ninth-century king of Wessex, father of Alfred the Great.[2] According to the Anglo-Saxon Chronicle he inherited the West-Saxon throne in 836, but a charter of 839 is dated *primo . . . anno regni Eðeluulfi regis post obitum patris sui*.[3] The later date is correct.[4] Before his accession to the throne of Wessex Æthelwulf was king of Kent *vita patris*, and he appears as *rex Kanciae, Cantrariorum* or *in Cantia* in charters, the earliest surviving being from 828.[5] The Chronicle gives the date of his death as 857 or 858, though his name is on a charter, presumably spurious, of 859.[6] Asser states that Æthelwulf surrendered Wessex to his rebellious son Æthelbald on his return from the Continent late in 856, and further evidence tends to confirm this.[7] Even if it is true Æthelwulf would have retained the title *rex* to the end of his life by virtue of his kingship of the dependent territories of Kent, Surrey, Sussex and East Anglia.

On this identification the ring may be as early as 828 or even somewhat earlier, but cannot be later than 858.

(d) The Æthelswith finger-ring (no. 1) inscription reads:

+ E A | Ð E L S V I Ð | R E G N A

The last line is perhaps to be transcribed REGI/NA.

The name on the ring is that of the queen of Burgred of Mercia.[8] Daughter of the royal house of Wessex and sister of Alfred the Great, Æthelswith was married to Burgred, according to the Anglo-Saxon Chronicle, in 853 or 854. The entry for 874 (or 875 in some versions) tells of Burgred's expulsion from his kingdom by the Danes, his journey to Rome where he settled, and adds that *his lic lið on Sancta Marian ciricean on Angel-cynnes scole*. The Chronicle does not date Burgred's death, but Asser puts it not long after his arrival in Rome.[9] It is not clear whether Asser had additional material here, or was only drawing an inference from the fact that Burgred's burial place is mentioned under the year 874. Of Æthelswith after her husband's loss of his kingdom nothing is known apart from the Chronicle entry for 888 (or 889) which records her death and the burial of her body in Pavia.

Æthelswith signed as *regina* Mercian charters between the years 855 and 872.[10] It is not certain that she would have kept the title *regina* after her husband's expulsion, and unlikely that she would have used it after his death, though most of the Chronicle entries

[1] *BMASG*, 110.
[2] *BMASG*, 114.
[3] Birch (1885–93), no. 421.
[4] Earle and Plummer (1892–9), ii, 75, Smith (1935), 18.
[5] Birch (1885–93), no. 395. The date on the charter is 823.
[6] Birch (1885–93), no. 497.
[7] Stevenson (1904), 196.
[8] *BMASG*, 114.
[9] Stevenson (1904), 35.
[10] Birch (1885–93), nos. 487, 535.

of her death call her *Æþelswiþ cuen*. The possible dates for the ring are, then, 853–89, the most likely ones 853–75.

The spelling *Eaðel-* is unusual. It is presumably a form of *Æðel-*, confusion perhaps arising from the existence of the variant *Eðel-*. Equally well it may be an error of cutting of a semi-literate craftsman, or a possible though rare variant spelling. Another epigraphical example of *ea* where we would expect a single vowel symbol is found on the Great Edstone (N.R. Yorkshire) sundial,[1] one inscription of which reads +LOÐAN| MEÞRO|HTEA (= + *Loðan me wrohtea*). However, this text is so cramped into one corner of the stone that it may be unfinished. It was perhaps to be completed + *Loðan me wrohte a(nd +* a second maker's name); cf. the double signature of the Kirkdale (N.R. Yorkshire) sundial + HAÞARÐ MEÞROHTE 7 BRAND|PRS.[2]

(e) The Bvredrvð finger-ring (no. 85) inscription reads:

+ B V R E D R V Ð + ⦂ꝏ·Ⅴ

Bvredrvð is a feminine personal name, presumably that of the owner. OE *Bure-* is found only in the moneyer's name *Burewine* on coins of Cnut to Harold II.[3] Searle regards it as a form of *Burg-* and he may be right; the final vowel could be a reduced form of the glide which develops between *r* and the following guttural, as in the simplex *buruh*. *Bure-* also occurs in early post-Conquest personal names used as place-name elements: so, for example, *Burewinestoch* Domesday Book (Burstock, Dorset), *Burewoldiscumbe* 1173–5 (Burlescombe, Devon).[4] So far *Bure-* has been evidenced only before a second element beginning with *w*, but early post-Conquest place-names again suggest that *Bure-* developed before other consonants, as in *Burestou* 1121 (Burstow, Surrey), *Burebeche* 1172 (Burbage on the Wye, Derbyshire).

-drvð must be related to the OE element *-þrȳþ*, the vowel of which is the reflex of *ū͡i*. *-drvð* is either cognate with *-þrȳþ*, deriving from an original without mutating *i*, or a variant spelling of it. ON has the unmutated vowel in *þrúðr* and the common name element *-þrúðr*, but the word was probably an *i*-stem originally.[5] More likely is the second alternative. M. Ångström has noted a very few examples from manuscript texts of OE *u* where we would expect *y*.[6] In inscriptions confusion of *u/v* and *y* is quite common. Coin legends supply a number of forms of CVNE- for *Cyne-*, VVN-, ÞVN- for *Wyn-*, as well as spellings in *y* for *u/v*, as EDELYYLF, YYILSIG, ÞYLFNOÐ, CYDBERHT.[7] A stone from Ripon bears the name ADHⅤSE, presumably a spelling of the rare OE name *Adhyse*.[8] The significant vowel is damaged at the base, but what remains suggests that it was V not Y. A parallel to -DRVÐ = *-þrȳþ* is perhaps the Domesday Book *Quendrud monacha*, a name from Lincolnshire. Feilitzen suggests that *u* here may be an AN spelling for [y], though in fact *u* is rare in this capacity in Domesday.[9] -DRVÐ may also reflect influence from the Continental Germanic element *-drud*. The use of *d* and *ð*

---

[1] Green (1928), 510.
[2] Blair (1956), plate XII.
[3] Searle (1897), s.n.
[4] Ekwall (1960), s.n.
[5] Noreen (1923), 265.

[6] Ångström (1937), 68, 96, 135, 145.
[7] Keary (1887), 50–1, Grueber and Keary (1893), 16, 26, 64, 78, 175, 187, 190, 233.
[8] Collingwood (1927), 94.
[9] Feilitzen (1937), 54.

for the two spirants of the element presents no difficulty; OE parallels are the forms *Aeðildryðam, Aelfdryð, Cynidryð, Eandryð*.[1]

If this account of BVREDRVÐ is correct, the name is a variant spelling of the *burgðryð* of the *Liber Vitae* of Durham.[2] There is, however, another possibility. If -DRVÐ = -*þrȳþ*, then BVRE- could be *Byre-*. OE *byre* 'son, child' could perhaps be used as a name element, though no certain OE example is recorded. Förstemann tentatively suggests a cognate *buri* in such Continental Germanic names as *Burigunda, Purehart, Purihilt*.[3]

The A ω symbols which follow the name probably had amuletic significance. *Alpha omega* formulae are common in OE charms.[4] Epigraphically they are found on grave furniture, on memorial stones from Hartlepool and Billingham, for example,[5] and on a funeral cross from St. Augustine's Abbey, Canterbury.[6] Elsewhere they are found on a coin of Æthelred II,[7] while they are common on finger-rings from early Christian times onwards.[8]

(f) The Cuxton brooch (no. 14) inscription reads:

+ Æ L F G I V V   M E A H

+ *Ælfgivv me ah*. '+ Ælfgifu owns me.'

Ælfgifu is an OE feminine name, too common for any identification of the lady to be possible.[9] The letters of the inscription are set radially round the brooch, spaced quite evenly. The engraver probably intended a space after the personal name, but there is none between ME and AH. The text spacing then compares with that of the Sutton, Isle of Ely, brooch.[10]

(g) The Pershore censer-cover (no. 56) has the inscription:

+ G O D R I C M E Þ V O R H T

+ *Godric me þvorht⟨e⟩*. 'Godric made me.'

The inscription is badly spaced. The personal name is well spread out, perhaps intentionally to give it prominence. The last two words are cramped into the right-hand half of the inscription fillet, which was not long enough to receive them. Consequently T had to be cut on the side of the animal head at the corner of the censer, while the final vowel was missed out altogether. This shortage of space was intensified by the craftsman's cutting a superfluous *v* in *þvorht⟨e⟩*.

(h) The Exeter sword-pommel guard (no. 17) inscription has been read LEOFRIC MEFEC (=*Leofric me fecit*),[11] but this is wrong. The letters are cut between incised lines running parallel to the guard edges. On one side of the central hole are clearly visible the letters EOFRI. After I the metal surface is worn, the incised framing lines become very faint, and no letter can be certainly seen, though there is room for a small character. Nor is there now a clear initial L, free of the framing at the base, as shown

[1] Ström (1939), 157, Sweet (1885), 155, lines 41–2.

[2] Sweet (1885), 154, lines 23–4.

[3] Förstemann (1900), cols. 351–2.

[4] See above, p. 79.

[5] Scott (1956), 201, 208, 212.

[6] Potts (1925).

[7] Brooke (1950), plate xvi, 7.

[8] Cabrol (1907–53), i, 15, Dalton (1912), nos. 4, 31, 960a.

[9] *BMASG*, 103 and below p. 129 f.

[10] See below, p. 87.

[11] *BMASG*, 94.

in some early drawings.[1] Initial L can only be read if the end and base framing lines are taken into use. Small incisions perpendicular to these suggest the serifs of upright and horizontal strokes of L, but there is also a similar incision at the upper framing line, approximately opposite that of the base one, which does not fit such an interpretation. Moreover, similar marks precede the M of the second part of the inscription. This suggests rather that they form part of a crude decorative pattern preceding each of the two halves of the text. Other arguments against reading initial L are: that none of the other letters of this part of the inscription makes use of the framing lines, the following E being quite clear of them: that such an L would be considerably taller than EOFR, which are all of a height despite the narrowing of the guard towards its ends; that no other letter in the inscription is serifed.

The second half of the text has the letters MEF clear, then follows a possible but uncertain E. Final C would be deduced more from the context than from the faint remains, which could in any case be part of a decoration edging the inscription. Since the M of this part touches framing lines at top and base it could be argued that the marks which precede it give a square form of C, most of the letter coinciding with the frame. EOFRI|C is then possible, though unlikely.

There is no reason to doubt that the Exeter inscription is a maker's signature, *NN me fe[c](it)*. The only comparable example on a sword—on the Sittingbourne scramasax[2]— is in the vernacular, but Latin signatures are known from other sources, DEINOLT ME FEC and TEDVVINVS mE FC on memorial coins of St. Edmund,[3] ÞVDEMANFECIÐ on the Canterbury coin brooch.

The maker's name must be considered under the forms *Eofri, Eofri[.], Eofric*. The first element could be *Eo-*, found in such names as *Eomod, Eomund, Eowine* and *Eumer*.[4] This is probably a reduced form of *Eoh-* (OE *eoh* 'stallion') which appears in the name *Eohric* (and perhaps too as a simplex in the Kirkheaton rune-stone 'eoh:woro|htæ'), cognates being found as elements of compound names in other Germanic dialects.[5] The full name could then be *Eofrið*, a name not otherwise recorded in OE, but with cognates in the ON feminine name *Iófríðr*, Old Danish *Iofrith, Iofridus*, Continental Germanic *Ehanfrid, Ehinfrit*.[6] Alternatively the first element could be *Eofr-*, a reduced form of *Eofor-*; for the loss of the unstressed vowel see such coin legend names as *Eofrmvnd, Efrard*.[7] The Exeter name could then be *Eofric* (=*Eoforric*) with simplification of *-rr-* as in the moneyer's name form *Eofred*.[8]

[1] See, for example, *VCH. Devon*, i, 373. The version in Shortt (*n.d.*), frontispiece and 143–4, though garbled, can readily be related to the inscription as it now stands. There has clearly been no deterioration of the inscription since Shortt's time.

[2] See below, p. 86.

[3] Keary (1887), 115, 130.

[4] Björkman (1920), 20–1, Ström (1939), 14–15.

[5] Förstemann (1900), col. 451, Krause (1932), 160 ff., Johannson (1933), 239 ff.

[6] Lind (1905–15), col. 646, Knudsen and Kristensen (1936–   ), i, cols. 649–50 (but see their derivation of the name), Förstemann (1900), col. 451.

[7] Grierson (1958), no 566, Grueber and Keary (1893), 110, 161.

[8] Grueber and Keary (1893), 460.

7

(i) The Sittingbourne scramasax (no. 80) has two inscriptions:

I   + S G E B E R E H T | M E A H
II + B I O R H T E L M M E þ O R T E
+ S⟨i⟩gebereht me ah. + Biorhtelm me þorte.
'+ S⟨i⟩gebereht owns me. + Biorhthelm made me.'

Both are indifferently set out. Neither is divided up into separate words, though in I the personal name subject is set apart from the rest of the sentence.[1] There is a space between M and EAH, which the interpretation of the text shows to be unintended. The letters of the final word of II are spread out to fill the space available.

The only difficulty is the form of the owner's name. Between S and G no letter was cut, though a space for one was left. It is very likely that *Sigebereht*, a common enough OE name, was intended, I being omitted in error.[2] That a space was left for it suggests that the engraver was illiterate or careless, copying from a text in which I had been accidentally erased.

The diphthong of *Biorht-* is characteristically Kentish.[3] *-elm* and *worte* show a common loss of *h*, the first at the beginning of the second element of a compound, the second in the three-letter group *rht*.[4]

(j) The Sutton, Isle of Ely, brooch (no. 83) has two inscriptions, the first, easy to read and interpret, in Roman characters, the second, which remains unread, in a cryptic script. Text I reads:

+ Æ D V þ E N   M E A G   A G E H Y O D R I H T E N
       5   10   15   20
D R I H T E N H I N E A þ E R I E Ð E M E H I R E   Æ T F E R I E
25   30   35   40   45   50   55
B V T O N H Y O M E S E L L E H I R E A G E N E S þ I L L E S
     60   65   70   75   80   85

Two types of evidence help to determine how this text is to be taken: (a) the spacing of the first part of the inscription.[5] There are deliberate spaces after *Ædvþen*, *ag*, *Drihten* (*1*), and possibly too after *age*, *Drihten* (*2*), though these are very small and most likely to be accidental. Spaces between A and G (10–11), E and A (75–6) are due to flaws in

---

[1] See below, p. 87.
[2] By a curious coincidence a fragmentary form . . . *geberhtus* appears in a charter (Birch (1885–93), no. 230). An OE name *Gebereht* could perhaps be defended, though initial S and the space following it are then unexplained. *Gebereht* could be a spelling of *Gebbereht*, the first element (=OE *gi(e)fu*, *gefu*) a variant of *Gef-* occasionally found in OE texts (Ström (1939), 17). Alternatively a

first element *Ge-* is perhaps found in two early names, *Geuuis*, *Giwis*, the eponymous hero of the *Geuissae* (Redin (1919), 30 and refs.) and *Gesecg*, who appears in the Genealogy of the East Saxon kings (Sweet (1885), 179, line 16).
[3] Sievers and Brunner (1951), 24.
[4] Campbell (1959), 188, Williams (1905), 129.
[5] Bruce-Mitford (1956a), 197–8.

the metal which antedate the cutting of the text. (b) metrical considerations. The text falls readily into verse, an OE alliterative line followed by two rhyming couplets:

Ædvpen me ag: age hyo Drihten.
Drihten hine aperie   ðe me hire ætferie,
bvton hyo me selle   hire agenes pilles.[1]

This is probably to be read: 'Ædvwen owns me, may the Lord own her. May the Lord curse the man who takes me from her, unless she give me of her own free will.'[2]

A space after the name *Ædvpen*, but no divisions in MEAG, AGEHYODRIHTEN is not surprising. OE inscriptions commonly have a subject personal name cut off from the rest of its sentence by punctuation or spacing, as on the Thornhill i rune-stone and the Cuxton brooch. Subject is divided from the rest of the sentence in the Sittingbourne scramasax owner formula and in the Brussels cross signature DRAHMAL|MEÞORHTE,[3] while in the Mortain casket text '+goodhelpe: æadan|þiiosneciismeelgewar|ahtæ'[4] there is similar isolation of a personal name object.[5]

Rhyming verse is rare in OE, but enough survives to suggest that the form may have been in quite common use among some social classes and for certain purposes. Mixture of rhyming couplets and alliterative lines in non-stanzaic form is typical of early ME, found frequently in twelfth-century texts. Occasional earlier examples suggest that this mixture of verse forms may have been a feature of OE literature too.[6] Most OE examples extant are from late in the period, though we must acknowledge the possibility that such verse—which has not survived perhaps because of the nature of its audience or the purposes to which it was put—was also an early phenomenon. The Christian curse of the Sutton brooch is paralleled in numerous examples, both in Latin and OE, in Anglo-Saxon wills.[7] For both matter and form compare the formula *crist hine ablende þe þis*

---

[1] This text should therefore be included in the OE poetic corpus. Dobbie (1942) includes the verse inscriptions of the Ruthwell and Brussels crosses and the Franks casket, but omits all other inscription verses. Apart from the Sutton brooch there can be named the Great Urswick rune-stone and the Dewsbury fragment, whose texts fall readily into alliterative verse, while alliterative lines can perhaps be traced on the Thornhill rune-stones and the Falstone 'hog-back'.

[2] Stephens (1866–1901), i, 292 reads *age hyo Drihten* 'may she possess the Lord', which is grammatically possible, though the meaning is less satisfactory than that given here. G. M. Young's translation of *Drihten . . . aperie* as 'Lord, mayest Thou curse . . .' (Bruce-Mitford (1956a), 197) is also possible.

[2] B. Dickins divides *Ædvpen me ag: age hyo. Drihten, Drihten . . .* 'Aedwen owns me. May she own me. Lord, lord . . .' (Fox (1923), 300). This too is grammatically possible, but conflicts with the metrical division.

[3] Logeman (1891), plate II.

[4] Cahen, Olsen and Osieczkowska (1930), 24.

[5] The practice is found outside England, as in the inscription 'boso:wraetruna' on the Freilaubersheim brooch (Arntz and Zeiss (1939), 217 ff.; cf. also Jacobsen and Moltke (1941–2), text, cols. 995–6). There is some resemblance here to the use of spacing to indicate sense divisions in some Anglo-Saxon manuscripts (Clemoes (1952), 10–11).

[6] Rankin (1921), 419 ff.

[7] Whitelock (1930), 4, 16, 28, 34.

geprit apende in four manumissions in a single hand in MS. Corpus Christi College, Cambridge, 140, fol. 1.[1]

The text presents few difficulties. *Ædvpen* is a spelling of *Ædwen*. I know of no other case of *vp* for *w*, though the Pershore censer-cover has *pv* in ᚹVORT. *Ædwen* is a rare name. There is a single example in Searle (1897), that of the mother of St. Godric, the twelfth-century hermit of Finchale; her name appears variously as *Aedwen, Adwen, Edwenna, Eadwenna* in the early biographies of the saint.[2] *Æd-* is a late form of *Ēad-*. *-wen* may be OE *wēn* 'thought, hope', cognate with *-van, -wan* in Continental Germanic names.[3] Alternatively the element may be OE *wyn* 'delight, pleasure', with unrounding and lowering of *y* to *e*, typical of the south-east but extending as far north as Cambridge-shire.[4] The name is then a variant of the recorded *Eadwynn*.

Two linguistic features help to date the Sutton brooch. The change from *ēa* to *æ* in *Æd-* is one which took place *c.* 1000.[5] The third person pronoun has the forms: acc. sg. m. *hine*, nom. acc. sg. f. *hyo*, gen. dat. sg. f. *hire*. This series of forms has been ascribed to the south-east in the eleventh and twelfth centuries.[6]

(k) The second, fragmentary, inscription of the Sutton brooch is roughly scratched on a band of silver fixed by two rivets to the back. Some 2 inches of the band remains, part having been lost at either end, though how much it is impossible to determine. From the time of Hickes scholars have not doubted that this text is in runes. Hickes himself called them *Runæ sive potius Runarum jugationes, ut opinor, Magicæ*.[7] To Stephens they appeared 'stave-runes, several runes on the same stave',[8] while H. M. Chadwick thought they were 'an attempt to write Scandinavian runes by someone who did not understand them'.[9] S. B. Jansson, the latest runologist to study the characters, has commented, 'These are not eleventh-century Scandinavian runes, nor an ignorant attempt to imitate them. It is more a case of degenerate Anglo-Saxon runes. In many cases the writer has tried to make bind-runes. . . . Two r-runes of a late type, one þ and possibly one œ might be read, but I cannot get any intelligible meaning from the damaged inscription.'[10]

In fact the characters bear only a slight, and probably misleading, resemblance to OE runes. Two framing lines have been scratched along the length of the silver strip, *c.* 0·05 inches from each edge. Perpendicular to these are cut seven staves which in most cases run through the frames to the edges of the strip. These staves are differentiated from one another by the addition of half- or quarter-circles or straight lines which join or cut them.[11] Numbering outwards from the brooch centre, stave 5 has a half-circle right of its centre, a quarter-circle adjoining beneath it; 6 has a half-circle left of its top and a quarter-

---

[1] Noted in Stephens (1866–1901), i, 292–3.

[2] Stevenson (1847), xxi, 22.

[3] Förstemann (1900), col. 1521.

[4] Luick (1914–), 168, Reaney (1943), xxxv. Reginald of Durham misinterprets when he comments *Aedwen, quod consone significat 'Beatitudinis amicam', seu 'Societate beatam'* (Stevenson (1847), 22). He confuses the second

element with OE *wine* 'friend'.

[5] See above, p. 77.

[6] Gericke (1934), 86.

[7] Hickes (1705), iii, 187.

[8] Stephens (1866–1901), i, 292.

[9] Fox (1923), 300.

[10] Bruce-Mitford (1956a), 198.

[11] See fig. 34, above.

circle right of its base; 7 has a half-circle left of its centre between two straight lines cutting the stave at right angles. These forms could be the runes 'r', 'w/c', 'þ'; 'w' and 'þ' being retrograde. Such a sequence makes no sense, while retrograde runes are rare in OE and never mixed with ordinary forms. The lines cutting the stave of 'þ' are unexplained, save perhaps as vestiges of a serifed form. 4 has the same half- and quarter-circle right of the stem as 5, but also a small half-circle left of centre with a line running into it. 3 has half-circles at both sides of the head, and quarter-circles at both sides of the base. This could be the occasional 'œ' form φ, bound to inverted 't'. I know of no OE parallel to such a use of an inverted form in a bind. 2, 1 are complexes of half- and quarter-circles and straight lines, best studied in fig. 34. These are not OE runes or even complicated binds of them.

If a comparison with runes must be made, the Sutton characters most closely resemble, not those of the OE *fuþorc*, but the cryptic forms based on half- and quarter-circles occasionally found in Scandinavian inscriptions; in, for example, Rødven I,[1] Bratsberg II,[2] Kingigtórsoak,[3] Storhedder R,[4] Maeshowe 22[5] and the Roskilde amulet.[6] Even here, however, the resemblance is only a general one. I would suggest that the identification of the Sutton inscription II as runic, which after all derives only from Hickes's guess, is incorrect. It might be more profitable to treat the script as cryptic, used perhaps for magical purposes, possibly based on the *fuþorc*, possibly not. Other cryptic scripts have been found in OE contexts. A well-known example on a Christian monument is the 'Ogam' inscription of the Hackness cross.[7] Less famous is an undeciphered inscription on a bronze object, perhaps a strap end, found at Mildenhall and now in Cambridge University Museum of Archaeology and Ethnology (pl. X, c). This too is cut between framing lines. It contains forms resembling runic or Roman B, I, a reversed 'þ' and perhaps a square form of O. The other characters are unknown to me.

(l) The *Eawen* finger-ring (no. 145) legend reads:

+ E A Þ E N : : M I E Λ H S P E T R V S · S T A N C E S
  5   10   15   20   25

This text has been described as 'a mixture of Roman and Greek characters'.[8] There is only one case (apart from that of runic Þ) where there is difficulty in identifying a Roman letter. Λ (11) could be a Greek capital, but is surely more likely in the context to be a variant A. Such a form, without horizontal stave, is common in coin legends and occasionally elsewhere, and Λ, A are sometimes used in the same legend.[9] The ring has also A (3), which stands midway between Λ, A.

The meaning of the text is unknown, though a few suggestions can be made. If Λ, A are read as A, its beginning, +EAÞEN:MIEAH, bears a striking resemblance to an

[1] Olsen *et al.* (1941–   ), iv, 270–1.
[2] Olsen *et al.* (1941–   ), ii, 185.
[3] Olsen (1932), 193.
[4] Hagen and Liestøl (1947), 194–6.
[5] Farrer (1862), plate XI.
[6] Jacobsen and Moltke (1941–2), text,

cols. 296–7.
[7] Baldwin Brown (1903–37), vi, 66–7.
[8] *BMASG*, 116.
[9] So, for example, on Grierson (1958), no. 554.

owner formula +*Eapen mie ah* 'Eawen owns me', punctuation dividing the subject from the rest of the sentence. Pronominal *mie* for *me* is irregular, and could be a dialectal or an erroneous form, perhaps produced by a semi-literate engraver. *Eawen* is not otherwise recorded, though both elements are used in the formation of OE personal names.

Other OE examples show an owner formula followed by a maker formula (Sittingbourne scramasax and Lancashire ring), or by a prayer for protection (Sutton brooch). A possible owner's name may be followed by the rank (Æthelwulf and Æthelswith rings), by religious symbols (Bvredrvð ring) or a religious formula, as on the NOMENEHLLA-FIDINXPO ring from Bossington, Hampshire. None of these types of continuation can certainly be traced on the *Eawen* ring. The group PETRVS·STAN suggests a Christian text, and the whole may be a protection charm parallel to the A ω of the Bvredrvð ring. SPETRVS can hardly be other than *S(anctus) Petrvs*, though S is not the common OE abbreviation for *sanctus*. St. Peter appears quite often in OE charms.[1] STAN may also refer to Peter, for *stan* 'stone, rock' glosses Vulgate *petra* in OE versions of Matthew 16, 18.[2] SPETRVS·STANCES could then be *S(anctus) Petrvs stan ces* 'St. Peter, the Rock, has chosen (her)', the form *ces* showing lWS smoothing of *ēa* after palatal *c*.[3] However, such a translation does not make particularly good sense. CES could be an abbreviation, though an odd one, of *Cristes*, giving *S(anctus) Petrvs Stan C(rist)es* 'St. Peter, the Rock of Christ'. Perhaps STANCES should be regarded as an anagram of *Sancte* or of *Sancte S(piritus)* or possibly the whole phrase SPETRVS·STANCES is a corrupt form of (*in nomine*) *spiritus sancte*.

(m) Welded into the imported blade of the Lincoln sword (no. 32) is the legend:

+ L E U T L R I ⊥

The only ambiguous character is the last one, which could be a badly formed L, but is probably an inverted T. The name, presumably that of the smith, is a Continental Germanic one. The first element is *Leut-* (or perhaps *Leuti-*, *Leute-*), cognate with OE *Lēod-*. The second can be read as *-rit*, a generally late form of *-rid*, and the whole name is then equivalent to the recorded *Liudrid*.[4] This does not account for the sixth character, a clearly-formed L, whose base however runs into the stem of the following R. This could be a mistake for I or E, which would then give an acceptable form *Leutirit* or *Leuterit*. Alternatively it could be an error for F, which would give a second element *-frit*, earlier *-frid* (OE *-frið*), the whole name equivalent to the recorded *Leutfrid*.[5]

[1] Storms (1948), 206, 218, 288.

[2] Skeat (1887), 136–7.

[3] Campbell (1959), 131.

[4] Förstemann (1900), col. 1047.

[5] Förstemann (1900), col. 1039.

APPENDIX B

ICONOGRAPHY OF THE FULLER BROOCH (No. 153)
by R. L. S. Bruce-Mitford[1]

General. Early attempts to explain the iconography of the Fuller brooch were rather ingenuous. Sir Charles Robinson, in his note in *The Antiquary*,[2] recorded suggestions that the four roundels with busts represented the four evangelists; that the central figure 'held two scourges of leather thongs tipped with leaden balls'; and that two of the four subsidiary figures (those to the right of Pl. XLIV) were bound hand and foot, while those to the left, in the acts of running and eating, were free, so that these four figures 'typify the pretensions of the Church to bind and loose its votaries', while the 'contorted and involved monsters in the marginal roundels may probably represent evil spirits of paganism'. It was E. T. Leeds who, with characteristic acumen, perceived the correct explanation of the five central figures. In a letter to the writer (18 April 1949), Leeds said with characteristic forthrightness:

'The five figures in the middle are another story, and no one, I hold, could possibly have invented them in modern times. To put it frankly, these figures are as genuinely Saxon as anything I know. There is, as I have always maintained, an element in Anglo-Saxon art, early or late, that is inimitable, and my instinct tells me that the Robinson piece has got it.... One point that bothered me was the geometrical roundels in the borders' [i.e. the 'rosettes' or 'floral themes']. 'They did not quite seem to harmonize with the rest, and I could not quite place them.... I had already on the Wallingford' [Abingdon] 'sword detected the four symbols of the evangelists, and wondered if the disc could yield some similar interpretation. But the figures round the centre had an almost too jaunty look to be biblical. They seemed to belong to civil life. And yet they are symbolic enough; for I have no doubt whatever that they can, with the central figure, be interpreted as the five senses, read as follows:

Taste		Smell
	Sight	
Hearing		Touch

And if you will argue that any modern forger could have evolved that idea in Saxon spirit out of his inner consciousness, then it is as well I should have retired to sit in the sun, as now, in my garden, and contemplate on the amount of learning that drives away common sense.'

There is no doubt that Leeds's explanation of the five central figures is correct, and that this is the key to the whole iconographic scheme. This being so, this ninth-century

[1] This appendix is reprinted, by kind permission of Messrs. Methuen, the publishers, from Bruce-Mitford (1956a).
[2] XIX, no. 10, 1910, 268–9.

91

brooch is by far the earliest illustration of the five senses in any guise, the next representations of them dating from the thirteenth and fourteenth centuries; and it is further unique both in its representing the senses as human beings and in its association with them of the four vital factors of human, animal, bird and plant life; for this, it seems, is what the border roundels must represent.

Even with the assistance of scholars in various fields[1] and after consulting the Index of Christian Art at Princeton, and the Warburg Institute, I have not been able to clinch this identification by finding an early illustration dealing with five senses in the manner of the brooch, or any text linking them with the four factors of human, animal, bird and plant life. The senses enter frequently into medieval allegory, but usually in other guises, roles or contexts; as guardians of the soul, and ruled over by reason; or associated with the four elements, earth, air, fire and water; with the four humours; with the idea of *microcosmus*; or with the seven deadly sins and other things. Perhaps, however, no iconographic model, or text specifically linking the senses with the four aspects of life, exists, or is necessary. The roundels might have been invented by the artist himself or his patron as a fairly obvious way of symbolising the external world of living things, which we know only through the senses; and the iconography may have been largely determined (as suggested below) by the form of the brooch on which the subject had to be depicted; there are, nevertheless, other difficulties beyond the lack of a prototype or model in the way of accepting the five senses as a complete explanation of the iconography. Is a quadripartite design, with a dominant central figure, an appropriate way of illustrating five senses, which one might suppose to be equals? Why is the inanimate world, which is equally perceived with the senses, excluded from the iconography? And if the figures are the five senses, is there any method in their arrangement or sequence? It is necessary to look into the matter more closely before the identification can be taken as established, particularly when we remember that our brooch is 400 years earlier than the first known appearance of this subject in the graphic arts in any form.

The figures. The principal figures on the Fuller brooch may, at first sight, seem comical to modern eyes, but their ingenuousness will not surprise anyone familiar with early medieval allegorical illustration, as seen, for example, in the many Psychomachia manuscripts. The senses, after all, have no fixed iconography, no special symbols or attributes, by which they can be readily identified without having to be depicted performing some sort of rudimentary and pointed actions. They are not easily conveyed, and we can greatly admire the success and ingenuity with which the artist of the Fuller brooch has solved his problem; I say the artist of the Fuller brooch, rather than of his model or prototype, for the iconography of the Fuller brooch has the stamp of complete originality.

[1] In dealing with the iconography I am greatly indebted to Mr. Chu-tsing Li, of the State University of Iowa, for much valuable advice and many useful bibliographical references to the senses in allegory and art, a subject of which he is making a special study. I also acknowledge my debt to Professor Dorothy Whitelock for advice, and to Miss Enid M. Raynes for references to the five senses in Ælfric. Mr. Peter Clemoes, of Cambridge, supplied further references in Ælfric, and referred me to Isodore's *Etymologies* and to Byrtferth's *Manual*.

There is, in the first place, nothing of the late antique about it. The animals, birds, rosettes and foliate details, fill-ups and scraps of interlace, and even the figures, are pure Saxon and quite masterly in their clear, perfectly balanced, vital and cleanly finished rendering; they are not the work of a copyist. Secondly, the whole scheme clearly is thought out with reference to, or adapted to suit, an established Saxon brooch-type. The quadripartite design is inherent, as has been explained, in this brooch-series, in which it persists from start to finish, making the differentiation between the central field and the four equal segments and the distribution of the five figures inevitable in this case and unlikely to have originated in this form in any other way. Moreover each figure is exactly designed to fit the space provided for it—and not only designed to fit the space, but also with reference to the position on the brooch which the space is to occupy. Thus the two uppermost of the four subsidiary figures (Taste and Smell) form a pair—both in profile, with pellet-hair and ear-lobes with central nick—both, as positioned, facing outwards. The two lower figures (Hearing and Feeling) are also a pair, heads seen half from the front, hair in plain lobes, ear-lobes plain (no nicks)—both, as positioned, facing inwards. All four, as placed, face upwards, stressing the vertical axis of the brooch, the consistency of which is maintained in the bird and animal roundels, but depends primarily on the ingenious placing of the four static, rigid busts in the border at top and bottom, set off by foliate sprays, and with vertical lines stressed in the openings of their tunics and their general upright positioning; and on the central figure, and the tapering fill-up over its head. These details anchor the circular disc in one position. With design of such purposefulness in evidence, we must suppose that the details and emphasis of the figures are deliberate and meaningful, and with this in mind, we may consider the appositeness of the drawing of each to the interpretation put forward; for the strength of Leeds's interpretation is simply that the figures do by their attitudes and actions illustrate the senses, while other suggested interpretations—that they might represent, for example, (with *Annus*, *Helios* or *Terra Mater* for the central figure) the four seasons or the four parts of the earth, or the four elements—have nothing concrete whatever to support them, except for a possible reading of the bottom right-hand figure (Feeling), considered alone, as Winter warming his hands; an interpretation with which neither his bare head, nor his clothes (apparently essentially the same as those of the other figures[1]) nor the accompanying foliage very well agree. The fact is that the only essential differentiation between the figures lies in their gestures or actions. The whole emphasis of the central figure, which is otherwise symmetrically composed and at rest, is in the eyes. These contrast with those of the other figures, and the staring expression, marked by inverted eyebrows, is obviously deliberate. Of the other figures Feeling is well indicated by the gesture of the hands, and Taste by the hand in the mouth (the gesture perhaps emphasised by the absence of any lateral line marking the end of the sleeve). The branch which Taste holds in his hand is no doubt intended to represent the source of what is being tasted. Smell and Hearing are less obvious, but just as unequivocal. They are inherently more difficult to convey than Touch and Taste. The hands of Smell are carefully and necessarily concealed behind his back, in order to avoid confusing the issue and to con-

[1] But see Bruce-Mitford (1956*a*), 176.

centrate attention on the head. Here the mouth and eye remain negative, the only gesture being the turning of the head, which brings the nose towards one of the two plants that flank the figure. If this figure does not represent Smell, it represents nothing. Hearing is somewhat cramped for space, but one hand is raised towards the ear, while the figure is shown running. He can be regarded as having heard a cry and as shown moving in answer to it. Of the figures in the border roundels the human figures, by the same negative device as is employed in Smell, are carefully and uniformly shown doing nothing at all. They are merely a symbol of humanity, repeated four times. The other roundels, as has been said, contain in each quadrant a bird, an animal and a rosette or floral theme: so that each of the four subsidiary senses is shown in connexion with the four manifestations of life on earth. The iconography thus recognises, as has been said (p. 92), animate, or living, but not inanimate creation, as associated with the senses.

The finding of a precise source of this idea as uniquely expressed in the Fuller brooch, if one exists, must be left to specialists in early medieval texts and ideology, and to art-historians expert in iconography and the illustrations of early encyclopaedias, patristic writings and allegorical treatises. Some preliminary observations which seem sufficient to settle the identification may, however, be offered here.

The figures on the Fuller brooch are lay figures, nor has any of the disc brooches any specifically religious context or content. Nevertheless the Fuller brooch seems to have a Christian background.

In the works of Abbot Ælfric, the tenth-century Saxon homilist, whose first work was issued about 990,[1] when he was a monk at Cerne Abbas, Dorset, and most of whose writings are believed to precede his becoming Abbot of Eynsham in 1005, the five senses are referred to on many occasions. Ælfric writes at least a century after the Fuller brooch was devised, but his *Homilies* serve to show that the five senses had a place in the religious teaching of Saxon England at this time, and his reference to Gregory the Great's eluci-dation of a biblical allegory in terms of the five senses,[2] quoted below, further implies a continuity of religious teaching on the subject from earlier times, and so an earlier back-ground to explain the theme on the brooch.

In the homily for the third Sunday after Pentecost[3]—on the text 'A certain man prepared a great feast and thereto invited many', Ælfric gives Gregory the Great's interpretation of this parable. One of those invited made the excuse 'I have bought five teams of oxen and I wish to go to try them'. Gregory's interpretation is given by Ælfric as follows (the italics are mine):

> The five teams of oxen betoken the five senses of our body, which are Sight, Hearing, Taste, Smell, Touch. These five senses he who has is whole. *Through our eyes we see and distinguish all things; through the ears* we hear; *in the mouth* (on ðam muðe) we have taste and distinguish whether it be sweet or bitter, what we eat; *through the nose* we smell what is clean, what foul; *in the hands* and in all the body we have touch, that

[1] Whitelock (1952), 220.

[2] Gregory, *XL Homiliarum in Evangelia Libri Duo*, Liber Secundus, Hom. XXXVI

(Migne, *Patr. Lat.*, LXXVI, 1268, col. 2).

[3] Thorpe (1846), 372–5.

we may feel what is hard, what smooth, what unsmooth, and so everything. These senses are rightly compared with the five teams of oxen, because they are doubled in the two persons, that is in man and in woman. He goes and tries these five senses who through curiosity or unstillness wastes them uselessly. Immoderate curiosity is a grave sin; for we should turn our look from evil sight, our hearing from evil speech, our taste from unhallowed aliments, our noses from hurtful smells, our hands and whole body from foul and sinful contacts, if we are desirous of coming to the delicacies of the eternal refection. . . .

Ælfric's homily for 25 December, the Nativity,[1] contains the following:

The soul is mistress of the body and governeth the five senses of the body. The senses are thus named: Visus, that is, Sight; Auditus, Hearing; Gustus, Taste, *with the mouth*; Odoratus, Smelling, *with the nose*; Tactus, Touching or Feeling, with all the limbs *but most usually with the hands*. The Soul directeth these five senses according to its will and it behoveth it that, as a mistress, it should carefully consider what it will commend each limb to do, or what it permitteth to each limb as regards its natural desire, that nothing unseemly should befall by means of any limb's service.

The homily on the Nativity of a Confessor[2] refers to the parable of the rich man who would go into a strange country, and, calling his servants, committed to one five pounds, to one two, to another, one. . . . 'The five pounds are the five senses of our body, that is, sight and hearing, taste, smell and touch.'

In the homily on the Nativity of Holy Virgins,[3] in which the Church is compared to the five wise and five foolish virgins, Ælfric says:

With five senses, as we have often said to you, every man lives that has his health; that is, sight and hearing, taste, smell and touch. Everyone who abstains from unallowed hearing, from unallowed taste, from unallowed smell, from unallowed touch, has the name of maiden for that purity.

In the homily for February 2 on the Purification of St. Mary[4] the following occurs:

God, in the Old Law, commanded his people that they should offer to him every first born male child, or redeem it with five shillings. . . . Our evil thoughts or actions we should redeem with five shillings; that is we should repent of our wickedness with our five senses,[5] which are sight, and hearing, and taste, and smell, and touch.

In addition to these extracts there are plentiful references in Ælfric to the senses in general, or to one or other of them, particularly to the New Testament miracles in which sight was restored to the blind, hearing to the deaf, etc.

[1] Skeat (1881), i, 22.
[2] Thorpe (1846), 549–53.
[3] Thorpe (1846), 562–4.
[4] Thorpe (1846), 1.

[5] 'We sceolon ure yfelnysse behreowsian mid urum fif andgitum, ðæt synd gesiþ, and hlyst, and swæc, and stenc, and hrepung.'

95

Three points in these five extracts from Saxon texts are directly relevant to the iconography of the Saxon brooch. In each, Sight is mentioned first and seems to have primacy —'*Through our eyes we see and distinguish all things*'; in each reference the senses are placed in the order in which they appear on the brooch; Sight first, followed by Hearing, Taste, Smell and Touch. Thirdly, the *organs* of sense are stressed, Sight through the eyes; Taste, *in the mouth*; Feeling, *especially in the hands*; and the *nose* and *ears* for Smell and Hearing. This association of the senses with the human body and its sensory organs is important, for we shall see that in the only other representations of the senses in the medieval era this is not so; in the text of Alanus ab Insulis's *Anticlaudianus*[1] and its illustrations published[2] by Mütherich they appear as horses pulling a chariot driven by Reason (*ratio*); in the *De Natura Rerum* of the mid-thirteenth-century encyclopaedist Thomas de Cantimpré, and the early-fourteenth-century Longthorpe Tower illustration of his text,[3] they are represented by animals (the 'sensory champions'—cock or lynx, sight; pig or boar, hearing; monkey, taste; vulture, smell; spider, feeling) sitting on a wheel, which is turned by Reason. The correspondence of the *Homilies* of Ælfric with the brooch is thus notable. In the only other medieval illustration of the senses known, in the Pierpont Morgan Library's manuscript of Richard de Fournival's *Bestiaire d'Amour*, they are again represented as animals, but in a simpler version appropriate to the bestiary, without the introduction of Reason or other philosophic trappings.[4] The *Homilies* not only show an emphasis on the five senses in Saxon religious teaching at a date not far removed from the brooch, but a conception of the senses, as on the brooch, in terms of the human body and its functioning; precedence given to Sight; a consistently maintained sequence or precedence of the senses identical with that on the brooch, and emphasis on those sensory organs that are emphasised on the brooch. The same sequence of the senses is found at the same date (1011) in Byrhtferth of Ramsey's scientific *Manual*.[5] In the section 'Of the Symbolism of Numbers', under the number 5, we have 'Five doubled up makes ten; There are five books of Moses; There are five Senses of Man, viz. Sight, Hearing, Taste, Smell, Touch.' Both Byrhtferth and Ælfric used Alcuin's pupil Rabanus Maurus (d. 856) as a source. It is very probable that Rabanus discusses the senses also, but I have not as yet found the passage.

In the quadripartite arrangement of the brooch, Sight is not directly associated with the four forms of life, as are the other senses; but it may, in its central position, facing directly to the front and at the centre of the scheme, be fairly taken as cognisant of the emblems that surround it. Since we have seen how carefully every detail of the iconography is worked out, we must suppose that the branches held by Sight are more than mere foliage: he is probably intended to be shown possessing the fruits of the earth— in other words, these are *cornucopia*.

As we have said, a striking feature of the Fuller brooch is the dominance of the central

[1] Alanus ab Insulis, IV, cap. iii (Migne, *Patr. Lat.* CCX).

[2] Mütherich (1955). Also noted by Audrey Baker, see Janson (1952), 255, note 12.

[3] Rouse and Baker (1955). Janson (1952), 240–1, pl. xliv, a.

[4] Janson (1952), 241 and pl. xliv, b.

[5] Byrhtferth's Manual (A.D. 1011) (ed. S. J. Crawford, *Early English Text Society*, London, 1929), i, 207.

figure. Why should Sight be accorded such primacy over the other senses? It is natural enough, for sight is the sense *par excellence* by which we comprehend the outside world. But apart from this, Sight's primacy was consistently assumed, as we have seen, in Anglo-Saxon sources more or less coeval with the brooch. Sight seems invariably to be mentioned first in medieval or antique sources that refer to the five senses. It does not necessarily follow that Sight is the most important. In the *Anticlaudianus* of Alanus, although the senses are mentioned in the sequence Sight, Hearing, Smell, Taste, Touch (Smell and Taste, incidentally, transposed from the normal sequence as seen on the brooch), it is in the final event Hearing which alone is able to carry Prudence into the heavenly kingdom and to the throne of the Almighty.[1] There is, however, a tradition in which Sight is supreme over the other senses. It is embodied in the mid-twelfth century *De Mundi Universitate* of Bernadus Silvestris of Chartres.[2] In his second book, the *Microcosmus*, the creation of man is described, the final stage being the making of the five senses and man's endowment with them. The work is discussed and in part translated by C. S. Lewis,[3] and Sight's primacy is described in the following words:

As the world's eye, the Sun, exceeds by far,
And claims the heaven from every vulgar star,
So doth the eye all other senses quite
Out-go, and the whole man is in the sight.[4]

The next in the hierarchy, Hearing, is on a lower plane altogether:

Auditus sede inferior, virtutibus inpar,
Tardior in sensu, commoditate minor.

Taste and Smell follow, in that order; 'Touch comes last, even as, among the organs, those of generation come last.'[5] Later by some centuries though it is, this passage fully justifies the treatment of Sight on the Fuller brooch, its dominance in the iconographic scheme. For the tradition of the primacy of Sight goes back at least to the end of the sixth century A.D. In the *Etymologies* of Isidore of Seville (570–636), book XI, ' *De Homine et partibus eius*', after the naming of the five senses, the following occurs[6]:

Visus dictus, quod vivacior sit ceteris sensibus, ac praestantior sive velocior,

[1] Lewis (1936), 101.
[2] Bernardus Sylvestris, *De Mundi Universitate, Libri Duo, Sive Megacosmus et Microcosmus*, herausgegeben von Dr. Carl Sigmund Barach und Dr. Johann Wrobel (Innsbruck, 1876), 65–9.
[3] (1936), 97.
[4] Sed oculus mundi quantum comminibus astris
Praeminet et Caelum vindicat usque suum,
Non aliter sensus alios obscurat honore
Visus et in solo lumine totus homo est.
Cf. also the *Reductorium Morale* of Petrus
Berchorius, written 1340–2, which contains a lengthy discourse on the senses. 'Visus est sensus subtilior et nobilior inter sensus et ideo remotiora potest percipere, et de objectis coloribus a longe judicare' (*R. P. Petri Berchorii Opera Omnia*, ed. nov., I, Cologne, 1730, cap. vii).
[5] Lewis (1936), 97.
[6] *Isidori Hispalensis Episcopi Etymologiarum Sive Originum, Libri XX*, ed. W. M. Lindsay, II (Oxf. Class-Texts, 1911), liber XI, De Homine et Portentis, De Homine et partibus eius, sections 18, 21. Cf. Saxl (1927), 43 and fig. 24.

ampliusque vigeat, quantum memoria inter cetera mentis officia. Vicinior est enim cerebro, unde omnia manant. . . .

Summary. The conception of the senses expressed in the Fuller brooch seems to have no relation to the classical treatment of the subject, as in Pliny, in which two senses (Taste and Touch) are most acute in man, but the others in various beasts: nor to the Christian version of it, as in the *Bestiaire d'Amour*, and in Thomas de Cantimpré, in which these vehicles of temptation are all found at their acutest, not in man, but in creatures. Nor is there any connexion in the iconography of the brooch with the philosophic schemes that relate the senses to *microcosmus*, to the elements, the humours, the seasons and other concepts, except that *microcosmus* is concerned with the senses in man, and (in Bernardus Sylvestris at any rate) stresses emphatically the primacy of Sight. On the contrary, these are the traditions which lie behind the medieval representations of the senses in animal form, and their inclusion (by name only) in cosmological diagrams. The Fuller brooch, which depicts the senses in man, and associated with organs of the human body, and which is some 700 years earlier than the next known representation of the senses in human form,[1] except for the explanatory or identifying sketches that accompany the horses in the Italian (Verona) Anticlaudianus MS.[2] stands apart and seems rather to reflect the moral teaching of the early Church, perhaps especially of the Saxon Church. But again it must be admitted that the brooch, apart from the small casual-looking cross on the garments of Sight, seems to dwell on the senses for their own sakes, in an almost secular way, with no indication of the essential theme of the homilist, namely that they are sources of temptation, which must be kept under control. Nor do the homilies (so far as I have been able to discover) anywhere associate the senses with the four forms of life, which are reiterated round the brooch. Even so, while the texts adduced do not explain the iconography in every particular, there can now be no doubt that it is the five senses that are depicted on the Fuller brooch, and furthermore that this subject is in no way out of place in the ninth century.

[1] Mr. Chu-tsing Li refers me to a seventeenth-century painting in the Prado by J. A. Escalante, 'The Triumph of Faith over the Senses', as the only comparable representation of the senses (personified, not symbolised) known to him.

[2] Bruce-Mitford (1956), pl. xxv.

APPENDIX C

ANGLO-SAXON ORNAMENTAL METALWORK, 700–1100, OUTSIDE THE BRITISH MUSEUM—A HAND-LIST

The following list lays no claim to completeness. It is meant to serve as a hand-list on which future studies can be based. I have been fairly ruthless in rejecting objects which do not fall within the scope of this catalogue, but a few controversial objects have been retained. References to objects illustrated in this catalogue are entered in the final column.

The list should be used in conjunction with the general index.

Find-Place or Name of Object	Museum	Publication	Remarks
Abingdon, Berkshire.	Oxford: Ashmolean Museum.	Evans (1887)	Sword (pl. VI).
Abingdon, Berkshire (near).	Oxford: Ashmolean Museum.	—	Buckle.
Æthelstan's ring.	—	—	See: No Locality.
Alhstan's ring.	—	—	See Llysfaen.
Alfred jewel.	—	—	See Newton Park.
Attleborough, Norfolk.	Norwich: Castle Museum.	—	Finger-ring.
Avfret ring.	—	—	See Rome.
Avon Valley, nr. Chippenham, Wiltshire.	Coventry Museum.	—	Stirrup.
Bamberg, Germany.	Munich: Bayerische Staatsbibliothek.	Messerek (1952), pls. 32 and 33.	Plates of a book-cover.
Barnham, Norfolk.	Cambridge: University Museum of Archaeology and Ethnology.	—	Circular brooch.
Barton Mills, Suffolk.	Cambridge: University of Archaeology and Ethnology.	—	Bronze-gilt roundel.
Bath, Somerset.	Bath: Roman Baths Museum.	Davis (n.d.).	Lead cross.
Battersea (Thames)	—	—	See London (Battersea, River Thames).
Belstead, Suffolk.	Ipswich Museum.	—	Inlaid scramasax.
Berkeley Castle.	—	—	See: No locality.

Find-Place or Name of Object	Museum	Publication	Remarks
Bischofshofen, Austria.	Bischofshofen Church.	Jenny (n.d.).	Altar cross.
Birdoswald, Cumberland.	Housesteads Museum.	—	Disc-headed pin.
Bjørke, Hjørundfjord, Møre, Norway.	Bergen: Historisk Museum.	Bøe (1932).	Gilt-bronze plaque (pl. I, c).
Blaise Castle, Somerset.	Bristol: City Museum.	—	Strap-end.
Bledlow, Buckinghamshire.	Aylesbury: County Museum.	Head (1955), 99 and fig. 32.	Strap-end.
Bolnhurst, Bedfordshire.	Bedford Museum.	—	Gilt-bronze disc brooch.
Bologna, Italy.	Bologna: Museo Civico.	Bruce-Mitford (1956a), pl. XXII, B–D.	Finger-ring.
Bossington, Hampshire.	Oxford: Ashmolean Museum.	Badwin Brown (1903–37) iii, 311 and pl. 53, 5.	Finger-ring.
Bottisham Lode, Cambridgeshire.	Cambridge: Museum of Archaeology and Ethnology.	VCH. Cambridgeshire, i, 322 and pl. XII, e.	Roundel.
Bradwell, Essex.	Colchester: Castle Museum.	—	2 strap-ends.
Bramham Moor, Yorkshire.	Copenhagen: National Museum.	Wilson (1959b), 159, 66 and Page (1962a).	Finger-ring.
Branston, Suffolk.	Ipswich Museum.	—	Circular brooch.
Brussels, Belgium.	Brussels: Treasury of Sts. Michel and Gudule	Velge (1925) 363–5 and pl. 93	Reliquary cross.
Buckinghamshire.	Cambridge: University Museum of Archaeology and Ethnology.	—	Circular brooch.
Burford, Oxfordshire.	Oxford: Ashmolean Museum.	—	Strap-end.
Burgh Castle, Suffolk.	Ipswich Museum.	—	Circular Brooch.
Burghead, Elginshire.	Edinburgh: National Museum of Antiquities of Scotland.	Proceedings of the Society of Antiquaries of Scotland, iv (1860–2), 378.	Drinking-horn mount.

Find-Place or Name of Object	Museum	Publication	Remarks
Bury St. Edmunds, Suffolk.	Farnham: Pitt Rivers Museum.	*VCH. Suffolk, i,* 352 3.	Lead plaque.
Burton Fields.	—	—	See Stamford Bridge.
Butley Priory, Suffolk.	Ipswich Museum.	Brøndsted (1924), 146.[1]	Circular brooch.
Cam, River.	—	—	See Chesterton.
Cambridge, Magdalene Street.	Cambridge: University Museum of Archaeology and Ethnology.	*VCH. Cambridgeshire,* i, 323 and pl. XI, d.	Circular brooch.
Cambridge (?).	Cambridge: University Museum of Archaeology and Ethnology.	Almgren (1955), 106 and Tab. II: F/8.	Key.
Cambridge.	Cambridge: University Museum of Archaeology and Ethnology.	*VCH. Cambridgeshire,* i, p. 323, pl. XII, g.	Book mount.
Cambridge.	Cambridge: University Museum of Archaeology and Ethnology.	*VCH. Cambridgeshire,* i, 324, pl. XI, c.	Disc.
Cambridge.	Cambridge: University Museum of Archaeology and Ethnology.	*VCH. Cambridgeshire,* i, p. 324, pl. XII, c.	Disc.
Cambridge.	Cambridge: University Museum of Archaeology and Ethnology.	*VCH. Cambridgeshire,* i, 323, pl. XII, b.	Fragment of cheek piece.
Cambridge.	Cambridge: University Museum of Archaeology and Ethnology.	*VCH. Cambridgeshire,* i, p. 327. pl. XI, g.	Strap-end.
Canterbury, Kent.	Canterbury: Cathedral Treasury.	*Country Life,* cvii, no. 2788 (June 1950), 1890.	Portable sun-dial.
Canterbury, Kent.	Oxford: Ashmolean Museum.	*VCH. Kent,* i, 382 and fig. 27.	Coin brooch.
Canterbury, (St. Augustine's Abbey), Kent.	Canterbury: St. Augustine's College.	Radford (1940).	3 styli.
Canterbury, Kent.	Canterbury: Royal Museum.	Jessup (1950), pl. 31.	Bronze cross.

[1] Wrongly referred to by Brøndsted as from Felixstowe: recently transferred, with other Suffolk material from the Castle Museum, Norwich to Ipswich Museum.

Find-Place or Name of Object	Museum	Publication	Remarks
Canterbury, Kent.	Canterbury: St Augustine's College	Talbot-Rice (1952), 235.	Lead cross.
Cheddar, Somerset.	Taunton: Castle Museum.	—	Various objects.
Chelsea, R. Thames.	—	—	See London, Chelsea.
Chesterton, Cambridgeshire.	Cambridge: University Museum of Archaeology and Ethnology.	*VCH. Cambridgeshire*, i, 327 and pl. IV, b.	Inlaid scramasax.
Chichester, Sussex.	Chichester: Guildhall Museum.	—	2 bronze tags.
Chichester, Sussex.	—	—	Pin.
Colchester, Essex.	Colchester Museum	Moe (1955), 17 and fig. 16.	Oval mount.
Coldingham Priory, Berwickshire.	Private possession.	—	Strap-end (fig. 3).
Compton Hampshire.	Winchester: Cathedral Library.	—	Coin brooch.
Cologne, Germany.	Cologne: Domschatz.	Goldschmidt (1926), pl. II, 10.	Mounts on Crozier of St. Heribert.
Coombs, Sussex.	Alnwick Castle.	*A Descriptive Catalogue of Antiquities . . . at Alnwick Castle*, Newcastle-upon-Tyne 1880, 71–2.	Spearhead.
Coquet Island, Northumberland.	Alnwick Castle.	Stephens, (1866 1901), I, 480–1.	Finger-ring.
Cowlam, Yorkshire.	Hull: Mortimer Museum.	—	Strap-end.
Cricklade, Wiltshire.	Oxford: Ashmolean Museum.	Goddard (1898–9), 232.	Fragment of a strap-end.
Dolven, Berg, Brunlanes, Vestfold, Norway.	Oslo: Universitetets Oldsaksamling.	Bruce-Mitford (1956*a*), pl. XXIII, C and D.	Sword.
Dorchester, Oxfordshire.	Oxford: Ashmolean Museum.	Oman (1931), fig. A, 4.	Finger-ring.
Dover, Kent.	Dover: Corporation Museum.	—	Inlaid scramasax.
Driffield, Yorkshire.	Now lost.	Fowler (1870).	Finger-ring.

Find-Place or Name of Object	Museum	Publication	Remarks
Dunwich, Suffolk.	Private Possession.	—	Gilt-bronze mount.
Durham.	Durham Cathedral.	Battiscombe (1956), 326–335 and pl. XIX.	St. Cuthbert's altar.
Durham.	Durham Cathedral.	Kendrick (1938*b*).	Flambard's crozier.
Durham.	Durham Cathedral.	Kendrick (1938*b*), 242 and pl. LV, 2, b.	Spearhead.
Dymchurch, Kent	Sheffield: City Museum	—	Strap-end (fig. 1).
Eaton Socon, Bedfordshire.	—	—	2 strap-ends.
Ehlla's Ring.	—	—	See Bossington.
Ely, Cambridgeshire.	London: Society of Antiquaries.	*English Church History Exhibition, St. Albans* 1905, 3.	Shroud pin of Wolstan, Archbishop of York 1002–23.
Espinge.	—	—	See Hurva.
Farmen, Kvelde, Hedrum, Vestfold, Norway.	Oslo: Universitetets Oldsaksamling.	Petersen (1919), fig. 101.	Sword.
Felixstowe, Suffolk.	Bury St. Edmunds: Moyse's Hall Museum.	Brøndsted (1924), 146 and fig. 122.	Circular Brooch.
Felixstowe, Suffolk.	Ipswich Museum.	Kendrick (1934),	Strap-end.
Felixstowe, Suffolk.	Ipswich Museum.	—	2 strap-ends.
Flambard's Crozier.	—	—	See Durham.
Fordham, Cambridgeshire.	Cambridge: University Museum of Archaeology and Ethnology.	*VCH. Cambridgeshire*, i, 323 and pl. XII, h.	Book mount.
Fordham, Cambridgeshire.	Cambridge: University Museum of Archaeology and Ethnology.	*VCH. Cambridgeshire*, i, 323, p. xii, i.	Book mount.
Framlingham, Suffolk.	Norwich: Castle Museum.	Almgren (1955), 106 and Table II.E/5.	Bronze key.
Fremington Hagg, Yorkshire.	York: Yorkshire Museum.	Cowen (1935).	Book mount in openwork.

Find-Place or Name of Object	Museum	Publication	Remarks
Freswick, Caithness.	Edinburgh: National Museum of Antiquities of Scotland.	*Proceedings of the Society of Antiquaries of Scotland*, lxxxi (1946/7), 196 and pl. XXIV, 4.	Strap-end.
Fulda, Germany.	Fulda: Landesbibliothek.	Wilson (1961).	Mounts on bookbinding.
Fulset, Hegra, Stjørdal, Nordtröndelag, Norway.	Trondheim Museum	Shetelig (1940), v, 69 and fig. 77.	Mount.
Gandersheim, Germany.	Brunswick: Herzog Anton Ulrich Museum.	Scherer (1931), pl. 1.	Metal-mounted ivory casket (pl. I, *a*).
Glenluce, Sands, Wigtownshire.	Edinburgh: National Museum of Antiquities of Scotland.	Callander (1932/3), 31, fig. 5, 2–4.	3 strap-ends.
Goldsborough, Yorkshire.	Private possession.	Collingwood (1915), 179.	Strap-end.
Gooderstone, Norfolk.	Norwich: Castle Museum.	—	Sword.
Grønneberg, Tjølling, Vestfold, Norway.	Oslo: Universitetets Oldsaksamling.	Bruce-Mitford (1956*a*), pl. XXIII, A–B.	Sword.
Haithabu, Schleswig, Germany.	Schleswig: Schleswig-Holsteinisches Landesmuseum.	Jankuhn (1937), fig. 132.	Silver gilt ornament.
Haithabu, Schleswig, Germany.	Schleswig: Schleswig-Holsteinisches Landesmuseum.	—	Strap-end.
Halstock, Dorset.	—	Cuming, (1863), 215 and pl. 16, 6.	Strap-end.
Hauge, Sunelven, Møre, Norway.	Private Possession.	Haseloff (1950), pl. xx, c.	Quatrefoil (pl. III, *e*).
Hauxton Mill, Cambridgeshire.	Cambridge: University Museum of Archaeology and Ethnology.	*VCH. Cambridgeshire*, i, p. 327, pl. XI, h, i, j.	3 strap-ends.
Hauxton Mill, Cambridgeshire.	Cambridge: University Museum of Archaeology and Ethnology.	*VCH. Cambridgeshire*, i, 324 and pl. XII, a.	Fragment of pinhead.

Find-Place or Name of Object	Museum	Publication	Remarks
Hedeby.	—	—	See Haithabu.
Hegge, Kvam, Stod, Nord-Tröndelag, Norway.	Trondheim Museum.	—	Silver-mounted sword.
Hexham, Northumberland.	Alnwick Castle.	Wilson (1956*b*), 92.	Finger-ring (fig. 3).
Hexham, Northumberland.	Hexham: Priory Church.	Wilson & Blunt (1961), pl. XXVIII, a.	Chalice.
Hillesøy, Lenvik, Norway.	Tromsø Museum.	Sjøvold (1951).	Disc.
Hitchin, Hertfordshire.	Hitchin Museum.	Evans (1892), 257.	Disc-headed pin (pl. II, *a*).
Hon, Norway.	—	—	See Nedre Hon.
Hoven, Hof, Sundalen, Møre, Norway.	Trondheim Museum.	Brøndsted (1924), 149 and fig. 124.	Sword.
Hurly Hawkin, Angus.	Edinburgh: National Museum of Antiquities of Scotland.	—	Strap-end (Cf. Bledlow).
Hurva, Skåne, Sweden.	Stockholm: Statens Historiska Museum.	Holmqvist (1951), fig. 38.	Strap-end.
Icklingham, Suffolk.	Oxford: Ashmolean Museum.	Evison (1957), 220.	Circular brooch.
Icklingham, Suffolk.	Oxford: Ashmolean Museum.	*Journal of the British Archaeological Association*, 1865, 84 and pl. 4, 6.	Circular brooch.
Igelösa, Skåne, Sweden.	Lund: Universitets Historiska Museum.	Wilson (1956), 33 and fig. 2.	Disc.
Islip, Oxfordshire.	Oxford: Ashmolean Museum.	Seaby (1950), fig. 12.	Stirrup.
Ixworth, Suffolk.	Cambridge: University Museum of Archaeology and Ethnology.	—	Book mount (pl. X).
Ixworth (?), Suffolk.	—	*Proceedings of the Bury and West Suffolk Archaeological Institute* (1853), i, 223, fig. 314.	Gold ring.

Find-Place or Name of Object	Museum	Publication	Remarks
Ixworth, Suffolk.	Cambridge: University Museum of Archaeology and Ethnology.	Strömberg (1961), fig. 20.	Book mount.
Ixworth (?), Suffolk.	Oxford: Ashmolean Museum.	Oman (1931), fig. A, II.	Silver ring.
Ixworth, Suffolk.	Cambridge: University Museum of Archaeology and Ethnology.	Brøndsted (1924), 146.	Round brooch.
Ixworth, Suffolk.	Oxford: Ashmolean Museum.	Kendrick (1938c), 380 and pl. LXXIV 3.	Strap-end.
Ixworth, Suffolk.	Oxford: Ashmolean Museum.	—	Fragment of a disc.
Ixworth, Suffolk.	Oxford: Ashmolean Museum.	—	Strap-end.
Källby, Sweden.	Lund: Universitets Historiska Museum.	Wilson (1955).	Horse trappings.
Kaupang, Tjølling, Vestfold, Norway.	Oslo: Universitetets Oldsaksamling.	Blindheim (1960), fig. 6.	Roundel.
Kaupang, Tjølling, Vestfold, Norway.	Oslo: Universitetets Oldsaksamling.	Blindheim (1953).	Sword (pl. VIII, c).
Kegworth, Leicestershire.	Leicester: City Museum.	—	Pin and connecting plate (pl. III, a).
Kersey, Suffolk.	Ipswich Museum.	—	Sword.
Kilverstone, Norfolk.	Norwich: Castle Museum.	Clark (1960), 232 and pl. 52.	Stirrup.
Kingsholm, Gloucestershire.	Gloucester: City Museum.	—	Strap-end.
King's Lynn.	—	—	See Reffley Spring.
Knafhólar, Iceland.	Reykjavik: National Museum.	Eldjárn (1956), 268 and fig. 90.	Sword pommel guard (fig. 2).
Knock-y-Doonee, Andreas, Isle of Man.	Douglas: Manx Museum.	—	Strap-end.
Köln.	—	—	See Cologne.
Kroken, Fjære, Aust-Agder, Norway.	Oslo: Universitetets Oldsaksamling.	Shetelig (1940), v, 179 and fig. 144.	Strap-end.

Find-Place or Name of Object	Museum	Publication	Remarks
Lakenheath, Suffolk.	Cambridge: University Museum of Archaeology and Ethnology.	Brøndsted (1924), 146.	Round brooch.
Lakenheath, Suffolk.	Cambridge: University Museum of Archaeology and Ethnology.	*VCH. Cambridgeshire*, i, 327.	Strap-end.
Långtora, Uppland, Sweden.	Stockholm: Statens Historiska Museum.	Arbman (1936), 90–92 and figs. 2–5.	Silver-mounted sword.
Lansdown, Somerset.	Private possession.	Gardner (1955), 252.	Strap-end.
Leicester, Highcross St.	Leicester: City Museum.	*City of Leicester Museum and Art Gallery, Anglo-Saxon Leicestershire and Rutland*, 23.	Bronze openwork pendant.
Leicester district (?).	Leicester: City Museum.	Evison (1957), 220 and pl. XXVI, d.	Circular brooch.
Lejre Denmark.	Copenhagen: National Museum.	Wilson (1960d).	Hanging-bowl.
Letchworth, Hertfordshire.	Letchworth Museum.	Westell (1935), 350 and fig. 3.	Bronze mount.
Lilla Howe, Gothland, Yorkshire.[1]	Liverpool: City Museum.	Leeds (1911).	4 strap-ends.
Lindisfarne Priory.	Lindisfarne: Priory Museum.	Butcher (1955), 10–11.	Buckle.
Little Ouse, River.	—	—	See Ouse, River.
Llysfaen, Caernarvon.	London: Victoria and Albert Museum.	Brøndsted (1924), fig. 111.	Finger-ring of Alhstan.
Lode.	—	—	See Bottisham Lode.
London (Bastion 14).	Now lost.	Grimes (1956), fig. 47.	Bronze pendant.
London (Battersea, River Thames).	Oxford: Pitt-Rivers Museum.	*Proceedings of Society of Antiquaries of London* iv (1868), 142–3.	Sword (pl. VII).

[1] Provenance confirmed in *Transactions of the Historical Society of Lancashire and Cheshire*, xxiii (1870-1), 200.

Find-Place or Name of Object	Museum	Publication	Remarks
London (Cheapside).	London: Guildhall Museum.	—	Pewter bead.
London (Canning Town).	London: London Museum.	Wheeler (1927), 42 and fig. 19.	Inlaid spur.
London (Cheapside).	London: Guildhall Museum.	VCH. London, i, 160 and fig. 17.	Hoard of 26 brooches, 5 beads and 12 rings.
London (Chelsea).	London: Victoria and Albert Museum.	Brøndsted (1924), 155 and fig. 130.	Finger-ring.
London (St. Mary Hill).	Now lost.	Griffith (1786).	Brooch.
London (Sherborne Lane).	London: London Museum.	Wheeler (1935), 181 and fig. 43.	Sword-guard.
London (Smithfield).	London: London Museum.	Wheeler (1927), 42 and fig. 21.	2 copper plates.
London (Queen Victoria Street).	London: Guildhall Museum.	Wheeler, (1935), 189–90 pl. XIX and fig. 45.	'Chatelaine'.
London (River Thames near Tower Hill).	London: London Museum.	Wheeler (1927), 38 and fig. 17.	Inlaid stirrup.
London (River Thames).	—	Cuming (1868), 181, pl. 13, 2.	Spur.
London (River Thames).	London: London Museum.	Wheeler (1935), 148 and fig. 26, 7.	Pewter brooch.
London (Wallbrook).	London: Guildhall Museum.	VCH. London, i, fig. 23.	Strap-end.
London (Westminster).	Private possession.	VCH. London, i. fig. 10	Sword.
London.	—	Brøndsted (1924), 146.	Round animal brooch.
London.	London: London Museum.	Wheeler (1927), 43 and fig. 22.	Strap-end.
London.	London: Guildhall Museum.	—	Circular (coin) brooch.
Lullingstone, Kent.	—	—	Strap-end.
Lunde, Vangen, Voss, Hordaland, Norway.	Bergen: Historisk Museum.	Shetelig (1940), v, fig. 148.	Bronze quadrant (pl. II, d).

Find-Place or Name of Object	Museum	Publication	Remarks
Malton, Yorkshire.	Now lost.	Warterman (1951).	Finger-ring.
Meaux Abbey, Yorkshire.	London, Victoria and Albert Museum.	Oman (1930), 63.	Finger-ring.
Meols, Cheshire.	Chester: Grosvenor Museum.	Hume, (1863), pl. VIII, 5.	Buckle.
Meols, Cheshire.	Chester: Grosvenor Museum.	Hume (1863), pl. XII, 20.	Buckle-plate.
Meols, Cheshire.	Chester: Grosvenor Museum.	Hume (1863), pl. XI, 1, 2, 5, 10 and 15.	5 strap-ends
Meols, Cheshire.	Chester: Grosvenor Museum.	Bu'lock (1960), fig. 4, i.	Pewter brooch.
Meols, Cheshire.	Chester: Grosvenor Museum.	Bu'lock (1960), fig. 4 f.	Openwork strap-end.
Meols, Cheshire.	Chester: Grosvenor Museum.	Potter (1889), fig. 4.	Strap-end.
Meols, Cheshire.	Chester: Grosvenor Museum.	Bu'lock (1960), fig. 6a and pl. 6.	Stirrup-plate.
Meols, Cheshire.	Chester: Grosvenor Museum.	Kitson-Clark (1941), 335.	Pin-head.
Mildenhall, Suffolk.	Cambridge: University Museum of Archaeology and Ethnology.	—	Bronze mount with cryptic inscription. (pl. X, c).
Mildenhall, Suffolk.	—	VCH. Suffolk, i, 345, fig. 12.	Weight.
Mildenhall, Suffolk.	Oxford: Ashmolean Museum.	—	Book or box mount.
Mileham, Norfolk.	Norwich: Castle Museum.	Clark (1960), 232 and pl. 53.	Sword.
Minster Lovel, Oxfordshire.	Oxford: Ashmolean Museum.	Kirk (1948).	Jewel.
Mortain, France.	Mortain Church.	Cahen et al. (1930).	Casket.
Mottisfont, nr. Romsey, Hampshire.	Private possession.	Read (1887).	Inlaid stirrup.
Nedre Hon, Haug, Øvre Eiker, Buskerud, Norway.	Oslo: Universitetets Oldsaksamling.	Brøgger (1920–21), 18 and fig. 8.	Finger-ring.

Find-Place or Name of Object	Museum	Publication	Remarks
Nedre Store-Var, Stokke, Vestfold, Norway.	Oslo: Universitetets Oldsaksamling.	Petersen (1919), p. 113, fig. 95.	Sword.
Nedre Stjørdalen.	—	—	See Re.
Newbury, Berkshire.	—	Mentioned in Wanley papers 16 Feb. 1720/1.	Runic ring.
Newton Park, Somerset.	Oxford: Ashmolean Museum.	Kirk (1948).	The Alfred Jewel.
Northamptonshire.	—	MS. Notes of C. Roach Smith.	Fragmentary circular brooch (part of hoard).
Northampton, Castle.	Northampton: Central Museum.	—	Pin.
Northampton, Castle.	Northampton: Central Museum.	—	Buckle and plate.
Northampton, Castle.	Northampton: Central Museum.	—	Book mount.
Nottingham, Barker Gate.	Nottingham: City Museum.	—	Pewter round brooch with iron pin.
Old Sarum, Wiltshire.	Oxford: Ashmolean Museum.	Montgomerie (1947), 136 and fig. 6.	Circular brooch.
Old Windsor, Berkshire.	—	—	Various objects.
Ormside, Westmorland.	York: Yorkshire Museum.	Brøndsted (1924), figs. 72–3.	Bowl.
Østebø, Sandeid, Vikedal, Rogaland, Norway.	Stavanger Museum.	Shetelig (1940), v, 182 and fig. 147.	Strap-end.
Ouse, River.	Cambridge: University Museum of Archaeology and Ethnology.	VCH. Cambridgeshire, i, 327.	Inlaid scramasax.
Oveing, Sussex.	Now lost.	Camden (1806), i, 288.	Disc brooch.
Oxford, Brasenose College.	Oxford: Ashmolean Museum.	Chamot (1930), 25 and pl. 3, b.	Enamelled disc (fig. 5).
Oxford, River Cherwell, Magdalen Bridge.	Oxford: Ashmolean Museum.	Seaby (1950), 33 and fig. 14.	Two stirrups.

Find-Place or Name of Object	Museum	Publication	Remarks
Oxford, River Cherwell, Magdalen Bridge.	Oxford: Ashmolean Museum.	Seaby (1950), 34 and fig. 13, *f*.	Stirrup.
Pakenham, Suffolk.	Oxford: Ashmolean Museum.	Baldwin Brown (1903–37), iv, 422 and fig. 16c.	Spur.
Pike and Eel.	—	—	See Chesterton.
River Ray.	—	—	See Islip.
Re, Stjørdalen, Nedre Stjørdalen, Nord-Trøndelag, Norway.	Trondheim Museum.	Smith (1925), 247 and fig. 21.	Fragment of mount.
Reay Links, Caithness.	Edinburgh: National Museum of Antiquities of Scotland.	Callander (1932/3), 32 and fig. 7.	Strap-end.
Reffley Spring, King's Lynn, Norfolk.	King's Lynn Museum.	—	Stirrup.
River Reno.	—	—	See Bologna.
Richborough, Kent.	Richborough: Richborough Castle Museum.	Roach-Smith (1850), pl. V.	Strap-end.
Rome, Italy.	London: Victoria and Albert Museum.	Oman (1930), 64.	Finger-ring.
Romsey.	—	—	See Mottisfont.
Roos, Yorkshire.	Hull: Mortimer Archaeological Museum.	Kitson Clark (1941*a*),	Pin-head.
Røysehagen, Kolbu, Vestre Toten, Opland, Norway.	Oslo: Universitetets, Oldsaksamling.	Shetelig, v, 116.	Sword.
Royston Heath, Cambridgeshire.	Cambridge: University Museum of Archaeology and Ethnology.	*VCH. Cambridgeshire*, i, 322, No. 8, pl. XXII, d.	Buckle.
Rudford, Gloucestershire.	—	Wheeler (1927), 41.	Stirrup.
Rupert Cross.	—	—	See Bischofshofen.
Saffron Walden, Essex.	Saffron Walden Museum.	*VCH. Essex*, i, 330.	Pendants, etc. in a grave.

Find-Place or Name of Object	Museum	Publication	Remarks
St. Andrews, Fifeshire.	Edinburgh: National Museum of Antiquities of Scotland.	Wilson (1863), 331.	Runic ring.
St. Cuthbert's Altar.	—	—	See Durham.
St. Mary's Abbey, York.	—	—	See York.
St. Neots, Huntingdonshire.	—	—	Strap-end
Sandford, Oxfordshire.	Oxford: Ashmolean Museum.	Swarzenski (1954), 49, pl. 65, 148.	Plaque with Christ in Majesty.
Selsey, Sussex.	—	Salzmann (1912), 60 and pl. V.	Strap-end.
Shifford, Oxfordshire.	Reading Museum.	Grove (1938), 256 and fig. 4.	Sword.
Sigeric Ring.	—	—	See Ixworth (?).
Skrøppa, Breim, Sogn og Fjørdane, Norway.	Bergen: Historisk Museum.	—	Bronze gilt mount.
Snotra, Årfjørden, Sør. Trøndelag, Norway.	Trondheim Museum.	—	Strap-end
Souldern, Oxfordshire.	Oxford: Ashmolean Museum.	Bruce-Mitford (1952/3), 236, and fig. 49.	Strap-end.
South Ferriby, Lincolnshire.	—	Kitson Clark (1941), 333–334.	Pin-head.
Stamford Bridge, Yorkshire.	York: Yorkshire Museum.	Kitson Clark (1941b).	Toilet set and bracelet.
Standal, Hjørundfjord, Møre, Norway.	Bergen: Historisk Museum.	Shetelig (1940), v, 184 and fig. 154.	Roundel.
Staplehurst, Kent.	Staplehurst Church.	Talbot Rice (1952), pl. 91 b.	Door hinges, etc.
Stevenston Sands, Ayrshire.	Edinburgh: National Museum of Antiquities of Scotland.	Callander (1932/3), 31 and fig. 5, 1.	Strap-end.
Stillingfleet, Yorkshire.	Stillingfleet Church.	Talbot Rice (1952), pl. 91, a.	Door hinges, etc.
Stockholm, Sweden.	Stockholm: Statens Historiska Museum.	Bruce-Mitford (1956), pl. XXXI, B.	Disc brooch.

Find-Place or Name of Object	Museum	Publication	Remarks
Støle, Støle, Etne, Hordaland, Norway.	Bergen: Historisk Museum.	Shetelig (1940), v, 48 and fig. 47.	Mount, used as a brooch.
Storsletta, Hillesøy, Lenvik, Troms, Norway.	Tromsø Museum.	Petersen (1928), 146–8 and fig. 176.	Silver pendant or brooch.
Sutherlandshire, Scotland.	Oxford: Ashmolean Museum.	—	2 strap-ends.
Talnotrie, Kirk-cudbrightshire.	Edinburgh: National Museum of Antiquities.	Maxwell(1912–13).	Hoard containing 2 pins, strap-end, etc. (pl. IV, d).
Ten Foot Bridge.	—	—	See Shifford.
Thames.	—	—	See London.
Thetford, Norfolk.	Norwich: Castle Museum.	—	Buckle-loop.
Thetford, Norfolk.	Norwich: Castle Museum.	Kendrick (1938c), 380 and pl. LXXIV, 2.	Strap-end.
Thetford, Norfolk.	Norwich: Castle Museum.	—	3 circular brooches.
Thetford, Norfolk (St. Mary).	Norwich: Castle Museum.	—	Pin-head.
Threxton, Norfolk.	Norwich: Castle Museum.	Evison (1957), 220 and pl. XXVIc.	Bronze disc.
Trewhiddle, Cornwall.	Now lost.	Wilson and Blunt (1961).	2 finger-rings and a gold pendant.
Tuddenham, Suffolk.	Cambridge: University Museum of Archaeology and Ethnology.	—	Bronze disc.
Velds, Orum, Viborg, Denmark.	Copenhagen: National museum.	Brøndsted (1936), 104 and figs. 11 and 12.	Stirrup plates and trappings (pl. IX, a).
Wallingford.	—	—	See Abingdon.
Wareham, Dorset.	Dorchester: County Museum.	Acland (1928).	Sword.
Wensley, Yorkshire.	Private possession.	*Proceedings of the Society of Antiquaries of London*, XXVIII (1915–16), 228–30.	Sword.

Find-Place or Name of Object	Museum	Publication	Remarks
Westley Waterless, Cambridgeshire.	Cambridge: University Museum of Archaeology and Ethnology.	Fox (1923), pl. XXXV, 3.	Large leaden vessel.
Westminster.	—	—	See London, Westminster.
West Stow, Suffolk.	Oxford: Ashmolean Museum.	—	Square plaque.
Wilbury Hill, Hertfordshire.	Cambridge: University Museum of Archaeology and Ethnology.	Kendrick (1938c), pl. 74, 4.	Strap-end.
Willingdon, Sussex.	Lewes: Sussex Archaeological Society's Museum.	VCH. Sussex, i, 348.	Lead chest.
Winchester, Hampshire, S. side of the Cathedral.	Private possession.	The Numismatic Chronicle, 1908, 83–4.	Coin brooch.
Winchester, Hampshire, Cathedral precincts.	—	—	Filigree panel.
Winchester, Hampshire, Cathedral precincts.	—	—	Strap-end.
Winchester, Hampshire, St. Georges St.	Winchester: City Museum.	Butcher (1955), 10 and fig. 2.	Buckle.
Winchester, Hampshire.	Winchester: Cathedral Library.	Kendrick (1949), 100 and fig. 13 and pl. LXXVII.	Panel (pl. X, a).
Winchester, Hampshire.	Winchester: City Museum.	—	Circular brooch.
Windsor, Berkshire.	Oxford: Ashmolean Museum.	Brøndsted (1924), fig. 118.	Sword pommel.
Wisbech (Castle Ditch), Cambridgeshire.	Wisbech Museum.	Kendrick (1949), pl. LXXXII.	Openwork roundel (pl. X, e).
Witham River, Lincolnshire.	Now lost.	Kendrick (1941a).	Hanging bowl (pl. II, c).
Witham, River, Lincolnshire.	Sheffield: City Museum.	City Museum, Sheffield, Annual Report, 1955/6, 9 and pl. 26.	Sword.

Find-Place or Name of Object	Museum	Publication	Remarks
Witham, River, Lincolnshire.	—	—	Stirrup-iron.
Woodeaton, Oxfordshire.	Oxford: Ashmolean Museum.	Leeds (1911), 6.	Strap-end.
York, College St.	York: Yorkshire Museum.	Waterman (1959), fig. 10, 12.	Coin weight.
York, Fishergate.	York: Yorkshire Museum.	—	Finger-ring.
York, Hungate.	York: Yorkshire Museum.	Richardson (1959), 81 and fig. 18, 1.	Buckle.
York, Hungate.	York: Yorkshire Museum.	Richardson (1959), 81 and fig. 18, 3.	Rectangular brooch.
York, Hungate.	York: Yorkshire Museum.	Richardson (1959), 81 and fig. 18, 2.	Circular brooch.
York: New Market St.	York: Yorkshire Museum.	Waterman (1959), fig. 10, 8.	Brooch.
York, Pavement.	York: Yorkshire Museum.	Waterman (1959), fig. 25, 5.	Circular brooch.
York, St. Mary's Abbey.	York: Yorkshire Museum.	Wilson (1956b), 92.	Finger-ring.
York, St. Mary's Abbey.	York: Yorkshire Museum.	—	Pin-head.
York, St. Mary's Abbey.	York: Yorkshire Museum.	—	Strap-end.
York, Tanner Row.	York: Yorkshire Museum.	—	Strap-end.
York, Tanner Row.	York: Yorkshire Museum.	—	Strap-end.
York.	York: Yorkshire Museum.	Baldwin Brown (1903–37), iii, pl. XLVI, 6.	Coin brooch, Croft Colln.
York.	York: Yorkshire Museum.	Waterman (1959), fig. 10, 7.	Circular brooch.
York.	York: Yorkshire Museum.	Waterman (1959), fig. 10, 11.	Clasp.
York.	York: Yorkshire Museum.	Waterman (1959), fig. 10, 2.	Strap-end.
York.	York: Yorkshire Museum.	Waterman (1959), fig. 10, 1.	Strap-end.
York.	York: Yorkshire Museum.	Waterman (1959), fig. 10, 5.	Strap-end.

Find-Place or Name of Object	Museum	Publication	Remarks
York.	York: Yorkshire Museum.	Waterman (1959), fig. 10, 4.	Strap-end.
York.	York: Yorkshire Museum.	Waterman (1959), fig. 10, 3.	Strap-end.
York.	York: Yorkshire Museum.	Waterman (1959), fig. 10, 9.	Brooch.
York.	Private possession.	—	Lead brooch.
No locality.	Bonn: Rheinisches Landesmuseum.	—	Bronze mount (pl. I, *b*).
No locality.	Bury St. Edmunds: Moyse's Hall Museum.	Oman (1931), fig. D, 34.	Finger-ring of Æthelstan.
No locality.	Canterbury: Royal Museum.	—	Circular brooch.
No locality.	Carlisle: Tullie House Museum.	Cowen (1934), 180–1, fig. 3.	Sword.
No locality.	Copenhagen: National Museum.	—	Mount similar to that in pl. I, *b*.
No locality.	London: Guildhall Museum.	—	Strap-hook.
No locality.	Norwich: Castle Museum.	*Proceedings of the Society of Antiquaries of London*, 2nd ser., xxiii, 302–7.	Sword pommel.
No locality.	Norwich: Castle Museum.	—	Circular brooch.
No locality.	Oxford: Ashmolean Museum.	Moe (1955), fig. 25.	Bronze mount.
No locality.	Oxford: Ashmolean Museum.	Oman (1931), fig. A, 7.	Finger-ring.
No locality.	Paris: Musée de Cluny.	Mitchell (1923).	Portable altar.
No locality.	Private possession.	Talbot-Rice (1952) 236 and fig. 18.	Finger-ring.
No locality.	Private possession.	—	Circular brooch (like Felixstowe).
No locality.	Private possession.	—	Sword (like Gooderstone).
No locality.	York: Yorkshire Museum.	Talbot-Rice (1952), 235 and pl. 90, a.	Bronze Virgin and Child.
No locality.	York: Yorkshire Museum.	Roes (1958).	Openwork mount.

COMPARATIVE MATERIAL

PLATE I

(a) The Gandersheim Casket. *Herzog Anton Ulrich Museum. Brunswick.* (Scale $\frac{1}{1}$.)

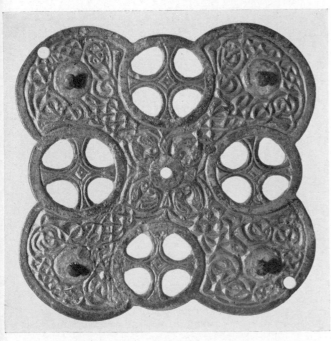

(b) Bronze mount of unknown provenance. *Rheinisches Landesmuseum, Bonn.* (Scale $\frac{1}{1}$.)

(c) Gilt-bronze mount from Bjørke churchyard, Hjørundfjord, Møre, Norway. *Historisk Museum, Bergen.* (Scale $\frac{1}{1}$.)

PLATE II

(a) Silver-gilt pin from St. Andrew's Street, Hitchin, Hertfordshire. *Hitchin Museum.* (Scale: $\frac{1}{1}$.)

(b) Fragment of a stone cross from Brixworth Northamptonshire. *Brixworth Church.*

(c) A lost hanging-bowl from the River Witham, Lincolnshire.

(d) Bronze fragment from Lunde, Vangen, Voss, Hordaland, Norway. *Historisk Museum, Bergen.* (Scale $\frac{3}{2}$.)

PLATE III

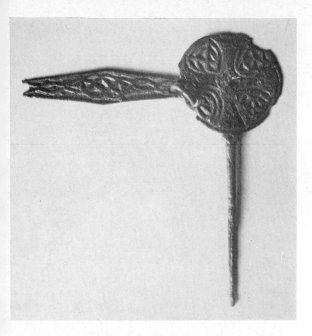

(*a*) Pin and link, from Kegworth, Leicestershire. *Leicester City Museum.* (Scale $\frac{1}{1}$.)

(*b*) Detail of fol. 3*a* of the Book of Cerne. *Cambridge University Library MS* Ll. 1. 10.

(*c*) Fragment of a silver boss from the Terslev hoard. *National Museum, Copenhagen.* (Scale $\frac{1}{1}$.)

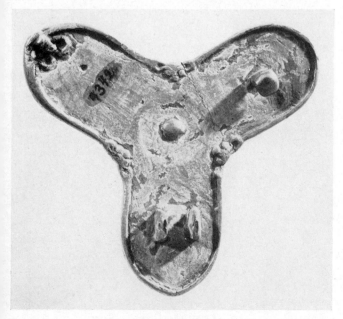

(*d*) Back of a brooch from Mosnæs, Rogaland, Norway. *Historisk Museum, Bergen.* (Scale $\frac{1}{1}$.)

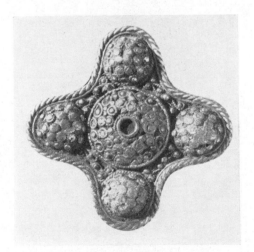

(*e*) Quatrefoil object, Hauge, Sunelven Møre, Norway. *Photo of an electrotype in Historisk Museum, Bergen.* (Scale $\frac{1}{1}$.)

PLATE IV

(*a and b*) Two silver-gilt mounts from the St Ninian's Isle Treasure. (Scale: $\frac{1}{1}$.)

(*c*) Group of bronze *Styccas. British Museum.* (Scale $\frac{1}{1}$.)

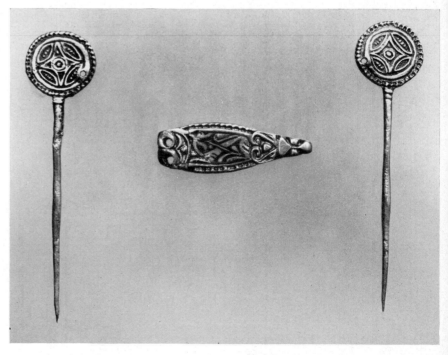

(*d*) Two pins (originally linked) and a strap-end from the Talnotrie hoard. *National Museum of Antiquities of Scotland, Edinburgh.* (Scale $\frac{1}{1}$.)

Folio 4*a* of the British Museum manuscript Royal i.E.VI.

PLATE V

PLATE VI

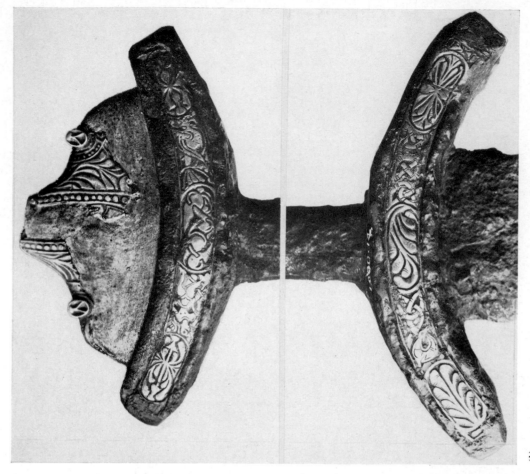

(b)

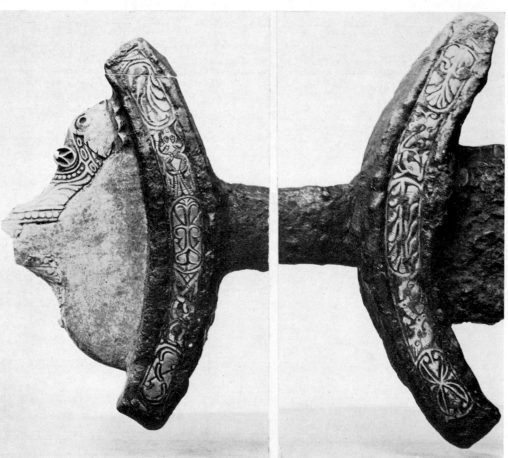

(a)

Details of the pommel and guard of the Abingdon Sword. *Ashmolean Museum, Oxford.* (Scale about $\frac{1}{1}$.)

PLATE VII

Hilt of sword from the Thames at Battersea. *Pitt-Rivers Museum, Oxford.*

PLATE VIII

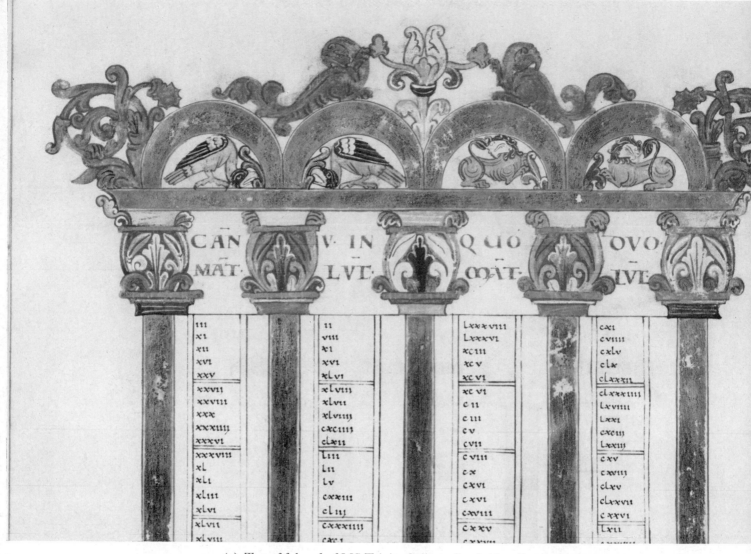

(a) Top of fol. 13b of MS Trinity College, Cambridge, B.10.4.

(a) Detail of fol. 5a of MS Trinity College, Cambridge, B.14.3.

(c) Pommel of a sword from Kaupang. Tjølling, Vestfold Norway. *Universitetets Oldsatsamling, Oslo.*

PLATE IX

(*a*) Stirrup-plates, Velds, Jutland, Denmark. *National Museum, Copenhagen.* (Scale $\frac{1}{1}$.)

(*b*) Detail of book-box. Seitz a.d. Lahn, Germany. *Germanisches Nationalmuseum, Nürnberg.*

PLATE X

(c) Bronze strap-end from Mildenhall, Suffolk. *Museum of Archaeology and Ethnology, Cambridge.* (Scale ⅟₁.)

(b) Bronze mount from Ixworth, Suffolk. *Museum of Archaeology and Ethnology, Cambridge.* (Scale ⅟₁.)

(d) Strap-distributor, no provenance, Gotland, Sweden. *Gotlands Fornsal Visby.*

(a) Gilt-bronze plate from Winchester. *Winchester Cathedral Library.* (Scale ⅟₁.)

(e) Openwork bronze mount from Wisbech, Cambridgeshire. *Wisbech Museum.* (Scale ⅟₁.)

CATALOGUE

The objects catalogued here are ordered alphabetically by find-place. Objects of known provenance are followed in this catalogue by unprovenanced objects and are ordered by their date of acquisition. This seems to be the sequence most likely to avoid subjective judgement.

The date of acquisition is indicated by the first element of the registration number. The first two figures of the registration number of objects acquired in the nineteenth century indicate the year of acquisition: the full date of the year of acquisition has been used as the first element of the registration number since 1900; thus: 22, 12-14, 1, was acquired in December 1822, and 1959, 2-10, 1, was acquired in February 1959. Objects with registration numbers beginning with letters were acquired as follows:

> AF......1897.
> OA......Date of acquisition not known.
> Sl.......1753.
> W.......1949.

1. Gold finger-ring. The ring has a hoop of circular, slightly bevelled, cross-section and a round bezel with semi-circular shoulders; both bezel and shoulders have beaded borders. Set against a background of niello in each of the shoulders is a formalised animal. The animal to the left is more naturalistic and has an open squared mouth, a circular eye and rounded ear. The body, which leans slightly forward, is given a three-dimensional effect by a linear representation of the muscles and by double nicks. The back leg is bent and the front leg is straight. The

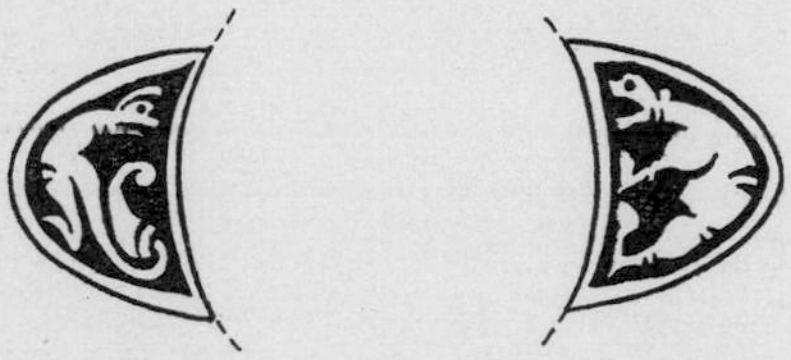

FIG. 8. Ornament from the shoulders of the Æthelswith ring (no. 1).

animal to the right is more amorphous. It has a squared snout, the mouth is open and there is a round eye; the ear is rather floppy and the body degenerates into a leaf-like scroll, one of the scrolls approximating in form to a leg.

Within the bezel is a quatrefoil; the spaces between this central element and the border are filled with a leaf-like ornament set against a niello background. The centre of the quatrefoil is a roundel—the rest being taken up by fields, carved with formalised ornament of pointed ovals between a bifoliate motif; these fields are not nielloed. In the centre of the field is an *Agnus Dei*, flanked by the letters Ā Đ, each of which has a line of abbreviation above it. There is a chevron below the Đ. The *Agnus Dei* is haloed, the halo being broken in two places and the break filled with a billet. The head is upright and the mouth is open, a small round eye appears below a curved eyebrow. A line separates the head from the neck. The back and chest of the animal have a double contour, there is a billeted break in the contour above the tail and in the centre of the chest. The animal has four rather spindly legs. The near-side legs have a shaped hip, the near hind-leg has a double nick at the hip: the feet stick out at right-angles to the hip. The background is nielloed.

Scratched on the back of the bezel, in three lines divided by a double line, is the inscription:

Diameter: 2·6 cm.

Reg. no. AF.458; *Ring Cat. no.* 180. Bequeathed by Sir A. W. Franks, K.C.B. From Aberford, nr. Sherburn, Yorkshire.

BIBLIOGRAPHY
Proceedings of the Society of Antiquaries of London,
  vi, 2 ser. (1875), 305–7.
British Museum, Alfred the Great Millenary
  Exhibition, London 1901, 13.
Smith (1908), 72 and pl. xiii, 7.
VCH Yorkshire, ii, 98–9.
B.M. Ring Cat., 30 and pl. ii, 180.
Brøndsted (1924), 133 and fig. 110.

BMASG, 114 and fig. 144.
Leclerq (1930), 2402 and fig. 7185.
Oman (1931), 105 and fig. B, 17.
Elgee (1933), 188 and fig. 33.
Kendrick (1938*a*), 183–4.
Jessup (1950), 68, 131, pl. xxxvi, 2 and fig. 9.
Hodgkin (1952), ii, pl. iv.
Wilson and Blunt (1961), 96 and 107.

The ring was ploughed up in 1870 between Aberford and Sherburn, West Yorkshire and, it is said, was attached by the finder to the collar of his dog. It was purchased by a York jeweller who sold it to Canon Greenwell. An extract from the Minutes of a Council Meeting of the Yorkshire Philosophical Society on 5 May 1873 runs as follows[1]:

'The Secretary made the following Statement.

'The Rev. Canon Raine having informed Mr. Noble that a Gold Enamelled Ring evidently of Saxon Workmanship and bearing in Saxon Characters the words "Ethelswith Regina" had come into the possession of a York Jeweller and was purchasable and that it was desirable so important an object of Antiquity should be secured to the Museum. The price asked being £30 Mr. Noble at once offered to secure the Ring and pay the money, many Members of the Society having expressed a desire that the Ring should be obtained.

'The Rev. Canon Greenwell of Durham a short time afterwards called on Mr. Noble and stated that if the Yorkshire Philosophical Society would abandon their claim at present to the Ring he would purchase it on the following conditions:

1. That the Ring should be handed over to the Society after his death and that he would give such guarantee in writing in respect of this Condition as the Treasurer and Secretary should approve.

2. That he would on consideration that the Society would allow him to have possession of the Ring for his life on the above terms hand over to the Society as a free gift his valuable collection of Saxon Antiquities found in Yorkshire.

[1] I am very grateful to Mr. G. F. Willmot, F.S.A., for this reference.

So far as could be judged the Ring appeared to be of the date assigned to it and the enamelled work was similar in character and colour to the enamelled design on the Ring of Ethelwulf King of Wessex the Father of the Lady who is supposed to have owned the Ring. King Ethelwulf's ring is a well known specimen of Saxon Antiquity and is now in the British Museum.

'The statement respecting the finding of the Ring is to the effect that it was found in a ploughed field in the neighbourhood of Sherburn in the W.R. Yorkshire.'

The ring was never again seen in Yorkshire. The matter is further raised in the Council Minutes of the same Society in November 1907, when it was recorded that representations had been made to Canon Greenwell on the subject of the ring which was by this time in the possession of the British Museum. The ring was still in the possession of Canon Greenwell in 1876 when it was exhibited to the Society of Antiquaries by Franks. It probably passed into Franks's possession a short time after this and it came to the Museum in 1897 with the rest of the Franks bequest.

The inscription on the ring 'Eathelswith Regina' associates it with Queen Æthelswith of Mercia (853–88).

Before 888. See above pp. 2, 5, 6, 22–27, 29, 34, 56, 75, 79, 80, 82, 83, 90 and pl. XI.

2. Silver and niello disc brooch. The brooch is made of a flat sheet of metal. In the centre of the brooch is a beaded circle, defined by a beaded border, within which is a cross with expanding arms. Within each arm of the cross is an engraved and nielloed triangle. In the circular centre of the cross is a rivet with a head in the form of three-quarters of a sphere. There are openwork spaces between the arms of the cross, but two of them are blocked by the metal strip which supports the catch plate and hinge on the back.

Equally spaced round the central circle—between it and the outer border of the brooch—are four circular fields. Inside each of these circles is an undecorated *fleur-de-lys* with its lateral leaves slightly faceted. Each *fleur-de-lys* stands on a plain semi-circular base and is executed in openwork. A beaded border surrounds each field, broken only at the foot of the *fleur-de-lys*.

Between each of these four fields, towards the border of the brooch, is a dome-headed rivet, similar to, but slightly smaller than, that in the centre; each of these is placed in a plain U-shaped field which touches the edge of the brooch. In the area surrounding each rivet is an animal reserved against a nielloed background. The formalised animal in the upper field has a prominent eye, thin neck and slightly beaked snout. A tendril emerges below the jaw to divide into two—one element crosses the neck to terminate in a pair of scrolls, while the other element of the tendril forms a double leaf at the bottom of the field. The leg extends straight down and slightly forward from the central hip (indicated on the body by two conjoined curved lines). Double nicks decorate the edge of the body —to give a three-dimensional effect. The rest of the body tails away into leaf and tendril ornament. The animal in the right-hand field has a prominent eye and a long pointed snout with an open mouth. From the open mouth runs a tendril with leaves at the terminal. A single line indicates the animal's collar and the leg extends vertically down from the hip, which is again made up of two conjoined curved lines; the paw bends slightly backwards and one of the claws is lobed. The body is U-shaped and nicked just below the rivet, the hind leg extends into the corner and the tail takes the form of a tendril. The animal in the lowest field is similar in many ways to that just described, the head is of the same form, but the tendril which issues from the mouth divides—one part crossing the neck and the other running underneath the leg to terminate in an interlace where the hind-quarters should be. Above this interlace is a small pellet. The body is of the same U-shape as the one just described and bears nicks in the same position. The leg, which is vertical from the hip, terminates in a claw. The bird in the left-hand field has a squared snout, open mouth, prominent eye and stumpy ear; a double line at the neck indicates a collar. In front of the snout is a long pointed billet. The body is U-shaped and the wing is indicated by a curved line. The leg is vertical from the hip, while the tail is indicated by three feather-like shapes. The leg terminates in a zig-zag line and is flanked on one side by a leaf and on the other by an elongated billet. Above the eye is a pellet. In those places where the niello is missing slight keying can be seen. The face of the brooch has a beaded border.

The pin and catch-plate with the connecting strip on the back of the brooch are made of one piece of metal. A double loop acts as a spring and the catch-plate is hook-like. The

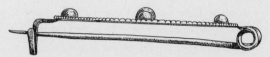

FIG. 9.   Side view of no. 2. $\frac{1}{1}$

strip is attached to the brooch by three of the five rivets which can be seen on the face, and sticks out slightly on either side of the brooch (fig. 9). The back is otherwise plain.

Diameter: 4·9 cm.

Length of pin and plate: 6·8 cm.

Reg. no. 1925, 1–14, 1. Purchased from the Rev. G. H. Wilson. From Beeston Tor, Staffordshire.

BIBLIOGRAPHY
Brooke (1924).
Smith (1925*b*).
The Antiquaries Journal, xii (1932), 173 and fig. 2.
Kendrick (1933*a*), 47.
Kendrick (1938*a*), 185 and pl. lxxviii, 2.
Shetelig (1940), iv, 31–32.
Jessup (1950), 68.
Moss (1953*a*), 61.
Moss (1953*b*), 76.
Bruce-Mitford (1956*a*), *passim* and pls. xxvii, B and xxix, A.
Thompson (1956), 14.
Dunning and Evison (1961), 143.

Found, by the vendor, in a chamber some 250 ft. from the entrance of the Beeston Tor Cave, Manifold Valley, Staffs., in 1924, with other objects (nos. 3–7) and coins, which date the deposition of the hoard to *c.* 873–5. The hoard was contained in a purse (or leather bag) of which nothing now survives and, together with the objects catalogued here, a certain amount of gold wire was found (some of which adheres to the back of the other brooch found in the hoard, no. 3).

Before 875. See above pp. 21, 22, 25, 27, 29–31, 33, 52 and pl. XI.

3. Silver and niello disc brooch. The brooch is made from a flat, circular plate and is decorated by carving, which is inlaid with niello (of which only a portion survives). Within a beaded border is a design based on a series of four overlapping circles. A series of lentoid fields are thus formed and are repeated twice on the remaining part of the circle's circumference—to form a hollow-sided quadrilateral in the centre of each circle.

At each end of these lentoid fields were nine dome-headed rivets—each of slightly different size (one is now missing). Where the four circles cut each other towards the border of the brooch a small triangle is constructed to form a tetrapsis. All the lines of division are billeted and are flanked by a plain border. The fields so formed are filled with different degenerate ornamental motifs. In the minor fields this mainly takes the form of leaves or tendrils in small, crude patterns, or of a complicated, enlongated interlace with pointed ends. In the four large quadrangular fields the ornament is rather more elaborate: two of them are divided by a plain line into four. Two of the subsidiary fields so formed are divided up by a nielloed line, into four plain areas, while each of the other two contains a trilobate leaf ornament. One of the other large fields contains a whirling, scroll ornament, between the four arms of which are small leaf ornaments. The other large field carries a series of leaves set plant-wise and topped by four lozenge-shaped billets.

Rusted to the back of the brooch is part of the iron pin and fragments of gold wire.

Diameter: 7·3 cm.

Reg. no. 1925, 1–14, 2. Purchased from the Rev. G. H. Wilson. From Beeston Tor, Staffordshire.

BIBLIOGRAPHY
Brooke (1924).
Smith (1925*b*).
Kendrick (1933*a*), 47.
Kendrick (1938*a*), pl. lxxviii, 2.
Shetelig (1940), iv, 31–2.
Jessup (1950), 68.
Haseloff (1951), 53, 54 and pl. ii, 7.
Moss (1953*a*), 61.
Moss (1953*b*), 76.
Bruce-Mitford (1956*a*), *passim* and pl. xxvii, A.
Thompson (1956), 14 and pl. vii, *c*.

Found with nos. 2 and 4–7. For details of find, etc. see entry for no. 2.

Before 875. See above, pp. 21, 27, 29–31, 35, 36, 40, 52 and pl. XI.

4. Bronze binding made of a strip of sheet metal, doubled to form a narrow U-shape, and riveted with a single rivet at the open end. The rivet is in the centre of a circular terminal, the plate narrowing to join it. One face of the mount is bordered by a series of serrations, which enclose an incised line. There are two rivet-holes in the body of the piece.

Length: 2·7 cm.

Reg. no. 1925, 1–14, 3. Purchased from the Rev. G. H. Wilson. From Beeston Tor, Staffordshire.

Found with nos. 2, 3 and 5–7. For details of find, etc., see entry for no. 2.

Before 875. See above, p. 65 and pl. XI.

5. Gold ring, undecorated, of lozenge-shaped cross-section.   Diameter: 3·0 cm.

Reg. no. 1925, 2–17, 1. Purchased from the Rev. G. H. Wilson. From Beeston Tor, Staffordshire.

Found with nos. 2–4. 6 and 7. For details of find, etc., see entry for no. 2.

Before 875. See above, p. 59 and pl. XI.

6. Plain bronze ring of wire with a break in its circumference.   Diameter: 1·8 cm.

Reg. no. 1925, 2–17, 2. Purchased from the Rev. H. G. Wilson. From Beeston Tor, Staffordshire.

Found with nos. 2–5 and 7. For details of find, etc., see entry for no. 2.

Before 875. See above, p. 59 and pl. XI.

7. Another similar, the ring is complete.   Diameter: 1·8 cm.

Reg. no. 1925, 2–17, 3. Purchased from the Rev. G. H. Wilson. From Beeston Tor, Staffordshire.

Found with nos. 2–6. For details of find, etc., see entry for no. 2.

Before 875. See above, p. 59 and pl. XI.

8. Bronze disc brooch. The brooch has a plain outer and a beaded inner border, within which is a backward-looking quadruped with raised tail. The animal has an open mouth and a ring-like eye. The suggestion of a mane is given by a ragged edge to the back of the neck. The legs are strap-like and terminate in a two- or three-element paw. The animal has a thin body and neck. The back of the brooch is plain and the catch-plate and lugs (which originally held an iron pin, of which traces remain) are of bronze.

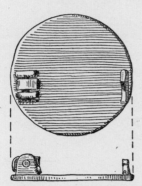

Maximum diameter: 3·3 cm.

Reg. no. 54, 12–27, 66. Purchased at Crofton Croker's sale through W. Chaffers, Jr. From Butley, Suffolk.

FIG. 10. Side and back view of no. 8. ⅟₁

BIBLIOGRAPHY
VCH Suffolk, i, 348.
Brøndsted (1924), 146.

Ninth/tenth century. See above, pp. 37, 52 and pl. XI.

9. Bronze censer-cover of tower shape. There is a gable on each of the four faces, from the tip of each of which rise the ridges of the pyramidal roof: the roof is carried down into the spaces between the gables and is crowned with a double cone the upper face of which is circled by a broad band of inlaid silver. The double cone is crowned by a small knob and equally spaced below it are the protruding heads of a bird with a hawk-like beak and three animals. The bodies of these creatures are placed in open work in the lozenge-shaped fields between and above each gable. One field contains a bird with a widespread claw, whose tail is crossed by the tail of an animal. The animal is narrow waisted and its three-dimensional head sticks out in the angle between the gables at the bottom of the lozenge-shaped field. The tail of the animal forms a scooped leaf motif which protrudes at the apex of the neighbouring gable. In the field to the right of this are two interlaced animals. The uppermost animal, the head of which sticks out below the crest of the object, has a narrow waist; while the lowermost animal, the head of which is modelled in the angle of the gables, has a body seen in three-quarter profile. This animal has only one leg and a tail which terminates in a protruding scooped leaf motif, as does the tail of the other animal in the field. The field to the right of this contains two interlaced animals in three-quarter profile, the heads of which protrude at top and bottom of the field. The tail of the uppermost animal interlaces with the body of the lower animal and joins the border. A plain ribbon crosses the field to join the leaf-like protrusions at the wide angle of the lozenge. Two more animals occur in the fourth field, each with its head in an equivalent position to that in the other lozenge-shaped fields. The tails of the animals form the leaf-like protrusions at the wide angles of the lozenge. The upper animal has a small body and stands above the lower animal in the three-quarter profile.

In the triangular gables of the cover, which are bordered by inlaid silver plates with an inlaid, median, nielloed line, are a series of openwork figures. Below and to the left of the first field described above the gable contains a three-dimensional, standing bird with bent neck and head in the bottom left-hand corner. The gable to the right contains another bird in a similar position, save that its head is in the bottom right-hand corner and that its open mouth bites the terminal of a ribbon which crosses the neck, passes under the leg, forms a loop at the tail and rises to a tendril above the body. The next field to the right contains a backward-looking animal, in a running position. Its tail forms a loop with the legs and is bitten by the animal, before forming a small tendril above the muzzle. The motif in the next field is unclear.

Below each gable is a square field bounded by borders which contain two inlaid silver plates with nielloed edges. Below the first gable are a pair of adorsed animals in a rampant position. Their tails appear from beneath their hind legs to cross the body and terminate in a tendril, below their heads. The next field to the right contains two birds, one right way up, the other upside down. The open mouth of each bird bites towards the other's tail. Their feet are respectively in the upper left and lower right corners of the field. Each bird has a displayed wing—these touch each other in the centre of the field. A backward-looking bird with an open mouth looking away to the centre from the top, right-hand corner has its tail gripped by a loop in the centre of the field. From this loop issues the double leaf on which the bird stands in the bottom-right of the field. In the centre bottom of the field is the head of an animal seen from above, the neck merges into a small front hip, from which issues a short leg (which almost touches the left-hand side of the field). The rest of the body is gathered by the central loop and forms a pair of tendril scrolls, one of which terminates in an animal head to the centre left. The next field contains two adorsed birds, with their heads reversed so that the bottom jaw of the open mouth lies along the top border. They stand on a tribolate element of stiff-leafed foliage, one elongated element of which rises between the two birds to touch their upper beaks.

The broad border at the bottom of the mount is inlaid with silver plates, which are in turn inlaid with niello. Below the first square panel the nielloed decoration consists of two semicircles and two quadrants, all barbed. In the central and left-hand plate is a roughly engraved foliate decoration. The other borders have the same motif without the engraved foliate decoration.

At each corner of the base is a lug of circular form with a central hole. The hips of all the animals and the wings of all the birds were inlaid with silver plates, sometimes patterned with niello; most of this panelling remains. Height: 11·8 cm.

Reg. no. 1927, 11–16, 1. Purchased from A. H. Crippen, Esq. From Canterbury.

BIBLIOGRAPHY
Proceedings of the Society of Antiquaries of London,
  2 ser., xxi (1907), 351–8.
Dalton (1909), 66.
Jackson (1911), i, 88–9 and fig. 120.
Brøndsted (1924), 265 and fig. 190.
Tonnochy (1933), 3 and pl. ii, B.
Tonnochy (1937), 55.
Kendrick (1938c), 379 and pl. lxxiii, 2.
Kendrick (1949), 41 and pl. xxxvi, 2.
Arbman (1958), 189 and figs. 18–20.
Wilson (1960a), 68, 163, 223 and pl. 79.

Found *c.* 1867 by the vendor's father and grandfather at the northern end of Palace Street, Canterbury, while laying a drain to connect with the main sewer, at a depth of about 9 feet.

Tenth century. See above, pp. 34, 39, 43–47, 53 and pls. XII–XIV

10. Silver disc brooch made up of two dished silver sheets, riveted together to clasp a number of gold sheets decorated with filigree ornament (see profile, fig. 11). The brooch is much damaged. The upper plate, in its original condition, was pierced by nine circular holes, four holes in the shape of slightly convex-sided squares and eight holes of comma-shape. The holes are disposed symmetrically and contain the gold plates of filigree. The

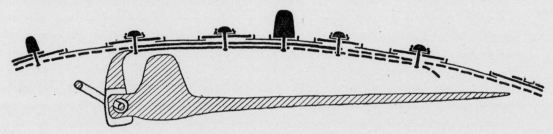

FIG. 11. Section through no. 10. $\frac{1}{1}$

area between these holes is filled with engraved zoomorphic and interlace ornament, the engraved lines being filled with niello. A silver band is applied to the edge of the brooch and set with ten slightly curved, sub-rectangular, gold plates embellished with filigree.

In the centre of the brooch is a gold roundel with a central, gold rivet-head in the shape of a truncated cone. The rivet-head is surrounded by a plain band of filigree, which is in turn surrounded by a running scroll pattern of filigree (each tendril of the scroll being linked to the next by a plain, flat, gold clip). Small granules of gold were, presumably, placed in each of the terminals of the seven tendrils of this scroll (one is now missing). Further granules occur (with one exception) at the joints of the scroll pattern and the whole field is surrounded by a filigree border. The filigree decoration of this field (as elsewhere on the brooch, except for the edges of the plates inlaid in the border) is made up of serrated gold bands stood on one edge. Spaced equally about the central roundel are four, small, dome-headed rivets of silver. They are collared by a band of twisted gold wire and set on small irregularly cut sheets of gold plate; the sheets protrude slightly

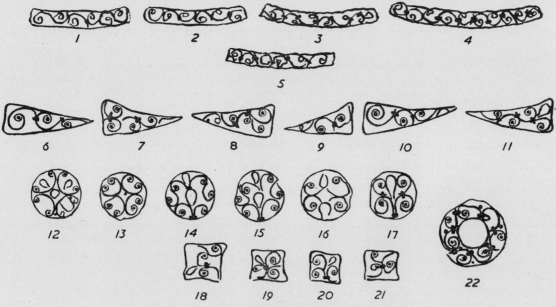

FIG. 12.   Ornament of filigree panels of no. 10. $\frac{1}{1}$

beyond the contour of the twisted wire. Each of these rivets occurs at one corner of each of the four, concave-sided, pierced, square fields. The rivets already mentioned are repeated at each corner of these fields and have similar underlying gold plates and twisted wire. A four-element knot, interlacing with a circle and inlaid with niello, is incised in each of the fields between the gold plates, and the field is bounded by an incised, billeted border. The gold plates are decorated with various filigree scroll designs and each is bounded by a border of filigree. Nine circular fields, inset with gold filigree, were disposed as a square round these central fields: two of the gold plates are missing. The designs of the filigree patterns of these plates vary and are illustrated diagrammatically in fig. 12. Most of them fall into one of two classes,

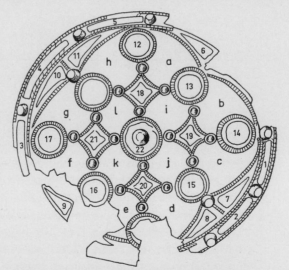

FIG. 13.   The division of the fields of no. 10.

(a) backed semi-circular scrolls or (b) tree shaped motifs. Surrounding the pierced holes, in which the gold plates are set, are incised billeted borders. Degenerate animal ornament

125

fills the fields between the pierced holes. Each field contains a single, amorphous, incised and nielloed animal which is often difficult to interpret. A description is attempted below (the fields can be identified in fig. 13 and the ornament is drawn out in fig. 14).

In field *a* the head is in the bottom corner of the field, the body bears double nicks and degenerates into a ribbon which interlaces with the neck, pierces the body, and develops into a pointed knot ornament; the edge of the ribbon is nicked in places. In field *b* the head is in the top right-hand corner of the field, the body is nicked and the

FIG. 14.   The ornament of the nielloed fields of no. 10. $\frac{1}{1}$

front leg lies below the neck and head of the animal. The field is damaged, but the hind-leg and paw can be seen along the left-hand side of the field. The body again degenerates into a ribbon which forms a triquetra-like knot between the head and the body. The animal in field *c* has its head in the right-hand corner, its body is nicked and the hind hip forms a spiral. The limbs and body degenerate into ribbons, one of which terminates in a spiral tendril. The head of the animal in field *d* is missing. The body is nicked and interlaced with ribbon ornament. Field *e* is much damaged and all that remains are traces of a spiral hip and the ribbon interlace. Field *f* is also damaged. The animal head lies along the upper left-hand side, the nicked body has almost disappeared but much of the interlacing ribbon ornament survives. The head of the animal in field *g* is in the centre top of the field, the body is decorated with double nicks and degenerates into a ribbon

126

interlace. One foot can be distinguished in the left-hand corner. The head of the animal in field *h* is in the topmost corner and is balanced by the front leg in the left-hand corner. The body is nicked, as is the ribbon interlace into which it degenerates.

The whole area of decoration so far described is confined within a billeted border of quatrefoil form with a large silver dome-headed rivet, in the shape of an inverted plant-pot, at the joint of each curve. The spaces between the quatrefoil and the border were taken up by ten comma-shaped fields, inlaid with gold plates bearing filigree scrolls, set in pairs and separated by a narrow billeted border of silver—of these only six survive (fig. 12). The border of the brooch is composed of a narrow applied band of sheet silver embellished with billeted borders. Originally ten gold plates, decorated with filigree scrolls, were inlaid in the border—each interspaced by large boss-headed, silver rivets of the type described above. Only five of the plates and six of the rivets survive. These gold plates are constructed and affixed in a manner different to that of the other plates. The edges of the gold sheets, which bear the filigree scrolls, are bent up and serrated to form a border. The edges of the holes pierced in the silver border are hammered over the edge of the gold border to hold the gold plates in position.

The back-plate was fragmentary when it reached the Museum and only part of it remains in position. The large pin was mounted on the back by means of a loop of silver wire, which passed through a hole in the flattened butt of the pin and the split, upturned end of a strip of silver which was riveted to the back of the brooch (which remains in position through about half its length). This strip presumably turned up at the other end to form a catch-plate for the pin. A heel at the butt-end presumably provided a fulcrum on which the pin could be bent into the catch. Maximum diameter: 14·2 cm.

Reg. no. 1959, 2–10, 1. Given by the headmaster and governors of the King's School, Canterbury. From Canterbury, Kent.

BIBLIOGRAPHY
Wilson and Hurst (1958), 186.

Wilson (1960a), 162.
Wilson (1960c).

The brooch was found on 3 February 1957 by a gardener in Palace Court, within the precincts of Canterbury Cathedral. It was given to the Museum on the condition that it be known as the King's School, Canterbury, disc brooch.

A few fragments of the back-plate are kept loose in the Department of British and Medieval Antiquities.

Tenth century. See above, pp. 3, 16, 25, 38, 40–42, 52 & pls. xv–xvi.

11. Pewter circular brooch. In the centre of the brooch is a low boss within a concave-sided lozenge; the sides of the lozenge are made up of ladder-like lines. The border consists of two ladder-like bands flanking a band containing a series of pellets. In the centre of the back is a cross, one of the arms of which has T-shaped terminals the other arm is recercele. The ornament is raised by casting. A loop and catch-plate survive on the back face. The metal has been confirmed by laboratory examination as a tin/lead alloy. Diameter: 4·1 cm.

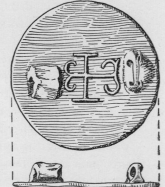

FIG. 15.   Side and back view of no. 11. ¹⁄₁

Reg. no. 1908, 10–5, 1. Given by E. M. Beloe, Esq., F.S.A. From Castle Acre, Norfolk.

BIBLIOGRAPHY
Proceedings of the Society of Antiquaries of London, 2 ser., xxii (1908), 66 and pl. facing p. 3, 4.

Found near the priory gate at Castle Acre.

Ninth/tenth century. See above, pp. 36, 52 and pl. XVII.

12. Bronze strap-end, of slightly tapering form. At the split-end is a single rivet hole. The upper leaf of the split-end is broken away across this hole. A formalised animal head, seen from above, cast in relief, looks towards the rivet hole, while another similar head occurs at the terminal. The heads have circular eyes and pointed ears and a small button-like snout. The area between the two heads, which consists of a ridged bar is plain and unornamented. The surface of the object is covered with a certain amount of encrustation and the back is plain. Length: 4·1 cm.

Reg. no. 80, 8–2, 163. Given by Sir A. W. Franks, K.C.B. From the Links at Coswick (? Goswick).

BIBLIOGRAPHY
Wilson and Blunt (1961), 121.

The provenance depends on a small label stuck to the back of the object which reads 'LINKS COSWICK'. The first letter might be G, in which case the object may be from Goswick, Northumberland. There is no place in the British Isles known as Coswick recorded in the gazetteers.

Ninth century. See above, 29, 62 and pl. XVII.

13. Silver strap-end. Between the rivet holes at the split-end are three pendant leaves within a fan-shaped field, the two outer ones turning back on themselves. At the terminal is a pattern based on a formalised animal head seen from above. The eyes are indicated by a pair of dots and the snout by a double curved line. The forehead bears a fan-shaped field containing a formalised pattern similar to that at the split end, while the ears are comma-shaped and cross-hatched centrally—between the ears is a small bifoliate pattern. In the centre of the strap-end is a sub-rectangular field with one convex end and slightly curved long sides, which are bounded by a beaded border. The field is ornamented by engraving and was originally inlaid with niello, of which some survives. It is divided by a cross, the arms of which have triangular terminals; at the junction of the arms is a square billet. In each quarter is a backward-looking animal. The hind-leg combines with the tail, crosses the body to interlace with a semi-circular ribbon behind the animal, and emerges to form a scrolled terminal. The animal has a squared snout, the mouth is open and the lower jaw is slightly shorter than the upper one, the forehead is domed and a small dot indicates an eye. The back is plain. The object is much worn. Length: 5·0 cm.

Reg. no. 41, 7–11, 456. Given by H.M. Queen Victoria, through the Chancellor of the Duchy of Lancaster. From Cuerdale, Lancashire.

BIBLIOGRAPHY
Hawkins (1842/3).
Hawkins (1847), 190 and fig. 90.
Shetelig (1940), iv, fig. 12.

BMASG, 109 and fig. 132, 5.
Brøndsted (1924), 131.
Wheeler (1927), 43 f.
Wilson and Blunt (1961), 121.

This object was found with the immense hoard from Cuerdale, near Preston, Lancashire, comprising coins, which date the hoard to *c*. 903, and much Viking and Hiberno-Saxon *Hacksilber* and bullion: it was originally deposited in a leaden chest. There were some seven thousand coins in the hoard and nearly a thousand ounces of silver. The hoard was found by some workmen carting soil to replace earth washed away from behind a retaining wall of the banks of the River Ribble. The find-spot was some 40 yards (37 metres) from the river bank.

Before 903. See above, pp. 7, 22, 27, 28, 62 and pl. XVII.

14. Silver openwork disc. Within a slightly peaned border is a plain field which contains the inscription:

+ÆLFGIVVMEAH

In the centre of the disc is an openwork ornament in low relief depicting a bird in profile with displayed wings gripping in its claws a fledgling or a small animal. Although the head of the bird is worn, the round eye and the pear-shaped head survive, as does the carved line of the folded wing which rises a little above the back. The tail is straight. The small animal, carried in the large claws of the bird, has a curled tail; the leg is bent and the head reaches up, with its open mouth, as though to bite the breast of the bird that carries it. The back is plain save where the central design has been hammered up. At the top of the back is a small round hole but this does not pierce the disc. The edge of the disc may be slightly clipped.   Maximum diameter: 3·3 cm.

Reg. no. 33, 1–1, 1. Purchased from E. Naylor Esq. From Cuxton, Kent.

BIBLIOGRAPHY
The Archaeological Journal, xii (1855), 202, and
    fig.
Stephens (1866–1901), ii, 586 and coloured plate.
Payne (1893), 112.

*British Museum, Alfred the Great Millenary
    Exhibition*, London 1901, 17.
VCH Kent, i, 383.
BMASG, 103 and fig. 124.
Jessup (1930), 238, 254 and fig. 33.

The object was found in 1830 and was purchased by the Museum from E. Naylor, Esq. This information is based on the British Museum register entry which says: 'January [1833] Purchased Anglo-Saxon brooch found at Cuxton, Kent in 1830 from E. Naylor.' An added note says 'see letters in Ants', unfortunately these letters are untraceable. In 1855 Westwood is reported as exhibiting a drawing of this object which 'was found about *1814* at *Chatham*'.[1] The date was repeated by Stephens[2], Smith[3] and Jessup[4] but we have no evidence for this date or for this find-spot. In the absence of other documentation we must accept the date and provenance supplied by the British Museum Register.

R. A. Smith suggests[5] that, although the name (Ælfgifu) is not uncommon, it may have belonged

---

[1] *The Archaeological Journal*, XII, 202. The italics are mine.
[2] (1866–1901), ii, 586.
[3] *VCH Kent*, i, 383.
[4] (1930), 238.
[5] *BMASG*, 103.

to the lady of that name (also called Emma) who was first the wife of Æthelred the Unready (*m.* 1002) and then of Canute—she died in 1052. This seems highly hypothetical.

Tenth century. See above, pp. 44, 47, 65, 79, 84, 87 and pl. XVII.

15. Bronze brooch with damaged border. The central, sunken, circular panel is surrounded by a double ribbon border forming a square with hollow sides. From each corner of this border a simple interlaced knot is produced, forming a loop on one side and an upturned tendril on the other (the pattern which is much damaged and worn is the same as that on no. 151). The back is plain and carries a broken, brazed-on catch-plate and loop (fig. 16).　　　　　　　　　Maximum diameter 2·7 cm.

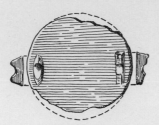

FIG. 16. Catch-plates of Fig. 15. $\frac{1}{1}$

Reg. no. O.A. 294. No recorded donor or vendor. From Dunwich, Suffolk.

A card with the object records that it was washed up by the sea from the sunken town of Dunwich. The provenance is confirmed in so far as the name of the site is written on the back of the brooch. No details of its acquisition by the Museum are available.

Tenth/eleventh century. See above, pp. 37, 48, 53 and pl. XVII

16. Gold finger-ring. The hoop is divided into panels by four pairs of animal heads in relief. The heads stand above the intervening oval fields. The heads of each pair face in opposite directions and a plain band divides them. Each head is in the form of a mask with two pointed ears and round bored eyes encircled by a ring of small dots—a feature which is not always visible due to wear. Traces of similar dots can be seen in a sub-triangular field between the ears of the animal heads. The jaws are open and grip the flat oval fields between each pair of heads. Three of these intervening oval fields contain an eight-petal rosette pattern with an annular centre. The fourth field is quartered and has an annular centre: in each of the four fields so formed is a bifoliate motif. The inside of the hoop is plain and slightly hollowed out behind each double mask.　　　　Diameter: 2·8 cm.

Reg. no. 1925, 11–18, 1. Purchased from Mrs. Arnold. From Ebbesborne Wake Vicarage, Wiltshire.

BIBLIOGRAPHY
The Antiquaries Journal, vi (1926), 186 and fig.

Found in 1916. The original publication of the ring suggests that the median line of the band dividing each mask was filled with niello, this is not apparent now and seems unlikely.

Ninth century. See above, pp. 23, 27, 29, 30, 34, 56 and pl. XVII.

17. Bronze pommel guard. The guard is formed of a curved bar of rectangular cross-section and tapers towards each rounded end. Towards the centre of the bottom edge the curve straightens for a short distance, defining the area of the space taken up by the pierced hole for the tang of the sword. The hole is rectangular and is flanked by two elongated hollows on the upper face.[1] On one face is a double contoured angular interlace pattern, flanking a truncated triangular field containing a roughly executed triquetra knot. On

---

[1] These hollows presumably acted as sockets for the pommel cap.

130

the other face is a simple fret pattern, built up of a series of interlocking Z-shaped elements. In the central, truncated, triangular field is a symmetrical linear pattern, which is perhaps a degenerate acanthus ornament. On either side of the tang hole on the bottom face is the inscription:

EOFRI   ME   F

The two halves of the inscription are reversed and placed back to back.

Length: 8·4 cm.

Reg. no. 75, 6–17, 15. Purchased from the Hon. Mrs. A. Way. From Exeter.

BIBLIOGRAPHY

Shortt, 143–4 and frontispiece.
The Reliquary and Illustrated Archaeologist, v (1899), 189–92 and fig. 1.

VCH Devon, i, 373–4.
BMASG, 94 and fig. 115.
Wilson (1960*a*), 109 and fig. 23.

The object was found in 1833 under the house of a Mr. Downe, a plumber, in South Street, Exeter. The premises occupied by Mr. Downe were leased to him in 1815 and appear marked in some detail in Coldridge's Map of Exeter, 1818–19, situated between the Black Lion Inn and what afterwards became Paragon Place. Besley's *Directory of Exeter and Suburbs*, 1885, lists the premises of Downe and Baker, plumbers and brass-founders, as no. 77 South Street. These premises were destroyed during the Second World War and the post-war Sun Street seems to occupy the site of the find.[1]

The inscription should perhaps be extended to:

EOFRI ME F[ECIT] (EOFRI MADE ME)

Ninth–eleventh century. See above. pp. 64, 79, 84, 85 and pl. XVII.

18. Bronze seal-die. The die is in the round base of a sub-conical openwork construction. Round the edge of the die is an inscription: ZIT̄ EĐILVVALDI: EP.⌐ The centre of the die is decorated with a floriated cross: between each of which is a leaf, while there is a bored dot at the centre of the cross. Round the inscription is a dotted line. Above the seal is a tiered openwork sub-conical construction, terminating at the apex in a solid trilobate motif. The bottom tier consists of three semi-circles, each of which contains, along the radius, an animal head with small circular borings for eyes. The ears are oval, with crescentic openings. Between each semicircle below the animal head is an inverted pear-shaped, blank field. Above this tier are another three semi-circles the edges of which touch at the top of the underlying tier, in each of the mushroom-shaped fields so formed is an animal-head of a type similar to those described above, in one of which a glass eye remains; again they surmount an inverted pear-shaped field. Three more semi-circles spring from a straight bar at the top centre of these fields and the bar is produced to form similar, though smaller, animal heads which bite the floriated cap of the seal.

Height: 6·9 cm.

Reg. no. 22, 12–14, 1 (*Seal Cat.* No. 1). Given by Hudson Gurney Esq., M.P., F.R.S., V.P.S.A. From Eye, Suffolk.

[1] I am grateful to the city librarian of Exeter, Mr. N. S. L. Pugsley, for information as to the location of Down's premises.

BIBLIOGRAPHY
Gurney (1824).
Madden (1856), 369–70.
Birch (1887), 213.
British Museum Alfred the Great Millenary Exhibition, London, 1901, 18.

VCH Suffolk, i, 352.
BMASG, 110 and fig. 135.
Leclerq (1930), 2403–4 and fig. 7191, 7.
Tonnochy (1952), 1 and pl. i, 1.
Wilson and Blunt (1961), 107.

It was dug up by a labourer, in a garden about two hundred yards from the site of the monastery at Eye. The labourer's child threw it on the fire, whence it was rescued by the child's mother. It later passed into the possession of a Mr. Fenner from whom it passed to Hudson Gurney who gave it to the Museum.

The seal probably belonged to Æthelwald, bishop of Dunwich (845–70).

Mid-ninth century. See above, pp. 2, 16, 31, 34, 60, 79–81 and pl. XVII.

19. Silver-gilt set of three linked pins with large circular heads. The head of the pin to the left, which is 4·4 cm. in diameter, has an empty central setting with an internal rivet-head (the riveted end of which can be seen on the back of the pin-head). The collar which surrounds the setting is straight sided internally and ragged at the top; externally the collar is surrounded by three bands of wire (two of plain wire, flanking one of twisted wire), which give the setting the appearance of a truncated cone. Four circular holes pierce the plate around this central boss. Each hole has a collar, back and front, which is formed from the waste metal from the piercings. The pin-head has a plain border, embellished with a series of evenly spaced dots. The border forms a continuous band, by means of a median line, with the main divisions of the field which encircle the holes pierced in the face of the disc. The border is partly obscured at the bottom by the riveted socket which holds the head of the pin. The socket is rectangular and slightly waisted on the front face: one of the original two rivets survive. Below the socket is a plain moulding, which continues through three-quarters of the circumference of the pin. The shank of the pin has an abrupt swelling about a quarter of its length from the point. The bottom of the circular head is broken away at the joint with the pin. This portion has been repaired in antiquity, by means of an irregular patch attached by four rivets, but a small fragment is missing.

The four panels formed by the division of the pin-head are decorated with chip-carved interlacing ornament. The lower left panel contains plain, regular, ribbon interlace. The upper left panel has a similar interlace, but is given zoomorphic character by the addition of wing-like features at the joint of two of the knots in the interlace. The upper right panel contains a winged biped within an elaborately interlaced ribbon. The eye of the animal appears as a small punch mark within a pointed forehead. The joint of the uppermost wing is decorated with an incised spiral and two dots are engraved in the length of the wing. The long tapering wings terminate in a small scroll. One leg is bent and the other is straight, while the foot is divided to give the impression of a paw. The bottom right panel is decorated with a design which is basically the same as that in the top left panel, save that the interlace springs from a pedestal-like object in the centre of the outer edge. This pedestal is panelled and has a central upper projection in the shape of an exclamation mark—this latter separates the two emergent ribbons. A hole just below the upper border of this field holds the silver wire loop which fastens the pin to the link. The link is in the form of an elongated lozenge with pierced circular terminals. Within a plain, punched border is a degenerate, trumpet-spiral pattern. Further punched dots appear in the pattern and in the plain border to the circular terminals.

The basic design of the central pin is similar to that just described save that no median line bisects the radial divisions of the face. There are traces of glass within the rather ragged central setting. The pin-head has been broken away from the pin and repaired in the same manner as the left-hand pin. The hindmost element of the socket at the top of the pin is missing. The socket is pierced by a single bronze rivet. The head of this pin is slightly larger than that to the left (4·8 cm. in diam.). In the two topmost fields are two affronted winged quadrupeds with a regular chip-carved interlace formed from their extended tongues. Their front legs cross and their hind legs degenerate into tapering scrolled wing-like features. The jointing at the hip is suggested by two lightly inscribed lines; a collar executed in the same technique can be seen at the neck. The wings are pointed and panelled. The animals have punched eyes and short pointed ears. The same animals occur adorsed in a backward-looking position in the bottom right field. Here the animals bite the tips of their wings and are caught in the interlace of their back legs (or tails). In the bottom left field is a single animal similar to those in the two upper fields, but executed on a larger scale. Two pierced holes, in the border on either side, carry the wire loops of the two flanking links. The two links are of exactly the same form and design.

The design of the head of the right-hand pin (which has a diameter of 4·2 cm.) is different from that of the others, it is divided saltire-wise by plain lentoid openings (each surrounded by a plain border). The whole head has a plain border enclosing a carved rope-like border. The pin is apparently attached to the head without rivets, but is otherwise of the same form as the other two pins. The central setting is badly damaged but was originally similar to those on the other discs. In the left-hand field is a serpent-like quadruped seen from above, forming a simple loop. This animal has pointed ears (slightly more floppy than those on the other pin-heads). The eyes are inlaid with glass and the legs are spread-eagled. It is entwined with a thin ribbon interlace and its body and legs are speckled with small dots. The hindquarters of the animal are marked with V-shaped cuts and all four feet have a double nick to suggest a paw. The animal in the uppermost field is upside down, and is seen in profile. It is a quadruped, the back leg of which issues hipless from the tapering body. The front foot is club-like but the hind paw has three nicks. The head has a panelled cheek, a slightly opened mouth, an eye inlaid with glass and a faceted ear. The animal has a short stubby tail and the body is speckled all over. The animal is surrounded by, and interlaced with, a ribbon which terminates in a speckled leaf in the right-hand corner, and in a speckled billet in the left-hand corner. The right-hand field contains a spread-eagled animal, seen from above, set in a ribbon interlace pattern. The animal has eyes inlaid with glass and a speckled body. A mane and long hair on the hindquarters are suggested by shallow scratched incisions. Nicks in the end of its tail give it a bushy appearance and the front paws have three toes, while the hind paws have four. The lower field, which is partly obscured by the socket at the top of the pin, has an apparently illogical design. Immediately above the socket is an animal neck and head with inlaid eye, panelled cheeks and faceted ear. The neck, which is speckled, and from which emerges a tapering wing-like feature, apparently tails away into an interlaced ribbon ornament. In front of the animal head, and below it, are the hindquarters and upstanding tail of an animal, speckled all over. The back of this pin is gilt.

Length of central pin: 12·1 cm.

Reg. no. 58, 11–16, 4. Given by the Royal Archaeological Institute. From Fiskerton, Lincolnshire.

BIBLIOGRAPHY

Archaeological Institute, Memoirs . . . of the History & Antiquities of the County & City of Lincoln, 1850, xxxi.
Romilly Allen (1904a).
The Reliquary and Illustrated Archaeologist, new series, xiii (1907), 134 and fig. 2.
Smith (1908), 74.
BMASG, 98 and pl. ix.
Brøndsted (1924), 138–9, 140, 219 and fig. 113.

Smith (1925a), 241 ff. and fig. 13.
Weigall (1927), 172.
Jenny and Volbach (1933), pl. 44.
Kendrick (1938a), 170 and pl. lxxi.
Kitson-Clark (1941a), 334.
Pijoan (1942), fig. 80.
Wilson (1960a), 143, 149, 220, fig. 33 and pl. 55.
Dunning and Evison (1961), 145.
Wilson and Blunt (1961), 105.

The pins, which are usually known as 'the Witham Pins', were found (according to the Fiskerton parish registers) in the River Witham during the dry summer of 1826; they were presented to the Archaeological Institute (later Royal Archaeological Institute), by Robert Swan, Registrar to the Bishop of Lincoln. They were probably found, with many other antiquities, during the work of improvement of the navigation and drainage of the Witham, which was started in 1826 under Act of Parliament— they may be among the antiquities mentioned by a correspondent in *The Gentleman's Magazine* in that year.[1]

FIG. 17. Side view of Gravesend Cross (no. 20). $\frac{1}{1}$

Eighth century. See above, pp. 2, 10–14, 16, 17, 20–22, 31, 57, 58 and pl. XVIII.

20. Silver pendant cross. The cross is cut from a plate of silver (2 mm. thick). One of the arms has a loop for suspension, which is circular in profile and appears to have been bored from both sides and then soldered to the arm. The arms of the cross expand slightly and join each other in a curve. Each arm is decorated with a scratched ornament. The upper arm has a plain panel shaped as an inverted truncated triangle; the lower arm has three scratched chevrons within a quadrilateral panel and above it the segment and chord of a circle. On the arm to the left is a double chevron inside a quadrilateral field; on the arm to the right is a double chevron inside a field which follows the outline of the arm. In a setting in the centre of the cross, attached to the cross by a pair of silver rivets which can be seen on the back, is a dome-shaped glass roundel. The glass is green and irregularly marbled with a blue and white inset. The setting is made up of an outer

[1] xcvi, pt. 2, p. 300, see also *Annual Register*, 1826, 127.

composite, filigree band in gilt bronze encircling the plain collar containing the glass The outer band of filigree consists of twisted plain wire, enclosing a broader band composed of two strands of plain and twisted filigree wire; within this is a plain band of beaded wire.

The back is plain, save for the butt ends of the two rivets.

Height: 6·2 cm.

Reg. no. 39, 3–19, 1. Purchased from J. Whiteaves, Esq. From Gravesend, Kent.

BIBLIOGRAPHY
Hawkins (1841–2), 34.
Rashleigh (1868), 150.
British Museum, Alfred the Great Millenary Exhibition, London 1901, 17.
VCH Kent, i, 381 and fig. 25.
BMASG, 102–3 and fig. 123.
Jessup (1930), 238, 256 and fig. 33.
Hencken (1950), 148 and fig. 72.
Philip (1954), 36.

Found in 1838 in association with coins, according to Jessup (1930) and Philip (1954), in Pelham Road, Gravesend.[1] The coins are dated by Mr. R. H. M. Dolley, to *c.* 872. The cross was purchased from Mr. J. Whiteaves, who may have had it from H. P. Borrell, Esq., who was the owner of the coins in 1838.[2]

Before 872. See above, pp. 10, 17, 59 and pl. XIX.

21. Bronze strap-end. The split end has two rivet-holes in which one rivet survives; one of the holes is broken, but it can be seen that the end originally terminated in a double curve. Below the rivet-holes are bordering lines, between which are two concentric curved lines. In the centre of the field, within a simple linear border, is a geometric design within a circle. The design consists of an equal-armed cross within a double-contoured, hollow-sided quadrilateral. At the terminal is a formalised engraved animal head, seen from above, formed out of a series of curved lines. The back is plain.

Length: 5·8 cm.

Reg. no. 92, 11–4, 15. Given by Sir A. W. Franks, K.C.B. From Great Wakering, Essex.

BIBLIOGRAPHY
BMASG, 107 and fig. 131, 1.
Wilson and Blunt (1961), 121.

The strap-end was originally in the collection of Philip Benton, Esq., of Great Wakering. Franks obtained it from him.

Ninth century. See above, pp. 28, 62 and pl. XIX.

22. Fragmentary and much corroded iron scramasax. Only the back of the blade survives. A slight angle is formed at the back of the blade, some 18 cm. from the existing tip. The tang survives, almost to its full length. On one face two channels run along the edge of the blade just below the back; below this, and a short way above the existing edge of the blade, is another groove inlaid with twisted copper and bronze wire—which is broken

[1] R. A. Smith (*VCH Kent,* i, 381) says that it was found between Perry St. and the cemetery.
[2] The fact that Borell owned the coins is, as far as I can see, only based on the evidence of Thompson (1956), 65.

in a few places. The process of hammering the wire into the blade has accidentally spread a few patches over contiguous areas. Similar traces can be seen on the two upper grooves, showing that they were also inlaid, a fact which is confirmed on the other face where a fragment of inlay remains, towards the tip, beyond the angle in the back. This face, however, is much corroded and, although a broken strip of inlay survives in the groove corresponding to the inlaid groove of the other face, little trace of the other two grooves survives. The blade is pattern welded and traces of the wooden hilt survive on the tang.   Length: 71·3 cm.

Reg. no. 1912, 7–23, 2. Purchased from Rev. Canon W. Greenwell. From Hurbuck, Co. Durham.

BIBLIOGRAPHY   *VCH Durham*, i, 213.
Archaeologia Aeliana, new series, vol. v, 159–61.   Wheeler (1935), 179.

The object was found in association with a sword and tools in a hoard in the bank of a small stream flowing past Greencroft, Harbuck, nr. Lanchester. They were for some time in the possession of a Mr. Balleny, of Little Greencroft who was the owner of the land on which they were then found. They passed thence into the hands of Canon Greenwell.

On acquisition by the Museum in 1912 this object and the other objects in the hoard were cleaned by the 'Adrien Oger' process.

Ninth/tenth century. See above, pp. 39, 60 and pl. XIX.

23. Bronze strap-end. The end has been broken away and re-pierced by two rivet-holes. The field of decoration, which is not complete, is filled with a linear ornament (which has possibly been punched out); a central line is flanked by two pairs of lines made up of arcs of a circle, placed end-to-end. An incised line defines the field. At the tip of the object three lines converge on a small terminal, decorated with three dots and faceting to give it a zoomorphic character. There is a crack across the face of the strap-end just above the terminal. The back is plain.   Length: 4·1 cm.

Reg. no. 1926, 11–16, 1. Purchased from G. F. Lawrence, Esq., with No. 24. From Icklingham, Suffolk.

BIBLIOGRAPHY
Wilson and Blunt (1961), 121.

Ninth century. See above, pp. 28f., 62 and pl. XIX.

24. Bronze strap-end. Between and below the two rivet-holes at the split end is a small fan-shaped field containing three pendant leaves. Below this, in the main panel, is an animal with its mouth open along the short side towards the split end. The top of the head is rounded and there is no eye. The animal has two floppy ears and a short body set across the field. There is a nick in the body above the front leg. The front leg is short but the two hind legs form a complicated and muddled interlace towards the terminal. The front paw has two nicks to suggest toes and one of the back paws has one nick only. At the terminal is a formalised animal head seen from above, with scrolled, comma-shaped ears and an inverted 'V' on the forehead. The terminal is slightly rounded and plastic in form. The sides of the strap-end are scalloped and there is a moon-shaped cut in each scallop. The central field appears to have been keyed for niello. The back face is plain.   Length: 4·6 cm.

Reg. no. 1926, 11–16, 2. Purchased from G. F. Lawrence, Esq., with No. 23. From Icklingham, Suffolk.

BIBLIOGRAPHY
Wilson and Blunt (1961), 121.

Ninth century. See above, pp. 27, 28f., 62 and pl. XIX.

25. Bronze-gilt disc brooch, slightly dished, gilded on the front only. In the centre is a much corroded knurled rivet-head of bronze on which traces of gilding remain. The face of the brooch, which is corroded in parts, is divided by an equal-armed cross and the edge of the disc is defined by a plain ridge-like border; within the fields so constructed are interlaced, chip-carved animal ornaments. A hole, half way along each arm of the cross, probably carried a rivet-head similar to that in the centre. A series of eight secondary holes occur round the edge, and traces of another survive in one of the damaged parts of the rim. The animals, which occur in all four quadrants, are similar, although there is a certain irregularity in the interlacing ribbons which surround them. The animals are in a rampant position; the front leg rises in front of the nose, while the back leg stands out straight. The tail is straight and has a curled end. Both the body and neck are arched, and the head is treated in detail with an upstanding scrolled ear. The eye is formed of a dot, and on three occasions is surrounded by a ring from which is produced a pointed pear-like tail. The feet are over-emphasised and clawed. A single line of dots decorates each arm of the cross and the animals' bodies are similarly decorated. This speckling appears to have been carried out with a pointed punch. There are nine secondary holes pierced in the brooch, mainly towards the border.

The back of the brooch bears the marks of a straight plate with one pointed end, which presumably carried the pin of the brooch (the pin can be seen in old photographs —see below). There is a fleck of gold on the back which is perhaps a spill-over from the gilding on the front.   Diameter: 5·0 cm.

Reg. no. 1927, 12–12, 23. Purchased from G. F. Lawrence, Esq. From Ixworth, Suffolk.

BIBLIOGRAPHY
Journal of the British Archaeological Association,   Brøndsted (1924), 138 and fig. 114.
   xxvii (1871), 259 and pl. 12, 3.   Smith (1925*a*), 245, and fig. 16.
VCH Suffolk, i, 337 and fig. 7.   Bruce-Mitford (1956*a*), 199 and pl. xxx, A.
The Reliquary and Illustrated Archaeologist, new
   series, xiii (1907), 133–4 and fig. 1.

Said to have been found in January 1871 near the Cross House at Ixworth, Suffolk. The vendor purchased it at the Fenton sale (Messrs. Sotheby, 28 November 1927, lot 194). Mr. S. G. Fenton presumably had it from Mr. J. Warren, who exhibited it before the British Archaeological Association in 1871. Warren was not a very trustworthy person as regards provenances and the find-place must not be too readily accepted.

The pin, which extended slightly beyond the edge of the brooch, can be seen on old photographs as in pl. XIX. It was probably lost during the Second World War.

Eighth century. See above, pp. 3, 10, 11, 13–17, 52 and pl. XIX.

26. Bronze mount. The object is roughly triangular in shape, at the terminal is a loop and above it is a panel which contains an interlaced animal. The head of the animal is seen from above. Behind the terminal loop, the body extends from the head and forms a complicated interlaced ornament which, because of the corroded surface, cannot be clearly traced. The back is plain and concave. Traces of iron rivets occur in the down-turned flange at the base of the triangle. Length: 5·4 cm.

Reg. no. 83, 12–13, 579. Purchased from George Payne Junior, Esq., F.S.A. From Kemsley Downs, nr. Milton, Kent.

BIBLIOGRAPHY
BMASG, 104.
Kendrick (1949), 116.
Wilson (1961), 212 and pl. xxxviii, a.
    The provenance is usually described as 'Milton-next-Sittingbourne' or 'Sittingbourne'.

FIG. 18. Section through no. 26. $\frac{1}{1}$

Eleventh century. See above, pp. 48, 51, 58 and pl. XIX.

27. Gold finger-ring consisting of a plain, flat, hoop bordered by two continuous lines filled with niello. Between these lines is a runic inscription which reads:

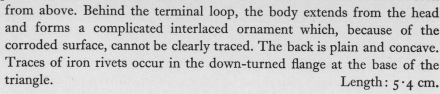

Each letter is serifed. The inside of the ring is plain save for the three characters: ᛏᛒᛁ
Diameter: 2·7 cm.

Ring cat. no. 184. Given by the Right Hon. the Earl of Aberdeen, P.S.A., Kingmoor, Cumberland.

BIBLIOGRAPHY
Magnusen (1820).
Magnuson (1822).
Hedley (1822), 245 f.
Hamper (1827).
Douce (1827), 122.
Liljegren (1833), 218.
Rask (1838), 294–303.
Kemble (1840), pl. xx, vi.
Newton (1851–4), 25.

Catalogue of the Archaeological Museum formed at Carlisle during the meeting of the Archaeological Institute of Great Britain, Carlisle 1859, 14.
Haigh (1861), 46 and fig.
Dietrich (1867), 197 and 201.
Franks (1876), 481.
Stephens (1866–1901), i, 496–7.
Stephens (1884), 157.
Jones (1890), 150.
Ferguson (1893), 509.

Stephens (1894), 30.

British Museum, Alfred the Great Millenary Exhibition, London 1901, 15.

VCH Cumberland, i, 281.

Collingwood (1906), 308.

B.M. Ring Cat., 31.

BMASG, 116 and fig. 148.

Agrell (1927), 206–7.

Harder (1931).

Dickins (1935).

Harder (1936).

Stierke (1939), 91.

Brade-Birks (1953), 127.

Wilson (1959*b*), 166–7 and fig. 8.

Transliteration is 'ærkriuf ltkriuriþonglæ∫tæpon|tol'. As it cannot be interpreted it must be assumed that the inscription is meaningless and of magical import.

The ring was found by a young man employed in levelling a fence on Greymoor Hill, in the hamlet of Kingmoor, two and a half miles from Carlisle. It passed into the possession of the Earl of Aberdeen before 1822. Sometime after 1823 it was given to the Museum.

Ninth century. See above, pp. 23, 27, 69, 70, 71, 73–75 and pl. xix.

28. Silver trefoil ornament; the terminals of the arms and the angles between them are rounded. On a heavy silver back-plate, in the centre of which is raised a boss, are mounted a series of filigree wires set in a tendril design. Surrounding the whole object is a border made up of two lengths of twisted double-strand wire—the twists opposed to form a herring-bone pattern—laid upon which is a much worn, beaded wire. The central boss of the heavy base-plate has been surrounded by a collar made up of a strip of metal with serrated edges. The beads formed by the serrations have in some places been embellished by a median cut (perhaps in imitation of *Äquatorschnitt*). But this is by no means a regular feature of the filigree. It stands on one of these edges and has been soldered to the sides of the boss. Above the collar are a series of annulets of plain beaded wire (each annulet surmounted by a small granule) which cover the area of the central boss as far as a central collar, consisting of a plain wire surrounded by a beaded wire collar, enclosing a now empty setting. The spaces between the beaded collar and the annulets are filled with a number of granules. The decoration of this boss was placed directly on the back-plate. A similar, somewhat lower, boss evidently occurred at the end of each arm, but here the boss was made from a separate sheet of metal soldered to the back-plate: only a small fragment of one of these bosses and a larger fragment of another survive. The smallest fragment consists merely of a single granule and a fragment of the thin back-plate of the boss adhering to the main border of the object. The other boss survives more completely: a serrated wire band surrounds the boss, which has a thin base-plate on which are set annulets and granules similar to those on the central boss. In the centre of the boss is a setting consisting of a plain collar surrounded by a beaded wire. The setting contains a flat garnet. About a third to a half of this boss survives (the garnet is at present supported by a cylinder of perspex). The bosses at the terminals had a diameter equivalent to the width of this portion of the arm. The central boss was of similar width and did not touch the borders. Filling the remaining available space of the field is a formal scroll pattern arranged symmetrically on either side of the centre of each arm. The scrolls, which are soldered to the base-plate, are made up of serrated bands similar to that which surrounds the central boss. The joints of the scrolls are covered by small horseshoe-shaped collars which have been slipped over, and soldered to, the two continuous bands.

Granules, either singly of in groups of three, mounted on the scrolls give a suggestion of grapes.

The back is plain and bears no pin or catch, but traces of an attachment occur on two of the arms, parallel with the third arm of the object, and it may be that these are the remains of the catch-plate and the hinge of a brooch.

Maximum overall length: 9·0 cm.

Reg. no. O.A. 21. From Kirkoswald, Cumberland.

BIBLIOGRAPHY

Gough Sale Catalogue (Leigh and Sotheby, 19 July 1810), 10, Lot 240.
Lysons (1816), iv, ccviii and pl. opp. p. ccvii.
Adamson (1834), 280.
Jefferson (1840), 296.
Ferguson (1893), 509.
British Museum, Alfred the Great Millenary Exhibition, London 1901, 17.
VCH Cumberland, i, 282 and pl. opp.
Proceedings of the Society of Antiquaries of London, xxiii (1911), 304–5 and fig. 3.
Friis-Johansen (1912), 244.

BMASG, 102 and fig. 122.
Weigall (1927), 64.
Wheeler (1927), 40–1.
Jenny and Volbach (1933), pl. 58.
Arbman (1937), 206–7.
Kendrick (1938*a*), 184 and pl. lxxviii, 3.
Haseloff (1950), 172–3 and pl. xx, b.
Thompson (1956), 81.
Holmqvist (1959), 45 ff. and fig. 10.
Wilson (1960*a*), 96, 143, 221 and pl. 62.
Wilson (1960*c*), 24.
Dunning and Evison (1961), 151–2.
Wilson and Blunt (1961), 94, 95 and 102.

The object is mentioned in the Gough Sale Catalogue of 1810 where it is described as 'a triangular silver ornament of Saxon work, weight 2 oz. 12 dwts, found near Kirkoswald, Cumberland'. It sold for £1 6s.[1] We know that this piece came into the Museum before 1816, the year in which Lysons illustrated it in *Magna Britannia*, it is not known how it was acquired. It is conceivable that the Museum bought it at the Gough Sale, for it is not listed in the donations register of the period.

Ruding,[2] quoting a Mr. Richard Miles, says that the hoard was found in 1808 and adds that it was found with 542 coins. Lysons says that there were about 700 coins. Ruding says that they were 'turned up by the plough', but a remarkably circumstantial account in the Acquisitions list of the Society of Antiquaries of Newcastle-upon-Tyne for 1814[3] describes the find thus: 'They were found [i.e. 6 copper stycas] a few years since near Kirkoswald in Cumberland by the blowing down of a large tree, the roots of which had taken hold of, and brought up with them, a large earthen vessel full of similar coins.' The phrase used by Ruding is a conventional phrase of the period and the account of the acquisitions list must be taken as the more accurate description of the circumstances of the find.

The remarkably accurate, if schematic drawing in Lysons, shows all the bosses whole; this would seem to be intelligent reconstruction.

The deposition is dated by the coins *c.* 855.

Before 855. See above, pp. 2, 7, 17–19, 40, 52, 65 and pl. XIX.

29. Bronze strap-end. The upper face is broken away at the split end and the single rivet-hole in the lower portion appears to be secondary; traces of two rivet-holes may perhaps be seen in the smoothed-off break. The end of the central panel is missing. The panel contains an indistinct, carved, zoomorphic, interlace pattern. The double lateral border and the interlace ornament are inlaid with niello. The terminal takes the shape of a

[1] MS. entry in British Museum copy of the Sale Catalogue.
[2] (1817), 223.
[3] *Archaeologia Aeliana*, i, 124.

formalised animal head with faceted snout and oval ears with half-moon openings. On the forehead is engraved a double-contoured lozenge. The back is plain but much corroded.   Length: 4·5 cm.

Reg. no. 1938, 3–2, 1. Given by Mr. and Mrs. J. Hunt. From Lakenheath, Suffolk.

BIBLIOGRAPHY   Wilson and Blunt (1961), 121.
VCH Cambridgeshire, i, 327.

Found 'quite near' two bone pins and a bone comb—the association, however, is probably of little value. The pins and the comb were given to the Museum at the same time.

Ninth century. See above, pp. 28, 62 and pl. XIX.

30. Gold finger-ring. Flat, worn, hoop of gold with beaded edges and an inscription on a nielloed ground:

The inside of the hoop is plain.   Diameter: 2·3 cm.

Reg. no. Sl. 64. Sloane Collection 1753, catalogued under rings, and *Ring Cat. no.* 181. Found in Lancashire (?).

BIBLIOGRAPHY   *British Museum, Alfred the Great Millenary*
Hickes (1705), i, xiii and fig. facing p. viii, vi.   *Exhibition*, London 1901, 13.
Hamper (1821), 381.   Bugge (1908), 176.
Magnusen (1820), 351 and pl. iii, 4.   Smith (1908), 72.
Magnuson (1822), 140–141.   *B.M. Ring Cat.*, 30.
Liljegren (1833), 219.   *BMASG*, 115 and fig. 145.
Kemble (1840), 348.   Oman (1931), 107 and fig. B, 13.
Waterton (1862), 327 and fig. 2.   Harder (1932), 37–8.
Cuming (1863), 216.   Jessup (1950), 132, fig. 10 and pl. xxxvi, 3.
Stephens (1866–1901), i, 463.   Bennett (1950–1), 273.
Evans (1873), 332.   Moss (1953*a*), 61.
Stephens (1884), 139.   Moss (1953*b*), 76.
Sweet (1885), 130.   Ploss (1958), 34.
Stephens (1894), 30.

A transliteration of the inscription is

æDREDMECAHEAnREDMECagROf

The inscription can be transliterated 'Ædred mec ah Eanred mec agrof' and translated as 'Ædred owns me, Eanred engraved me'.

The provenance is not mentioned by Hickes,[1] but it does occur in the Sloane Catalogue (compiled by Sloane after Hickes's had published his book).

Ninth century. See above, pp. 1, 23, 27, 33, 56, 69, 75–77, 90 and pl. XIX.

31. Gold finger-ring, much squashed and dented, beaded along the lower edge, the upper edge being defined by a plain border. The ornament is, in the main, reserved in the metal

[1] (1705), xiii.

against a background of niello; where the niello has broken away the heavy striations of the keying can be seen. The bezel has the shape of a cocked hat and is decorated with two birds on either side of a formalised plant motif. The plant consists of three elements connected by a speckled line, which has roundels at the top and in the centre and a triangle at the bottom; the roundels contain quatrefoils and the triangle a bifoliate motif (these subsidiary motifs are not nielloed). The birds, which are lightly speckled, have sharply defined angular faces with squared snouts, a single nick below the eyes, heavy oval ears, a collared neck and a rounded forehead. The legs are bent up vertically in front of the birds and run from a long panelled hip; the wings are pear-shaped with scrolled ends. The tail consists of three lobes each with a billet and a ring at the terminal. On the back of the loop is a circular panel containing a quatrefoil between four dots (originally set against a nielloed background). On one side of this roundel is a pointed interlace motif with leaf-like terminals, while on the other side is a floriated saltire, between the arms of which are comma-shaped dots. On either side of the bezel are a pair of triangular fields containing two conjoined leaves (not nielloed). In a rectangular panel, below the two birds on the bezel, is the nielloed inscription:

ELHELVVLFR

The letters, the ornament of the loop and the border are speckled.

Maximum diameter: 2·8 cm.

Reg. no. 29, 11–14, 1; *Ring Cat.* no. 179. Given by the Earl of Radnor. From Laverstock (*Laverstoke*), Wiltshire.

BIBLIOGRAPHY

Archaeologia, vii, 421 and pl. xxx, 8–10.
Waterton (1862), 327 and fig. 3.
Proceedings of the Society of Antiquaries of London, ser. 2, vi (1875), 307.
British Museum, Alfred the Great Millenary Exhibition, 1901, London 1901, 13.
Smith (1908), 72 and pl. xiii, 5.
B.M. Ring Cat., 29 and pl. ii, 179.
Jackson (1911), i, 54 and fig. 70.
BMASG, 114 and fig. 143.
Brøndsted (1924), 133 and fig. 109.
Leclercq (1930), 2402 and fig. 7184.
Oman (1931), 105 and fig. B, 14.
Kendrick (1938a), 183 and fig. 25.
Jessup (1950), 130 , fig. 8 and pl. 36, 1.
Maryon (1950), 178 and fig. 2.
Hodgkin (1952), ii, pl. iv.
Moss (1953a), 61.
Moss (1953b), 76.
VCH Wiltshire, ii, 36–7.
Wilson and Blunt (1961), 96, 105 and 107.

The ring was found in a cart-rut at Laverstock (sometimes known as Laverstoke), Wiltshire, about August 1780 by one William Petty. Petty sold it to a silversmith (a Mr. Howell) in Salisbury and the then Earl of Radnor purchased it from him.

Ethelwulf, King of Wessex, was the father of Alfred the Great and reigned between 828 and 858.

Before 858. See above, pp. 2, 5, 6, 22–29, 34, 56, 79, 82 and pl. XIX.

32. Iron sword. The blade is complete and has a fuller on each face. On the blade towards the hilt and within the fuller is the inlaid legend: + L E U T L R I ⊥, while on the other face, also within the fuller, is an inlaid double scroll. The down-curved guard of the sword is inlaid with a series of lozenges, each lozenge is of copper surrounded by a bronze border and is hammered on to a cross-hatched, prepared field. The same pattern appears on the pommel-guard, while on the central element of the trilobate pommel a similar but rather elongated inlaid lozenge occurs. The two elements on either side of the plain central lobe of the pommel have two moulded shallow grooves, while deep grooves of rectangular section, between the pommel and the pommel guard and the three lobes of the pommel, were presumably inlaid with a twisted wire decoration—this is now missing. The tang of the sword is flat and plain and the grip does not survive; it decreases in width towards the pommel. The pommel is fastened to the guard by two rivets, hammered over beneath the guard.   Length: 91·4 cm.

Reg. no. 48, 10–21, 1. Given by J. Hayward, Esq. Found at Lincoln in the River Witham.

BIBLIOGRAPHY
Laking (1920), 14 and fig. 15b.
BMASG, 94.

Kendrick (1934), 396 and fig. 2.
Maryon (1950).
Bruce-Mitford (1953), 321–2.

Found in the river opposite Monk's Abbey, Lincoln.

Ninth/tenth century. See above, pp. 39, 64, 79, 90 and pl. xx.

33. Bronze openwork mount of sub-triangular shape, the base line is straight and the two long sides are slightly convex. At the apex is a circular lug. The mount has a rounded cross-section and at the base is a rectangular lug with a central, circular rivet-hole. The frame of the ornament is inlaid with niello on the edge of the two curved sides and on the front face of all three sides. The nielloed ornament of the edge consists of a line of niello inlaid with a zig-zag midrib of silver wire, the niello was inlaid in a narrow groove, which is keyed regularly along its length: little niello remains on the front face. The main ornament rises up above the border and consists of an animal seen from above. Its head is at the apex of the triangle and the faceted nostril and two bulbous eyes are prominently displayed; the body curves round to form a loop and the limbs form an interlace pattern with the single main loop of the body. The body of the animal has a central mid-rib, originally inlaid with niello, which is broken only where the interlaced limbs cross over the main body. The underside of the mount is concave and the openings in the mount are made by drilling, the holes being expanded slightly in the corners. The surface of the mount is much worn.   Length: 5·7 cm.

FIG. 19. Section through no. 33. ¼

Reg. no. 67, 3–20, 20. Purchased from Arthur Trollope, Esq. From Lincoln.

BIBLIOGRAPHY
BMASG, 104 and fig. 126.
Shetelig (1940), iv, 99 and fig. 65.

Kendrick (1949), 116 and fig. 19, a.
Moe (1955), 17 and fig. 15, a.
Wilson (1961), 212 and pl. xxxviii, a.

Found in soil carted out of Lincoln in 1850.

Eleventh century. See above, pp. 48, 51, 58 and pl. XXI.

34. Bronze buckle-loop. The loop is decorated and the straight bar is plain. In the centre of the loop is a blundered triquetra knot flanked by incomplete animals which bite the bar. The barbed upper jaw of each animal grips the bar which is slightly moulded at this point.

The eye of each animal is lentoid and stands up above the background. Behind the ear a double element tendril forks round the central triquetra. The back is plain and the casting is very poor. The surface is badly pitted and even pierced in one place (to the right of the triquetra knot). Length 7·1 cm.

Reg. no. 56, 7–1, 1474. Purchased from C. Roach Smith, Esq. From London: Barnes, found in the Thames.

BIBLIOGRAPHY
Shetelig (1940), iv, 90 and fig. 57.
Eleventh century. See above, pp. 48, 51, 53 and pl. XXI.

35. Iron stirrup-iron inlaid with copper. The loop for the stirrup leather is square and its flat lower portion is decorated with a series of almost vertical lines tilting slightly away from the centre. The back has lost its inlay. Below the loop is an oval knop, originally plated with a series of horizontally inlaid wires; much of this inlay is now missing. The main hoop has gently curved sides above a solid boss near the foot-plate. The hoop to this point has a triangular cross-section, beyond the boss it continues on both sides, past the foot-plate, to an irregular, flat hexagonal, side plate. The foot-plate is plain but slightly convex in cross-section. The bosses at the side are plated on the outside in the same way as on the nodus, while the hoop and side plates are decorated with a series of running spiral hooks. The pattern is incomplete on the hoop. On the side plates, this running spiral pattern is defined by a plain inlaid border. The surface was prepared for inlaying by cross-hatching and the wire was beaten into this keyed surface.

Height: 23·9 cm.

Reg. no. 54, 4–24, 1. Purchased from H. J. Briggs, Esq. From London; near Battersea.

BIBLIOGRAPHY
BMASG, fig. 110.
Weigall (1927), 183.
Wheeler (1927), 41.
Kendrick (1930), fig. 8.
Shetelig (1940), iv, 88 and fig. 56.

We know from the register that at some time in the nineteenth century this object was waxed. It has apparently been cleaned in recent years, but the condition of the metal would suggest that the object came from the River Thames.

Tenth/eleventh century. See above, pp. 39, 62 and pl. XXI.

36. Iron scramasax inlaid with copper, bronze and silver. It has a straight edge and back, save that 23 cm. from the tip the back runs off at an angle to form the tip. The tang is slightly offset from the blade; it is broad and decreases slightly in width towards the butt. On both faces is a median groove which runs the length of the blade from the tang. An inlaid line flanks the median groove on both faces and another line runs below the back of the blade. Within the area defined by these lines on the front face of the blade is an inlaid inscription:

immediately followed by a double running lozenge pattern executed in twisted silver and bronze wire. Further towards the tip is a single running lozenge pattern, each lozenge containing a billet of bronze or silver. Following on in the same line is the inscription:

beyond which is an indistinct pattern in silver wire which merges into a zone of running lozenge ornament from which much of the inlay is missing. In the centre of each of these lozenges was originally a rectangular billet—all are now missing. The inscription is inlaid in wire, either of twisted bronze and copper or of twisted bronze and silver. The long lines on both faces are made up of a herring-bone pattern executed in lengths of twisted bronze and copper, and bronze and silver, wire. Small triangles of copper are pendant from the lower line. The two bordering lines on the lower face of the blade border a continuous zig-zag ornament, which develops into a short stretch of interlace beyond the angle in the back of the blade. The running lozenge pattern consists of inlaid twisted silver and bronze wire, with a silver billet in the centre of each lozenge. In the triangular space, between each lozenge and the bordering line, is an inlaid triangle of bronze with its base on the border—a feature which can also be seen on the front face, where the single running lozenge pattern occurs. Across the squared back edge of the blade are nine, equidistant, inlaid double (and in one case treble) short lines of twisted bronze and silver wire. Length: 81·1 cm.

Reg. no. 57, 6–23, 1. Purchased from H. Briggs, Esq. From London: Battersea.

BIBLIOGRAPHY
Proceedings of the Society of Antiquaries of London,
    iv (1857), 83.
Haigh (1861), 46.
Stephens (1866–1901), i, xxxiii, 361 f. and iii,
    159 and *passim*.
Haigh (1870), 182.
Haigh (1872), 235–6.
Evans (1873), 333.
Haigh (1873), 252 and 285.
Wimmer (1874), 72, 76–7 and pl. iii, 3.
King (1876), 750.
Vigfusson and Powell (1879), 444.
Taylor (1879), 5.
Proceedings of the Society of Antiquaries of London,
    series 2, x (1883), 18.
Stephens (1884), 111.
Sweet (1885), 129.
Wimmer (1887), 82 f., 383 f. and pl. iii.
Chaillu (1889), i, 160.
Baye (1889), 31.
Taylor (1890), 505.
Bugge and Olsen (1891–1924), i. 147.

Baye (1893), 28.
Stephens (1894), 22.
Sephton (1895–6), 186 and pl. i, fig. 2.
Sievers (1896–1901), 255.
Greinberger (1898), 115 and 117.
Müller (1898), 99.
Hempl (1903–4), 136.
Ålund (1904), 12, 13 and 17.
Shore (1906), 41 and 43–4.
Kermode (1907), 83 and fig. 44.
Paues (1907), 10–11.
VCH London, i, 152 and fig. 7.
Paues (1911), 450.
Gosse (1911), 852–3.
Forbes and Dickens (1914), 25.
Baldwin Brown (1903–37), iii, 230.
Friesen (1918–19), 22, 24 and pl. 3.
La grande encyclopédie, 28, 1140 f. and fig. 1, b.
Buck (1919), 219, 221.
Royal Commission on Ancient and Historical Monuments (Scotland): Seventh Report, Edinburgh 1920, 238 and 274.
BMASG, 96 and fig. 117.

Schönaich-Carolath (1924), 6, 8 and pl. 3.
Agrell (1927), 155 f., 208.
Weigall (1927), 175.
Bork (1929), 69.
Friesen (1929), 659.
Grosleben (1930), 623–5.
Hammerström (1930), 42 and fig. 7.
Leclerq (1930), 2403–4 and fig. 7191, 4.
Shetelig (1930), 6.
Vulliamy (1930), 236, 258 and fig. 36D.
Agrell (1931), 246–8 and figs.
Agrell (1931/2), 9–10.
Brodeur (1932), 6.
Dickins (1932), 19.
Kummer (1932), 21.
Kendrick (1934), 398 and fig. 3, c.
Arntz (1935), 67, *passim* and pl. viii.
Harder (1935), 21–2.
Friesen (1936), 241 and fig. 4.
Jungandreas (1936), 231.
Reichardt (1936), 10 and fig. 11.
Reiss (1936), 7 and 59.
Pfeilstücker (1936), 208–9.
Krause (1937*a*), 438–40.

Shetelig and Falk (1937), 215.
Arntz (1938), 76.
Dickins (1938), 83.
Harder (1938), 146–8.
Reichardt (1938), 433 and fig. 4.
Neckel (1938), 105.
Arntz and Zeiss (1939), *passim*.
Daunt (1939), 120.
Sierke (1939), 72.
Baescke (1940), 124.
Weber (1941), 20–1.
Baeksted (1943), 44.
Krause (1943), 9.
Arntz (1944*b*), 176 f. and 249.
Altheim (1948), 234–5.
Oakeshott (1951), 70.
Baeksted (1952), 120 *et passim*.
Brade-Birks (1953), 175.
Derolez (1954), *passim*.
Blair (1956), 309.
Elliott (1957), 251.
Schramm (1957), *passim*.
Elliott (1958), *passim*.
Nerman (1959).

From the River Thames.

The purchase included a number of other iron weapons of Anglo-Saxon date found in the Thames at Battersea.

A transliteration of the runic inscription would be:

    I: 'fuþorcgwhnijȝpxʃtbeŋdlmœaæyêa'
    II: 'bêagnoþ'

Late ninth-century. See above, pp. 38, 60, 69ff. and pl. XXII.

37. Pewter circular brooch. The central, circular panel of this brooch is raised above the surrounding border and contains, within a beaded border, a backward-looking, stylised

FIG. 20.   Side view of no. 37.

animal with a conventionalised mane, open mouth and forward-bent legs. The tail rises behind the animal and curves gently forward. The background is filled with raised dots. A small secondary hole is pierced below the hind leg. The border consists of a heavy beaded band enclosing three lesser beaded bands: these are in turn enclosed by a band imitative of twisted wire and surrounded by a small and a large beaded border. The back of the flan is covered with cast annulets, in imitation of filigree. The centre of the back is plain. The catch-plate hinge and half of the pin of the brooch remain. The pin is made of thin wire, twisted into a loop at one end round a wire spindle; it may be secondary. All the ornament of the brooch is cast. The metal has been confirmed by laboratory examination as a tin/lead alloy.

Diameter: 4·3 cm.

Reg. no. 52, 3–25, 2. Purchased from Mr. J. Purdue. From London; Bird-in-Hand Court, Cheapside.

BIBLIOGRAPHY
Fairholt (1847), 313 f. and fig.
VCH London, i, 160 and coloured plate, 3.
Brøndsted (1924), 146 and fig. 121.
Wheeler (1935), 189.
Jessup (1950), 47.

Found on 1 August, 1844. The brooch was previously in the collection of Mr. W. Chaffers (a dealer). No trace can be seen of the gilding which Fairholt[1] described in his original publication.

Tenth century. See above, pp. 36, 37n, 52 and pl. XXII.

38. Bronze key with solid shank which tapers towards the tip. The ward has a forked terminal rising at right-angles. The bow is shaped as an inverted pear and is divided into nine openwork fields with a lozenge-shaped field in the centre and sub-triangular fields interspersed with oval fields surrounding it. At the top of the bow, and at right-angles to it, is a small loop for suspension issuing from a plain collar.

Length: 8·0 cm.

Reg. no. 50, 7–1, 1088.[2] Purchased from C. Roach Smith, Esq. From London; Bush Lane.

BIBLIOGRAPHY
Roach Smith (1859), 144 and pl. 38: 14.
Found in 1841.
Kessler (1932), 100.
Almgren (1955), 105 and Tab. II, G/4.

Ninth–eleventh century. See above, pp. 57 and pl. XXII.

39. Pewter circular brooch. Within four beaded circles and a double contoured plain border (broken in four places by small circlets) is a blundered three-line inscription filled out round the edge of the central field with a series of short comb-like motifs. The back is

FIG. 21.   Side view of no. 39. $\frac{1}{1}$

plain but retains the two hinge plates and a portion of the catch-plate. The brooch has been confirmed by laboratory examination as a tin/lead alloy. The brooch is broken into two pieces.

Diameter: 3·7 cm.

Reg. no. 56, 7–1, 1468. Purchased from C. Roach Smith, Esq. From London; Cloak Lane.

BIBLIOGRAPHY
Fairholt (1847), 312–13 and fig.
Roach Smith (1854), 106 and fig.
Found while excavating sewers in 1846/7.
VCH London, i, 160.
Wheeler (1935), 189.

[1] (1847), 314.
[2] The registration number recorded by Almgren (1955), 105 is incorrect.

I am grateful to Dr. Walker, Keeper of Coins and Medals in the British Museum for the following note:

'The central part of the brooch certainly resembles a Kufic *dirham*. There are traces of a magical legend which would appear to be a copy of an Arabic legend containing a date formula. The outer circles with four pellets are not unlike those on certain coins struck towards the end of the Umaiyad Dynasty in the Middle East, say a little before A.H. 132, *i.e.* A.D. 750.'

Tenth century. See above, pp. 35, 52 and pl. XXII.

40. Bronze key with hollow shank and long pierced tongue with upturned bifurcated end. The bow is a ring of oval cross-section containing an openwork cross. The arms of the cross expand from a sub-lozenge-shaped centre, which is decorated on each side, with a small punched dot. At right-angles to the bow a loop for suspension issues from a small projection at the top: the top of the loop is broken away.   Length: 7·2 cm.

Reg. no. 56, 7–1, 1087. Purchased from C. Roach Smith, Esq. From London; possibly from Copenhagen Fields.

BIBLIOGRAPHY
Almgren (1955), 105 and Table II, G/3.

Ninth–eleventh century. See above, pp. 57 and pl. XXIII.

41. Silver parcel-gilt pommel and upper part of the grip of a sword, inlaid in parts with niello. In the centre of the pommel is a tapering upright element, with rounded end, which is flanked by three cylinders of decreasing height and oval section. On the top of each of these cylinders is a dome-shaped rivet-head surrounded by a collar of beaded wire: the beaded wire collar is worn away on the outer edge of the outermost cylinder. The broader, central element is decorated on either side by two dissimilar conventionalised scroll patterns executed in low relief, the ornament on one side is given a semi-zoomorphic character by the central mask-like feature. Each of the cylinders is separated from the next, and from the central element, by a band of fine-gauge beaded wire. The whole of the pommel is gilt. The pommel guard is made of three separate pieces, two flat silver plates, bounded by a gilt rope moulding, and a plain moulding of semi-circular cross-section which is not gilt. The two rope mouldings differ: that at the top slopes at a different angle on one-half of one face to give an opposed stroke effect, this is not done on the other face (which slopes from top-right to bottom-left) or on the lower band (which slopes from top-left to bottom-right all the way round). The individual strands of the rope moulding are divided by a median incised line. Below the guard and at either end of it are the domed heads of two rivets, each collared with beaded wire. The shank of the rivet appears at the top of each dome. The tang of the sword ran through the grip into the pommel and the hole allowing for this, a pointed oval, can be seen in the plate at the bottom of the pommel guard, where it is separated from the grip.

The grip curves away from the guard to a collar of half-oval section decorated with an interlocking band of double zig-zags. Both the grip and the pommel are filled with modern wood—their shape being thus retained.

148

On the front of the grip four snakes swirl into the centre of the field, interspaced with leafy tendrils carved in the silver. The tail of each snake starts as a scroll in one of the corners of the field and passes through a three-quarter spiral to terminate in a head towards the centre. The bodies are segmented but, as they grow thinner towards the tail, two of them form a zig-zag line and two of them continue the segments merely as a definitive border. A line of small dots of triangular shape, executed with the corner of a graver, continue throughout the length of the body from behind the head. The head has a pear-shaped eye which is separated from the snout and straight mouth by an ogival line. The mouth and snout are gilded but the rest of the body of the snake is left plain against the gilded carved background of the leaves. The leafy tendrils of the background are interspaced between the bodies of the snakes, joining in the centre to separate the snakes' heads, they are carved below the general surface of the field. All the details of the segments, eyes, borders and zig-zags of the animals are nielloed and, where the niello is missing, the fine keying is visible.

On the other face is an animal in a four-pointed spread-eagled position. The head is in the top, right-hand corner and the barbed tail curls round from the opposite side under the head and the two legs (which are extended into opposing corners) and finishes, after crossing over itself, in a scroll beneath the right leg. The eye and nostril are formed of a scroll with a pear-shaped terminal. From the bottom of this scroll, and linked with it, runs a tendril which continues into a central scroll to interlock with other scrolls formed by the production of the bordering lines of the legs and a loop on the rump of the animal. A dotted line forms a midrib to the tail and follows the spiral scrolls and the edges of the limbs, head and body of the animal. Each dot is triangular in shape and was formed, presumably, by the corner of a graver. The incised ornament of the spirals and the borders is filled with niello. The animal retains the silver surface. The background is filled in with leaf and tendril ornament, carved in relief and gilt.

Inlaid in the areas between the deeply carved leaves on this object was a substance which has been confirmed by x-ray diffraction as a mixture of calcium carbonate and iron carbonate. This may well be primary.   Length: 8·7 cm.

Reg. no. 93, 7–15, 1. Given by Sir A. W. Franks, K.C.B. From London; Fetter Lane.

BIBLIOGRAPHY
VCH London, i, 154.
Proceedings of the Society of Antiquaries of London,
    2 series, xxiii (1910), 302–3 and fig. 2.
Brøndsted (1924), 144 and fig. 119.
BMASG, 93 and fig. 112.
Smith (1925a), 249 and fig. 23.

Weigall (1927), 210.
Vulliamy (1930), 256.
Kendrick (1938a), 189 and pl. lxxix, 1.
Wilson (1960a), 109, 145, 216 and pl. 24.
Dunning and Evison (1961), 140–5, 156, 157
    and pls. xli–xlii.

The pommel was found while excavating foundations for Smith's Printing Works (now Monotype House, Fetter Lane) and purchased by John Allen (son of the famous publisher) from a workman for half-a-crown (see letter from H. S. Gordon, 30.7.1927, in the Department of British and Medieval Antiquities).

c. 800. See above, pp. 2, 10, 11, 20–22, 24–26, 30, 33, 64 and pl. XXIII.

42. Bronze cast plaque, rectangular with a *fleur-de-lys* terminal. A raised border surrounds the decorated portion of the field, save at the top, and there is a plain space at the bottom of the plaque. The ornament consists of a much worn, floriate animal ornament set in a basic figure-of-eight design and cast in low relief. The animal head appears in the centre of the right-hand side and the body is interlaced and crossed by many tendrils, which are impossible to relate anatomically to the body. The surface of the object is much damaged, and with it the other termination (centre-left) of the main part of the animal (Moe has interpreted this as the head of an animal: I cannot agree). The side elements of the *fleur-de-lys* terminal form the curled terminations of the lateral borders. The back is plain, save for the blow holes of the casting which occur over the whole surface.   Length: 10·6 cm.

Reg. no. 1904, 6–23, 4. Purchased from G. F. Lawrence, Esq. From London: Hammersmith.

BIBLIOGRAPHY
Shetelig (1909), 95 and fig. 20.
Proceedings of the Society of Antiquaries of London, 2nd series, xxiii (1911), 400 and fig. 3.
Proceedings of the Society of Antiquaries of London, 2 series, xxvi (1914), 71.

BMASG, 113 and fig. 141.
Lindqvist (1931), 165 and fig. 18.
Kendrick (1949), 117 and pl. lxix, 2.
Moe (1955), 26 and fig. 24a and b.
Shetelig (1958), 143 and fig. 52.

Found in the River Thames.

Note that the reconstruction of the ornament published by Moe (1955), fig. 24a is inaccurate and misleading.

Eleventh century. See above, pp. 2, 48–50, 65 and pl. XXIII.

43. Iron scramasax inlaid with bronze and copper: the edge of the blade is straight and the back is high and pointed. It has a tang which is bent slightly out of line with the blade. The front face of the blade is ornamented with three inlaid lines of alternating bronze and copper wire, set in a herring-bone pattern, running parallel with the back of the blade. Towards the point the three lines merge into a triangle filled with a bronze and copper zig-zag pattern. The other face of the blade is inlaid with a single straight band of copper wire, which runs parallel with the back of the blade to the highest point, where it is crossed by another short inlaid line.   Length: 32·7 cm.

Reg. no. 56, 7–1, 1413. Purchased from C. Roach Smith, Esq. From London; Honey Lane Market.

BIBLIOGRAPHY
Gentlemen's Magazine (1836), 371.
Collectanea Antiqua, ii (1852), 243 and pl. lviii, 3.
Roach Smith (1854), 102.

VCH London, i, 152 and fig. 6.
Wheeler (1935), 179 and 193.
Dolley (1958), 99.

Charles Roach Smith in his diary describes the site of the find on 7 February 1836:

'This morning I went with James to the various sites of the late excavations and obtained the following confirmatory infor-.

Honey Lane

The knife inlaid with brass was found close to the corner of the Honey Lane Market, i.e. on the Cheapside side of the New School where also were found the coins of Athelred and numerous Saxon tiles, but as far as we could tell no pottery.'

From this context it seems that there is no definite association of coins and scramasax. But in *Collectanea Antiqua*[1] it is recorded that it was found 'on the site of the City of London School with several coins of Ethelred II', and in the Roach Smith catalogue the very definite statement is made that '. . . on the same spot and contiguous to the knife, were some coins of Ethelred II'.[2] The hoard is not recorded in Thompson[3] and, as it was unrecorded in the numismatic literature before 1958, no other evidence as to this association is available. Eight of the coins are listed in the Roach Smith Catalogue,[4] six are now in the Department of Coins and Medals in the British Museum.[5] The deposition of the coins has been dated to *c.* 1003.[6]

Ninth/tenth century. See above, pp. 39, 60 and pl. xxiv.

44. Bronze censer-cover of tower shape, much bent and damaged. Originally the ridges of the pyramidal roof rose from the points of the gables on each of the four faces. The roof above the gables has now largely disappeared. The object is ornamented in low relief with a series of animal and bird figures executed in openwork. In each of the three surviving gables is a standing bird, with a down-bent neck and open beak. Above two of the gables project stylised bird's heads. One side is badly dented and the gable is missing, but traces remain here of the ornament in the upper lozenge-shaped fields which originally stood between the gables; on the left is a tail and on the right the spread foot of a bird; the same features can also be seen on the opposite face. At each of the four corners, below the gables, an animal head, with a mouth indicated by an incised line and small bored eyes, sticks out like a gargoyle. The snouts of three of the animals are squared off, the fourth is slightly pointed. The square field on the damaged side is much worn and has been dented into a V-shape. It contains two adorsed birds on either side of an elongated leaf-like motif. One of the legs of each bird is raised against the side border, the other is stretched into the outer corner. The tail develops into a three-fold leaf-motif, the longest element of which passes between the legs of the bird. The necks of each bird are crossed by tendrils issuing from a cat-like mask in the centre of the upper border. The necks are twisted so that the bottom element of the open beak touches the upper border. The heads of the adorsed birds in the field to the right of this are in the same position. The birds' tails touch in the centre bottom and the legs, each with an enormous claw, project into the lower corners. From a mask (centre top) issue four tendrils (two of which are split), two of which cross the necks of the birds while the other two pass beneath their bodies, to terminate in a close curled element. On the third face are two animals with heads seen from above on either side of the cat-like mask. Two tendrils emerge below the mask to cut the animals' necks, and a pointed tongue extends from the mask half way down the centre of the field to a point where the legs of the animals rise to meet it. Each animal has a shaped hip, a single leg and a floriated tail, one tendril of which terminates in a trefoil. The fourth field contains two adorsed birds with heads raised to peck with open beaks against the upper border. The large claws are in opposite corners of the bottom, while the tails touch in the centre of the bottom border. Of the

[1] ii (1852), 243.
[2] Roach Smith (1854), 102.
[3] Thompson (1956).
[4] Roach Smith (1854), 108.
[5] Dolley (1958), 100.
[6] Dolley and Metcalfe (1961), 163.

tendrils which emerge from the mouth of the central mask, one pair crosses the neck, while the other pair curls beneath the animal to touch the upper part of the foot. In the centre is a very coarse acanthus leaf.

Four pierced lugs stand out at right-angles from the bottom corners of the cover. The interior has not been cleaned up after casting; many burrs remain. Height: 8·8 cm.
Reg. no. 37, 3–28, 1. From London; London Bridge.

BIBLIOGRAPHY
Proceedings of the Society of Antiquaries London. ser. 2, xxi (1907), 56–62.
Jackson (1911), i, 90–1 and figs. 121–3.
Brøndsted (1924), 264 f. and fig. 189.
Dalton and Tonnochy (1924), 184 and fig. 123.
Tonnochy (1932), 2–3, and pl. iiA.
Tonnochy (1937), 54–5.
Kendrick (1938c), 379 and pl. lxxiii, 3.
Arbman (1958), 189 and figs. 16 and 17.

The provenance depends on a note painted on the censer cover. The object was never registered and the details of its acquisition have been lost. But it was presumably found during the rebuilding of London Bridge, which was opened on 1 August 1831.

Tenth century. See above, pp. 34, 43–45, 47, 53 and pl. xxiv.

45. Fragment of a silver-gilt binding strip terminating in an animal's head in full relief. It consists of a strip of metal bent longitudinally so that it has a U-shaped cross-section. The curved top of the strip is decorated with oblique mouldings, each with an incised median line at its highest point. The mouldings terminate behind the animal head in three transverse incisions. The front face of the strip is inscribed with runic characters thus:

The back face is plain. The strip is broken at a rivet-hole adjacent to a complete one. In the centre of the surviving length of the strip two rivets with globular heads flank an empty hole. Three rivets survive behind the animal head, where two globular rivet-heads flank a knurled globular head: all are riveted over on the back of the strip. The long, scrolled, animal ears, modelled in relief, rise from the back of the head and join at the tips. The mouth is open and two canine teeth in the upper and lower jaws interlock on either side of the mouth to form an arch, through which the tongue issues from the back of the mouth. The tongue curls back on itself outside the mouth and forms a scroll on the throat. The head has blue glass eyes. Two moulded ridges rise from the circular nostrils (which were themselves, presumably, set with glass) to pass between the eyes, separate in diminishing relief, and terminate in a spiral scroll engraved beneath the ears. Two scrolls of groups of incised lines cross each other on the forehead to diminish and finish above the spiral termination of the eyebrows; they leave a plain lozenge-shaped field just above the eyes. Between the ears is a triangular field, with inscribed sides and a trefoil (?) design. The lip is billeted and the lower jaw terminates in the suggestion of a scroll. Below the throat the mount is broken away but another binding strip, of U-shaped cross section, apparently emerged here, below a panel of horizontal hatching within two bordering lines. The whole object is curved throughout its length and some of the gilding is missing. The back of the strip beyond the animal head bears no trace of gilding. The mount is slightly buckled. Length: 18·8 cm.

Reg. no. 69, 6–10, 1. Given by Thomas D. E. Gunston(e), Esq. From London: found near Westminster Bridge in the River Thames.

BIBLIOGRAPHY
Cuming (1868), 178–82 and pl. 31, 1.
Stephens (1866–1901), ii, 892 and iii, 204.
Dietrich (1869), 115–18.
Wincklemann (1883), 176–77 and fig. 8.
Stephens (1884), 147.
Bugge and Olsen (1891–1924), i, 120 and ii, 230.
Romilly Allen (1904a), 275 and figs. 3 and 7.
VCH London, i, 166–7 and fig. 30.
Grienberger (1913).
BMASG, 118 f. and fig. 152.
Vulliamy (1930), 266.
Arntz and Zeiss (1939), 37.
Arntz (1944a).

Dietrich's[1] provenance 'from the Thames at Aylesbury' may be dismissed, as based on secondary evidence. Cuming, however, makes a statement which seems eminently reasonable as it was made, presumably on the authority of its then owner T. D. E. Gunston(e), in England within two years of its discovery. Cuming writes that it was, 'dredged from the gravelly bed of the Thames, near Westminster Bridge in 1866', a statement repeated, without question, by R. A. Smith (*VCH London*, i, 166). A transliteration of the runic inscription would be: ' s b e/r æ d h t ʒ b c a i | e/r h/a d/æ b s '.

Eighth/ninth century. See above, pp. 10, 15, 16, 31, 65, 69, 71, 77–79 and pl. xxv.

46. Bronze key. The openwork bow is circular and contains a wheeled cross. A circular suspension-loop is set at right-angles to the bow. The shank is solid and the tongue is roughly rectangular with an upstanding nipple at the terminal. The object is much corroded. Length: 8·4 cm.

Reg. no. 1909, 5–18, 25. Purchased from G. F. Lawrence, Esq. From London: Wood St.

BIBLIOGRAPHY
Almgren (1955), 105 and Tab. II, F/8.

Ninth–eleventh century. See above, pp. 57 and pl. xxv.

47. Copper circular brooch. Within a double beaded border (each border made up of alternate larger and smaller beads) is a circular central panel defined by a plain line. The panel contains a pattern made up of three backed curves with recurved ends. The ends of these curves are split by a median line and between each curve is an S-shaped motif. In the centre of the motif is a single dot. The whole pattern has been stamped up from the underside. The back of the brooch is plain, save for the negative traces of the ornament on the face, and carries a loop and a broken catch-plate for the pin. The identity of the metal has been confirmed by laboratory examination.

Diameter: 3·4 cm. FIG. 22. Back of no. 47. ½

Reg. no. 56, 7–1, 1462. Purchased from C. Roach Smith, Esq. From London.

[1] (1869).

BIBLIOGRAPHY
Roach Smith (1854), 105 and fig.   *BMASG*, fig. 125.
VCH London, I, 157.   Wheeler (1935), 186.

Tenth century. See above, pp. 36, 52 and pl. xxv.

48. Bronze-gilt disc. The disc, which has a much corroded face, has a central dome-headed rivet. In the surrounding area are traces of an interlaced ribbon ornament. The back is plain, save for the end of the central rivet and possible traces of two, or more, other rivets.

Maximum diameter: 3·4 cm.

Reg. no. 56, 7–1, 1466. Purchased from C. Roach Smith, Esq. From London (?).

Most of the material obtained by the Museum from Charles Roach Smith came from London—any other provenance for this object is unlikely.

? Eleventh century. See above, p. 65 and pl. xxv.

49. Bronze buckle with a tongue made from a strip of sheet bronze. Two rivet-holes survive in a rectangular panel at the butt-end of the loop, which is cut to a slightly lower level. The rest of the loop is elongated and pointed, terminating in an animal mask seen from above, with moulded, round eyes from which springs a spiral ridge to form the eyebrows —spectacle-wise. The snout is plain. The tongue is carried in an oval hole. The underside of the loop is plain and concave.

Length: 4·6 cm.

Reg. no. 56, 7–1, 1473. Purchased from C. Roach Smith, Esq. From London.

BIBLIOGRAPHY
Roach Smith (1854), 106, No. 560.

Ninth/eleventh century. See above, p. 53 and pl. xxv.

50. Iron scramasax. The tanged end is broken away, but the core of the tang survives. The cutting edge is slightly curved. Towards the back of the blade, on both faces, are three bands of twisted copper and brass wire inlay—the two metals forming a herring-bone pattern. In one place, on the back of the blade, the two bottom lines are joined by a panel decorated with a zig-zag pattern. The bands are broken away at the fracture towards the tanged end and finish beyond the angle on the back of the blade.

Surviving length: 23·2 cm.

Reg. no. 59, 1–22, 12. Purchased from William Edwards, Esq., London: from the bed of the Thames (?).

The scramasax was purchased with a group of iron weapons which are described as, 'all from London, chiefly from the bed of the River Thames'.

Ninth/tenth century. See above, pp. 39, 60 and pl. xxvi.

51. Pewter circular brooch. The central panel is raised on expanding openwork struts above the rim and is defined by a laddered border. It contains three backed curves with scrolled ends, set round a triangle with a central dot. Between the scrolled ends is an S-shaped scroll. The rim has a beaded border inside which is a pattern made up of two rows of interlocking, curved, concentric lines. The ornament is cast and the central panel is soldered to the struts. On the back are the remains of a loop and catch-plate. The metal has been confirmed by laboratory examination as a tin/lead alloy.

Diameter: 4·4 cm.

Reg. no. 1942, 10–8, 4. Given by the Christy Trustees. From London.

FIG. 23.   Back and side view of no. 51. $\frac{1}{1}$

BIBLIOGRAPHY
Burlington Fine Arts Club, Catalogue of an Exhibition of Art in the Dark Ages in Europe (c. 400–1000 *A.D.*), London 1930, 31, No. 49.

Acquired at the Grantley sale in 1942 (lot 22), when it was said to have come from Kent. A MS., *Catalogue of the Antiquities in the possession of Cecil Brent*, written in 1884, now in the Department of British and Medieval Antiquities of the British Museum, illustrates this brooch (pl. 11); recording that it was found in 1864 in the Steelyard, London (but see note to no. 53).

Tenth century. See above, pp. 36, 52 and pl. xxvi.

52. Pewter circular brooch. In the centre of the front face is a small conical boss surrounded by a ring of small dots within a ladder-like border. Outside this a zig-zag pattern, made up of short lengths of ladder-like ornament, gives a star shaped effect: dots are added between the points of the star. A double ladder-like border surrounds the whole brooch. The back of the brooch has a central circular field containing a cross with expanded arms between each of which is a small cross pattée. Surrounding this field is a treble hatched border. The remains of the hinge and the catch-plate can be seen on the back. The whole ornament is cast in low relief. The metal has been confirmed by laboratory examination as a tin/lead alloy.

Diameter: 4·1 cm.

Reg. no. 1942, 10–8, 5, Given by the Christy Trustees. From London.

BIBLIOGRAPHY
Burlington Fine Arts Club, Catalogue of an   *Exhibition of Art in the Dark Ages in Europe (c.* 400–1000 *A.D.*), London 1930, 31–2, no. 50.

The brooch was purchased at the Grantley Sale in 1942 (lot 22), at which time it was said to have come from Kent. In a MS., *Catalogue of the Antiquities in the possession of Cecil Brent*, written in 1884, now in the Department of British and Medieval Antiquities in the British Museum, it is recorded as having come from the Steelyard, London, in 1864 (but see note to no. 53).

Tenth century. See above, pp. 36, 52 and pl. xxvi.

53. Pewter circular brooch. The brooch is imperfect, part of one side having been broken away. In the centre is a hollow conical boss divided into quarters by double lines; in each quadrant is an applied dot. The boss is surrounded by a double ladder-like border.

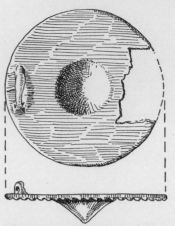

FIG. 24. Back and side view of no. 53.

Within the beaded border which surrounds the brooch, is a panel containing a series of triangles each containing two or three dots; further dots occur between the triangles. The panel is defined on the outer edge by two lines, the outer one forming the central rib of a feathered pattern. The ornament of the face is case in low relief. The back is plain, save for an applied loop. The metal has been confirmed by laboratory examination as a tin/lead alloy.   Diameter: 4·5 cm.

Reg. no. 1942, 10–8, 6. Given by the Christy Trustees. From London.

BIBLIOGRAPHY
Burlington Fine Arts Club, Catalogue of an Exhibition of Art in the Dark Ages in Europe (*c.* 400–1000 *A.D.*), London 1930, 31, No. 48.

In a MS., *Catalogue of the Antiquities in the possession of Cecil Brent*, written in 1884 and now in the Department of British and Medieval Antiquities in the British Museum, this brooch is figured (pl. 11) and catalogued as from the Steelyard, London, having been found in 1864. In another volume of what is apparently the same MS. this brooch is again illustrated and a later hand has added that it came from 'the Thames 1867'. The brooch is apparently mentioned (with nos. 51 and 52) in the Cecil Brent Sale Catalogue (Sotheby, Wilkinson and Hodge, Wednesday 17 December–Friday 19 December 1902), lot 88, it was sold in a miscellaneous lot for £5. It apparently passed into the hands of Lord Grantley, for it was purchased at the Grantley Sale (Messrs. Glendenning and Co., Wednesday 9 September 1942, lot 22). In the Burlington Fine Arts Club *Catalogue*, it appears with a Kentish provenance, which is almost certainly incorrect, stemming presumably from the Kentish origin of much of Brent's collection. The Steelyard provenance is probably correct as many other pieces in Brent's collection came from that site.

Tenth century. See above, pp. 36, 52 and pl. XXVI.

54. Pewter circular brooch, ornamented in low relief with a cast decoration. It has a ladder-like border and central panel containing a double-contoured, equal-armed cross. In the

FIG. 25. Back and side view of no. 54. $\frac{1}{1}$

centre of the cross, and at the terminal of each arm, is a small hemispherical boss. A small panel between each arm contains an indecipherable motif. The back is plain, save for part of a double concentric circle which is slightly off centre and runs out of the circumference of the brooch. There are remains of a catch-plate and loop. The metal has been confirmed by laboratory examination as a tin/lead alloy.

Diameter: 3·0 cm.

Reg. no. 1942, 10–8, 11. Given by the Christy Trustees. From Mildenhall, Suffolk.

The brooch was purchased at Lord Grantley's Sale (Glendennings, 9 September 1942, lot 66). In view of the uncertainty of provenance of a number of the objects in this sale (see above no. 53), this find-place should be treated with a certain amount of caution.

Tenth century. See above, pp. 36, 52 and pl. XXVI

55. Bronze disc. The front is decorated with an equal-armed cross, at the centre of which is a quadrangular field with concave sides. Inside this field is a circular hollow, surrounded by four annulets. The arms of the cross are produced to form a loose interlace pattern which is given zoomorphic character by the addition of a small circular eye. The arms of the cross, to the point where the interlacing starts, are ribbed between two bordering lines, the lines continue in the interlacing but the ribbing ceases. The roundel is bordered by a grooved plain band. The back is plain and rather pitted.   Diameter: 2·9 cm.

Reg. no. 1955, 10–2, 1. Given by A. Winter, Esq. From Oxshott Wood, Surrey.

BIBLIOGRAPHY
Wilson (1956*a*), 70 f. and pl. viii, a.   Evison (1957), 220.

Tenth/eleventh century. See above, pp. 48, 49, 52 and pl. XXVI

56. Bronze censer-cover of tower shape with a gable on each of the four faces, from each tip of which rise the ridges of the pyramidal roof. The panels of the roof are carried down into the spaces between the gables. The roof is crowned by a three-dimensional animal mask, with dot-and-circle eyes, pointed nose, faceted snout and linear mouth: two pointed ears appear low down on the back of the head and traces of the linear treatment of the hair can be seen. The animal head is set on a short pillar which issues from a nodus decorated with a herring-bone pattern with a dotted midrib. The snout and eyes of masks similar to that at the crest of the object project gargoyle-wise at each corner of the gables. The gables are decorated with a series of hollowed ovolos (representing shingles). The ridges of the roof and the ridges between the gables are all decorated with double rows of slightly curved, punched lines—set in a herring-bone fashion. The panels between the gables are filled with openwork ornament, cast in relief. The ornament takes the form of a pair of backward-looking, duck-like birds, one with its feet in the top corner of the field, the other standing upright with its feet on top of a developed plant motif. Tendrils emerge from the mouth of each duck and balance each other to form a similar motif in a horizontal position across the centre of the field. The birds have dot-and-circle eyes and similar motifs occur on their bodies above the front leg. The same pattern is repeated in all four fields with slight variations: one of the fields, however, is slightly damaged. At the apex of each lozenge-shaped field is a small engraved lozenge containing a dot-and-circle motif. The base of each gable is decorated: one with a series of stamped curved lines between two rows of punctuated dots, another with a row of dot-and-circle motifs between two rows of dots, the third with a dot-and-circle motif above a row of dots and the fourth with an inscription. The inscription reads:

⁜ᛒ Ο ᛑ ᚠ ᛁ ᛋ ᛘ ᛖ ᚿ ᛟ ᚠ ᚺ ᛏ

The last letter appears on the side of the animal head which sticks out at the angle.

157

The almost square base is arcaded and executed in openwork. The arcade is made up of round-headed arches, each with a slight rectilinear capital, the pillars stand on a broad rectangular base. The foot of the cover is splayed and there is a horizontal lug at each corner—the lugs are pierced vertically. The arcades are decorated with dots, dot-and-circle motifs, and curved lines. The base is decorated, above a line of punched curves, with a zig-zag motif made up of the same short curved lines with a dot-and-circle motif within each field thus created.   Height: 9·7 cm.

Reg. no. 1960, 7–1, 1. Purchased by K. J. Hewett, Esq., on behalf of the Museum, from Messrs. Sotheby and Co. From Pershore, Worcestershire.

BIBLIOGRAPHY
Gentleman's Magazine, xlix (1779), 536 and li (1780) 75 and 128.
Brassington, 108.
VCH Worcestershire, i, 233.
English Church History Exhibition, St. Albans, 1905, 3 and fig. 1.
Romilly Allen (1906).
Proceedings of the Society of Antiquaries of London, xxi (1906), 52–9.
Jackson (1911), i, 87–8 and figs. 118 and 119.
Brøndsted (1924), 264 and fig. 188.
Tonnochy (1932), 2.
Tonnochy (1937), 54.
Talbot Rice (1952), 232–3 and figs. 15 and 16.
Arbman (1958), 189–90.
Sotheby & Co., *Catalogue of Sale of June 17th* 1960, 8–9 and pl.

The account in *The Gentleman's Magazine*, 1779, records that it was 'found a few years ago in a mass of gravel in digging a cellar near the middle of the town of Pershore'. A note in the handwriting of its first owner, the Rev. Thomas Beale (filed as a *document* in the Department of British and Medieval Antiquities at the British Museum) records that it was discovered 'as far as is recollected between 1759 and 1769' (at this latter date Beale was curate at Pershore). It remained in the Beale family until it was purchased by the Museum on the death of Miss L. E. Lucas, a descendant of the original owner.

The inscription can be translated as 'Godric made me'.

Tenth century. See above, pp. 34, 44, 47, 53, 75, 79, 84, 88 and pl. XXVII.

57. Gold finger-ring. On either side of a hoop of circular cross-section is a round disc. Three globules are soldered to the ring at the joint between hoop and disc; and two smaller globules are interspaced with each group. Engraved on one roundel are three overlapping and interlaced triangles, each double contoured. On the other roundel is a small, centrally placed, equal-armed cross and the lines which make up its outline are extended into a symmetrical, interlacing, scroll pattern. The edges of each roundel are engraved with a zig-zag line. The outer face of the hoop is decorated with linear interlace (fig. 26). The ornament is inlaid with niello.

FIG. 26. Ornament from shoulder of no. 57. $\frac{2}{1}$

Diameter: 2·7 cm.

Reg. no. 55, 11–15, 1. *Ring Cat.* No. 202. Purchased from P. and W. Garrat. From Peterborough, Northamptonshire: from the River Nene.

BIBLIOGRAPHY
Archaeological Journal, xiii, 87 and fig.
Waterton (1862), 326–7 and fig. 1.
British Museum, Alfred the Great Millenary Exhibition, London 1901, 15.
Smith (1908), 72–3 and pl. xiii, 6.
B.M. Ring Cat. 33 f. and pl. ii, 202.
BMASG, 116 and fig. 147.
VCH Northamptonshire, i, 253.
Oman (1931), 105 and fig. B. 20.

Found while spearing for eel in the River Nene immediately under the Great Northern Railway viaduct, about 300 metres above the site of the ancient bridge. The vendors were Peterborough jewellers but the provenance is confirmed by a letter, from an interested Peterborough antiquary to Sir Augustus Franks, in the Department of British and Medieval Antiquities. The object is usually known as the River Nene ring.

See above, p. 56 and pl. XXVII.

58. Bronze mount of sub-triangular shape; the base line is straight and the two long sides have a slight curve towards the base. At the apex is a circular lug with a central rivet-hole. Two more rivet-holes have been bored, after casting, through the mount just above the base line. A plain plate, a little less wide than the length of the base line, projects at right-angles to the base. The mount is generally convex and has slightly sloping edges. In the field is an interlaced animal, seen from above, with its head at the apex, its two ears are comma-shaped and the snout is faceted. One front leg curves away gracefully from a spiral hip just behind the head and thence bends at right angles, to form a curled paw above the right-hand ear of the animal. The other front leg extends straight down into the right-hand corner. The body turns so that the hindquarters are within a loop formed by the body. The back legs interlace with the body of the animal, while the tail, with its curled terminal, emerges to balance the front leg on the opposite side of the head. The whole ornament is cast in low relief. The underside is plain and concave.
Length: 5·2 cm.

FIG. 27. Section through no. 58. ¼

Reg. no. 62, 3–21, 6. Given by Sir Augustus W. Franks, K.C.B. From Peterborough.

BIBLIOGRAPHY
Kendrick (1949), 116.

Moe (1955), 17 and fig. 15b.
Wilson (1961), and pl. XXXVIII, *a*.

Found on the site of 'the singing schools'.

Ninth century. See above, pp. 48, 51, 58 and pl. XXVII.

59. Silver-gilt spoon. The bowl is much fractured, but was originally pear-shaped: it is undecorated. The handle is composed of two elements, an elongated lentoid panel and a twisted rectangular rod. The lentoid panel contains a spiral scroll ornament, which has leaves between the spirals in the broad portion of the panel and in the centre of three of the spirals a frond-like terminal: the background was originally inlaid with niello. Towards the terminal the scroll degenerates into an interlace pattern. The field of ornament stands proud above the border, which is decorated with a beaded ornament in relief. At one end of the panel an animal head in relief joins the bowl of the spoon. The animal has lentoid eyes and a median, beaded line between the lobes of the forehead. At the other end of the lentoid panel is a square field containing four hollow squares. Beyond this field emerges a twisted bar, originally of rectangular cross-section—there is a beaded line on each face. The rod terminates in a small, collared beak-head with round eyes set in lentoid sockets. The back of the bowl and the lentoid field are plain, save for a pair of shallow steps behind the animal head. Length: 22·0 cm.

Reg. no. 1931, 12–15, 1. Given by H.M. Commissioners of Works. From Pevensey Castle, Sussex.

BIBLIOGRAPHY
Simms (1932).
Nørland (1935), 122 and fig. 3.

Ward Perkins (1939), 313 and 314.
How (1952), 28 and pl. 3.

Found during excavation and repair at Pevensey Castle, in a pit under the stairs at the entrance to the keep.

Eleventh century. See above, pp. 60, 61 and pl. XXVII.

60. Bronze-gilt disc brooch. The brooch is dished: within the border of laterally touching scalloped tongues is an openwork design of an interlaced animal. The body and the neck of the animal are represented by a thick band of contiguous plain and beaded lines. The

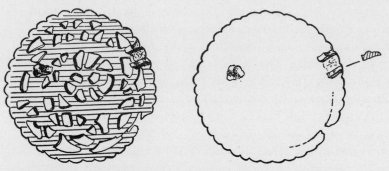

FIG. 28. Back view and fastening mechanism of no. 60.

head of the animal is rather amorphous but can be seen, with its almond-shaped protruding eye, at the top of the brooch. The body forms a heart-shaped loop and one leg emerges from a spiral hip at the bottom-left of the brooch and produces a three-claw foot. The hind leg is more formalised, springing from a spiral hip to terminate in a scroll, it produces a further scroll just below the knee. Interlacing with the animal is a snake with a head. Seen from above it has prominent eyes and the mouth bites the neck of the main animal; it terminates in a double-scroll (top-left). The remains of a broken catch-plate and hinge occur on an otherwise plain back. Diameter: 3·9 cm.

Lent by Miss Dudham, 1931. Found at Pitney, Somerset.

BIBLIOGRAPHY
Brøndsted (1924), 145 and fig. 120.
VCH Somersetshire, i, 380 and coloured plate.

Shetelig (1941), iv, 57 and fig. 24.
Kendrick (1949), 116–17 and pl. lxxxii.
Moe (1955), 17.

Found in the churchyard at Pitney.

Eleventh century. See above, pp. 3, 48, 51, 52 and pl. XXVIII.

61. Gold finger-ring consisting of a plain band divided on the outer surface into eight panels, each decorated with a carved motif. The worn outer edges of the ring show traces of a beading. Field 1 (the fields are numbered according to the drawing, fig. 29) contains a fleshy, balanced leaf motif growing out of a central lentoid feature, very much like a potted plant on its side. The two leaves which droop down on either side bear pairs of

FIG. 29. Ornament of no. 61: the fields are numbered from the left. $\frac{1}{1}$

nicks. Field 2 contains a related motif, save only that the leaves have stems, which interlace as they rise from a wedge-shaped trunk. The two leaves on either side of the trunk are lobed, those to the right of the field are made up of three elements and are nicked. Field 3 contains an octofoil, the four leaves in the corners of the field having pointed terminals, while those in the centre top and bottom of the field are bi-lobate. Field 4 contains a quadruped with its head in the top right-hand corner. The mouth is indicated by an incised line and a leaf protrudes from it below the lower jaw. The ear is extended into a lobed and doubly nicked billet which runs across the field. The body has two nicks on its back and a curved incised line occurs over the front hip. The front leg extends backwards and takes a nicked, floriate form. Field 5 contains a similar motif to that of field 2. Field 6 contains an interlaced-knot motif with the four ends of the ribbon in each corner of the field; between each pair of terminals and parallel with the central knot is a lentoid motif. Field 7 is very similar to field 3, save that it has less definition. Field 8, has an animal head in the bottom right-hand corner, the snout is squared, the mouth is slightly opened and there is no ear. The animal degenerates into a muddle of vegetable interlace. The divisions between each field are plain. The interior of the hoop is undecorated.   Diameter: 2·2 cm.

Reg. no. 1955, 12–1, 1. Purchased from Mrs. A. Deeks. From Poslingford, Suffolk.

BIBLIOGRAPHY
Wilson (1956b).   Wilson (1960a), 143 and fig. 34.

Found in 1955 in the garden of No. 4 Council Houses, Poslingford, and purchased from the finder.

Ninth century. See above, pp. 27, 33, 56 and pl. XXVIII.

62. Gilt bronze tweezers. The legs of the tweezers are made of strips of bronze; on each face is a long panel, containing a carved interlace pattern, above a pair of double scrolls and a plain chamfered roundel ended terminal. Each leg has an exactly similar design. At the top of the legs is a cylindrical knop with four circular collared settings, interspaced with billets. The knop has a hollowed top with central boring, which may have carried a handle.   Length: 10·8 cm.

Reg. no. Sl. 396. Purchased with the Sloane Collection. From Reculver, Kent.

Eighth/ninth century. See above, pp. 1, 10, 13, 64 and pl. XXVIII.

63. Silver-gilt, cast strap-distributor of trefoil shape. In the centre is a triangular field which contains an ornament of five small cast granules above five leaf-like features. Each of the arms has a field which contains five cast granules on top of a number of displayed leaves, one of which develops into a mask towards the terminal. The mask is seen from the front and has two raised eyes separated by a nose and curved eyebrows; striations cross the head above the mask. There is no mouth and the chin is produced to form part of the scrolled frame of the panel. The frame has the shape of a formalised animal head. At the

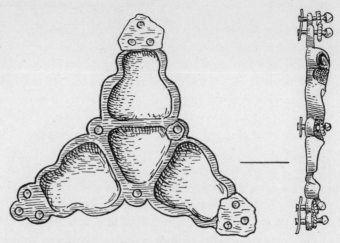

FIG. 30.   Back and side view of no. 63. $\frac{1}{1}$

terminal of each arm were a series of three dome-headed rivets each with a collar of beaded wire: on one of the terminals only two rivets and one collar survive. A similar, collared rivet pierces the loop at the angle of each arm, one rivet and its collar are now missing. The rivets at the terminals are hammered over underneath on to an irregularly shaped small plate, two of which survive at the terminals, a washer survives in the angle of two of the arms. Modern beeswax holds the rivets in position at two of the terminals. The back is hollow cast and quite plain, save for ridges which form a triangle at the centre (fig. 30).   Maximum overall length: 5·3 cm.

Reg. no. 47, 2–7, 1. Given by Henry Farrer, Esq. From Rome, Italy.

BIBLIOGRAPHY
BMASG, 156.   Haseloff (1950), 173–4 and pl. xx, d.

The donor was a picture dealer and restorer of 15 Wardour Street, London; he obtained the object in Rome. The register gives its provenance as from a hoard of tenth-century coins found in Rome. In *BMASG*, Reginald Smith, a most careful scholar, says that it was found with coins of Offa. By an unfortunate coincidence two Anglo-Saxon hoards, one of early ninth-century date (which contained coins of Offa) and one of tenth-century date, were found in Rome before 1847 (the date of acquisition). At this time the Departments of Coins and Medals and Antiquities were administered by the same Keeper and it is perhaps significant that at that time the tenth-century hoard was particularly well-known to the numismatists in the British Museum, for they had purchased many coins from this hoard from another dealer. An Anglo-Saxon coin which may have come from the ninth-century hoard was exhibited at the Numismatic Society in London in 1843 together with a denier of Pippin. Both were said to have come from Rome,[1] and tie in very well with the description of the ninth-century hoard.[2] But the fact that the hoard was not mentioned in print until 1849 need not exclude the possibility that the hoard was known in England in 1847.[3]

A third find of Anglo-Saxon coins was also made before 1847. This was an eleventh-century accumulation of offering coins (from the church of St. Paul-without-the-Walls), but this hoard was not published until 1849.[4] When Reginald Smith wrote *BMASG* in 1923, the tenth-century hoard had been forgotten: in fact it had already been forgotten forty years earlier when Kearey[5] failed to mention it in his discussion of another tenth-century find from the Forum. The first tenth-century Rome hoard was not mentioned in print until 1955.[6] It is possible that Reginald Smith had some source which has escaped the attention of subsequent scholars. On the other hand when Smith wrote *BMASG* no Rome hoard of tenth-century date, with the exception of the Forum hoard, was known to anyone. On the other hand only two other Rome hoards were known of which one, which was not *sensu strictu* a hoard but an accumulation of offerings, was far too late to fall in with his chronological ideas. Smith, therefore, naturally, assigned this object to the ninth-century hoard, which was known from San Quintino's publication. If the vendor's provenance is accepted there seems little reason to doubt the original statement of the register, which associated the object with the tenth-century hoard.

Eighth/tenth century. See above, pp. 10, 16, 62 and pl. XXVIII.

64. Silver coin brooch. An imitative coin of Edward the Elder is surrounded by a collar consisting of a ribbon of silver denticulated at top and bottom. This is flush with the coin on the reverse and stands up above the level of the face of the coin on the obverse. Below this, and flush with the reverse of the coin, is a series of four concentric bands of beaded wire. On the back of the brooch, on the border, is a catch-plate, hinge and pin. The catch-plate and hinge-plate are made of strips of longitudinally moulded silver.

Both inscriptions of the imitative coin are retrograde:

obv: +EADVVEARDREX
rev: FRAMVVISH—.

Diameter: 3·5 cm.

Reg. no. 1951, 2–6, 1. Purchased from Messrs. Spink & Son. From Rome, Italy.

BIBLIOGRAPHY
British Numismatic Journal, xxvi, (1950), 234
and pl. B.   Bruce-Mitford (1956a), 200.

Found at the Villa Wolkonsky in Rome. The attribution of this brooch to a hoard of Anglo-Saxon coins found in Rome can probably be dismissed on the basis of confidential evidence documented in the Department of British and Medieval Antiquities. At the same time the brooch is compatible with the Rome hoard dispersed in 1929/30, which is dated to 927.

Circa. 920. *See above*, pp. 8, 36, 52 and pl. XXVIII.

65. Silver and iron sword pommel. A silver band, inlaid with gold plates and niello, surrounds the remains of an iron core (fig. 31). Seen from above the band has a pointed oval

---

[1] *Proceedings of the Numismatic Society*, May 25, 1843, 104.
[2] San Quintino (1849), 7.
[3] A parcel of coins including coins of Offa, Coenwulf and Pippin, which seem to be part of this hoard were sold in Rome in 1879. *1° Catalogo*

del Museo Bartolomeo Borghesi (sold by R. Dura, 10 December 1879), 131–2.
[4] San Quintino (1849).
[5] Keary, (1884).
[6] Dolley and Strudwick (1955), 32.

outline and slopes and curves slightly outwards from top to bottom. In the centre of each side are three T-shaped panels inlaid with gold plates and interlocking with each other. They are separated from triangular, gold-inlaid fields by plain nielloed fields which follow the contours of their neighbours precisely. The final field at each end is in the form of an

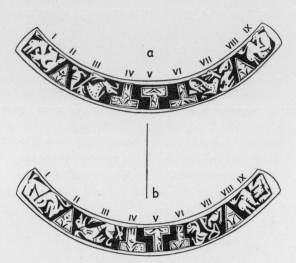

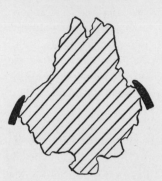

FIG. 31. Section through no. 65. $\frac{1}{1}$

FIG. 32. Ornament of no. 65. $\frac{1}{1}$

inverted truncated triangle. This arrangement of fields is repeated on both sides of the band, the ends being left plain.

Description of the ornament in the panels, from left to right (fig. 32):

Side *a* (i): In this field which is shaped as an inverted truncated triangle, is an animal with its head in the bottom left-hand corner, with a dot for an eye. The body rises from the head to the top of the field and crosses thence to the bottom right-hand corner, where it forms a hip and a short leg and tail. Another animal, with its head below the chin of the first animal, crouches upside down, the neck crossing the body of the first animal. The animal has an open mouth, a trailing ear and a dot for an eye. The background is nielloed.

(ii): This triangular field is filled with a gold plate. The decoration consists of a hollow triangle joined to two feet-like features at the base of the field. Traces of speckling survive.

(iii): In this field is an animal with an inverted head in the top right-hand corner of the field. The head has a bump over the eye and an open mouth. The lower jaw forms a hook. The animal is collared and the front leg rises up to the head. The body then crosses to the top-left, whence a shaped hip, decorated with a double nick, produces a bent leg. A stubby tail occurs in the top right-hand corner. The hind-leg forms an inverted animal head with a dotted eye, while another animal head springs from the neck of the main animal and bites across the body of the main animal with elongated jaws. The body of the main animal is speckled. The background was filled with niello of which much remains.

(iv): In to each arm of this gold-filled inverted T-shaped field an animal head emerges

164

from a triangular central element. Each animal had an open mouth and dotted eye. The topmost animal has an incised triangular ear. Traces of speckling remain on the ornament.

(v): This T-shaped field is filled with gold and surrounded by a nielloed, linear border. In the cross-piece of the T are backward-turned animal heads with pointed muzzles: their lower jaws join. In the shaft of the T is a feature shaped like one of the animal heads in the arms, but with no zoomorphic characteristics. The ornament is speckled.

(vi): In the cross-piece of this T-shaped field are two animal heads, one inverted and one which emerges from an angular, foliate-like body which fills the shaft of the T. Between the two animal heads is a triangle with notched base-line. The animal to the left has a squared snout, open mouth, pronounced forehead and no eye. The top of the animal head to the right is angular, fitting into the corner of the field, the snout is pointed and the mouth open. The ornament is speckled all over.

(vii): The ornament in this field (one end of which interlocks with the inverted T of the field *vi*, the other end of which slopes parallel with the side of triangular field viii) is muddled. In the top left-hand corner is an animal head which is bent back beneath the neck which runs down to the centre left of the field. The head is slightly curved and has an eye and an open elongated mouth. The lower jaw turns back to form a triangular leaf. Below the head is the paw which runs into the body in the centre of the field. The body terminates, in the top right-hand corner of the field, in what appears to be a hip with a leaf-like leg and foot. Crossing and cutting the body is a neck with a head at either end. The uppermost head has a billet-shaped ear, an open mouth, a bump over the eye and a square snout. The tongue of this head crosses the neck of the first animal and enters its mouth across the snout. The neck, which emerges from this head, passes under the leg of the first animal and joins the top of another head which has a thin snout, an open mouth, an eye and an upward curled neck.

(viii): This field is similar in design to field *a* (ii) save that the triangle is not hollow.

(ix): This field, which is shaped like an inverted truncated triangle, is much worn. It has an animal head with a beaded eye and open mouth in the bottom right-hand corner. The body rises to the centre of the field and has an indeterminate leg in the top right-hand corner. Another animal head crosses the body in the centre of the field but the details of the ornament are unclear.

Side *b* (i): In the field, which is shaped as a truncated, inverted triangle, is an animal with its head in the bottom right-hand corner and a foot with a three-element paw, above the head: the leg is nicked. Traces of niello remain at the bottom-right, but the rest of the field is much worn and the hind-quarters of the animal are barely distinguishable.

(ii): Triangular field inlaid with gold, engraved with a design (now rather worn) which is similar to that in field *a* (ii).

(iii): This field is of the same shape as field *a* (iii) and contains an animal with a head looking up and backwards into the top left-hand corner. The head has a round eye and an elongated snout with a nick below the forehead. The neck is collared with a double incised line. The fore-leg curves into the bottom left-hand corner and the body passes up into the top right-hand corner, where a hip and a bent leg are produced. Double nicks occur in various parts of the body. A collared animal head, with open mouth and dotted eye occurs below the belly of the main animal and appears to grow out of the front hip. Another head with flowing ear and tiny dotted eye occurs in the top right-hand corner. The field is nielloed.

(iv): This field is similar in outline to field *a* (iv). The gold plate contains a debased animal head in the shaft of the inverted T, in each of the arms is a ragged foot-like motif. Traces of speckling can be seen.

(v): Similar in outline to field *a* (v). In the shaft of the T is an animal head with open mouth and round eye which joins with two beak-like animal heads in the arms of the T. Traces of speckling are visible.

(vi): Similar in outline to field *a* (vi). The gold plate being engraved with an animal head in the shaft of the T, two leaves appearing in the cross-stroke. Traces of speckling can be seen.

(vii): Similar in outline to field *a* (vii). In the top left-hand corner is an animal head with a pointed snout and open mouth. The eye is detached from the top of the head and is attached to the neck by means of a string-like feature. The ear is produced to cross the body and finishes in a double knot in the bottom right-hand corner. The legs emerge from double nicked hips in the bottom-left and top right-hand corners. The field is nielloed.

(viii): This is a triangular field inlaid with gold containing three leaves, one large and lozenge-shaped, and two small triangular shaped; the former is embellished with a double nick.

(ix): Similar in outline to field *a* (ix) this one contains two animals of which one is inverted with its head in the bottom left-hand corner, while the other can be seen below the belly of the larger animal. The smaller animal is backward-looking and rather worn and is in a crouching position. The larger animal has a front leg in the top right-hand corner, while the rest of the body tails away above the smaller animal. The mouths of both animals are open and both have round eyes. The background is inlaid with niello.

Length: 6·6 cm.

Reg. no. 1944, 3–1, 1. Purchased from H. S. Tomlinson, Esq. From Scales Moor, Ingleton, Yorks.

BIBLIOGRAPHY
Bruce-Mitford (1952*a*), 74–5 and pl. xxxiii, d.   Wilson and Blunt (1961), 105.
Bruce-Mitford(1956*a*), 171, 181, 192 and pl. xxx, d.

The pommel was found by the vendor on 15 January 1944, at the foot of Scales Moor, near Ingleton, Yorkshire, near to Dale House Farm and Beezly Falls.

Ninth century. See above, pp. 3, 25, 27, 31, 32, 63 and pl. xxix.

66. Silver sword pommel mount, inlaid with a gold plate embellished with filigree. The pommel is cast and of trilobate form with a curved base. It is very worn. There is a narrow opening at the bottom of the mount which extends along most of its length and presumably to the top of the interior. The decoration of the piece is similar on either face. The curved border at the bottom is fairly broad and is decorated with an incised zig-zag line with a small punch mark at each angle; there are traces of speckling along the upper edge of the border on one side. The central lobe is tall, has a slightly convex side and a top crowned by a deckle-edged cap. An arched long panel on each side, in the centre of the lobe, has been cut away and a gold panel inserted. This panel consists of a gold sheet, larger than the aperture, placed in position from the underside. The surface of the sheet is decorated with gold filigree which consists of tape-like strips of gold each of which is roughly serrated, one of the serrated edges being soldered to the base-plate. Certain slight cuts across the tape, as though joining the individual serrations on either edge, are puzzling and irregular features of the filigree. Within a filigree border are a series of double scrolls interlocking with *occuli*-like scrolls. Two of the filigree scrolls of one plate have been broken in antiquity, while the plates themselves have been replaced with glue in modern times. The panels are bordered by incised lines which were originally inlaid with niello, of which a little remains on one face. The vertical borders continue above the arched part of the border to stop at the cap at the top of the lobe. Traces remain of a further dotted border outside this line, while, within the area between the cap and the top of the arch, a further series of dots followed the bordering lines.

On either side of the central lobe on both sides of the mount is a long panel, originally inlaid with niello, containing a fleshy leaf motif. Two nicks cut across one of the lobes of a leaf in one panel. Below these panels rivet-holes pierce the mount from side to side. The tips of the mount form animal heads, which are moulded in low relief on the two faces. Certain features of these heads are indicated by incised lines, one-half of each head appears on either face of the mount, the ears rise slightly above the normal level of the casting; they are short and stubby and too worn to show any features. Each eye is set in a deeply incised socket, has a pointed-oval shape and a central bored pupil. The mouth is wide open and lies along the border, the teeth are indicated by scratched lines and the incised, nielloed upper lines of the lip form a spiral terminal with an elongated pointed nielloed field continuing above it. The line of the lip is bordered on either side by a line of punched dots and a similar bordering line continues round the lower jaw, beneath the eye and between the ears. Various indeterminate incisions on the snout would indicate that this area was panelled, but they are so worn that they cannot be interpreted.

Length: 6·9 cm.

Reg. no. 62, 7–28, 1. Purchased from George Eastwood. Found in the River Seine.[1]

BIBLIOGRAPHY
Evans (1887), 535.
BMASG, 152 and fig. 205.
Wilson (1960c), 24.
Dunning and Evison (1961), 153.
Wilson and Blunt (1961), 153 and pl. xlv, b.

Ninth/tenth century. See above, pp. 40, 64 and pl. XXIX.

67. Silver double spoon and spatula; at one end is a flat, pear-shaped plate and at the other an oval plate with a hollowed centre. Between these terminals are long thin bars which join at a central, circular disc. Where the bars join the terminal plates and the central disc are four shaped raised billets. The raised billet above the hollowed plate bears the scratched representation of a human face with down-curved mouth, punched eyes and a

[1] 'Paris' has been added in the register at a later date by the same hand (Franks's).

continuous line, which forms the eyebrows, eye-socket and the nose. The next billet towards the centre represents an animal head seen from above, the ears of which have been faceted and nicked and the nostrils indicated by a scratched line. The eyes are shaped as inverted pears. The next billet is blank, while the one above the pear-shaped plate is scratched with four curved lines, opposed in pairs to indicate an animal head seen from above. The bowl of the 'spoon' is decorated with a scratched interlaced pattern; the tip of the bowl is missing. The two bars are decorated, within fields defined by a simple longitudinally scratched border, with an irregular interlace pattern. In the central disc is a further scratched pattern (which might have been intended as a formal acanthus pattern) within a plain scratched border. The back of the object is plain.

Length: 21·2 cm.

Reg. no. 88, 7–19, 98: Purchased through Messrs. Rollin and Feuardent at the Londesborough Sale. From Sevington, Wiltshire.

BIBLIOGRAPHY
Hawkins (1838), 305–5 and pl. 24.
Fairholt (1857), pl. 18, 1.
Jackson (1893), 117.
Jackson (1911), ii, 480 and fig. 571.
BMASG, 106 and fig. 130.
Leclerq (1930), 2403–4 and fig. 7191, 6.
Ward Perkins (1939), 314 f. and pl. 63.
How and How (1952) 18 and pl. 3.
Himsworth (1953), 44 and fig. 13, 4.
Thompson (1956), 122–2.

Found with nearly seventy coins and other objects listed below (nos. 68–79), in January 1834 at Sevington, on a farm occupied by a Mrs. Gough. The hoard was found in the middle of a meadow by some labourers and was possibly enclosed in a box. The objects appear to have passed through the hands of C. W. Loscombe, Esq., of Pickwick House, Corsham. Loscombe's collection was sold in 1854 and the objects from the Sevington hoard were bought by Lord Londesborough. At the Londesborough sale they were purchased by Messrs. Rollin and Feuardent for the British Museum. The hoard is dated *c.* 850.[1]

Before 850. See above, pp. 17, 42, 61 and pl. XXIX.

68. Silver fork and spatula; at one end is the surviving prong of a two-pronged fork, at the other is a pear-shaped spatula-like plate. Between these terminals are two bars, which join a central, truncated lozenge shaped plate. Raised billets, at the points where the bars join the central plate and the terminals, have been roughly faceted to represent animals' heads. The bars have a scratched border; further scratches on the raised billets indicate the ears and snouts of the animals. On the billet above the fork the scratches representing the ears occur. The back of the object is undecorated. The object has been broken into two across the central lozenge. Length: 19·9 cm.

Reg. no. 88, 7–19, 99. Purchased through Messrs. Rollin and Feuardent at the Londesborough Sale. From Sevington, Wiltshire.

BIBLIOGRAPHY
Hawkins (1838), 303–5 and pl. 24.
Fairholt (1857), pl. 18, 2.
British Museum, *Alfred the Great Millenary Exhibition*, London 1901, 18.
Jackson (1911), ii, 537, and fig. 736.
BMASG, 106 and fig. 130.
Leclerq (1930), 2403–4 and fig. 7191, 6.
Himsworth (1953), 44 and fig. 13, 4.

[1] Dolley and Skaare (1961), 64.

Found with nos. 67 and 69–79. For details of find, etc., see entry for no. 67.

Before 850. See above, pp. 17, 61 and pl. XXIX.

69. Bronze-gilt fragment. The object, which is made of thin sheet bronze, has a rounded end and a curved cross-section. The convex surface is decorated with a series of long lentoid fields, each containing pear-shaped ornament. The fields form a triangle on the main surviving part of the object, but traces show that the design continued over the whole object. The gilt has worn away over much of the surface: it can only be seen in the engraved lines of the pattern. The back is plain and the whole object is much cracked and torn. The upper edge is broken away.   Length: 4·3 cm.

Reg. no. 88, 7–19, 161. Purchased through Messrs. Rollin and Feuardent at the Londesborough Sale. From Sevington, Wiltshire.

BIBLIOGRAPHY
Hawkins (1838), 303 and pl. 24.

Found with nos. 67, 68 and 70–9. For details of find, etc., see entry for no. 69.

Before 850. See above, pp. 10, 16, 17, 65 and pl. XXIX.

70. Bronze-gilt disc. The disc is fragmentary and the gilt has worn off the broad, plain border. In the centre is a rivet-hole surrounded by a plain field and an engraved line: outside this central panel are four double C-shaped loops with the backs of their curve meeting the edge of the central field. The back of the disc is plain.

Maximum surviving width: 2·7 cm.

Reg. no. 88, 7–19, 162. Purchased through Messrs. Rollin and Feuardent at the Londesborough Sale. From Sevington, Wiltshire.

BIBLIOGRAPHY
Hawkins (1838), 303 and pl. 24.

Found with nos. 67–9 and 71–9. For details of find, etc., see entry for no. 67.

Before 850. See above, pp. 10, 16, 52, 65 and pl. XXIX.

71. Bronze strap-end. The split end is scalloped and two rivets survive with a pendant triangle in a segmental field between them. At the terminal is a faceted animal head with scratched snout and a scratched triangle on the forehead. The ears take the form of a double chevron within an oval. In the centre of the strap-end, between beaded curved sides is an irregular and clumsy interlace pattern. The object appears to be badly worn and has been over-cleaned, so that the decoration is not immediately clear. The back is plain.   Length: 4·0 cm.

Reg. no. 88, 7–19, 163. Purchased through Messrs. Rollin and Feuardent at the Londesborough Sale. From Sevington, Wiltshire.

BIBLIOGRAPHY
Hawkins (1838), 303 and pl. 24.

BMASG, 106.
Wilson and Blunt (1961), 121.

Found with nos. 67–70 and 72–9. For details of find, etc., see entry for no. 67.

Before 850. See above, pp. 26, 28, 62, 63 and pl. xxx.

72. Bronze blank for strap-end. The blank has a roughly shaped animal-head terminal (which stands proud) and a double scalloped and pierced split end. The sides are slightly curved but the object is otherwise featureless.   Length: 4·9 cm.

Reg. no. 88, 7–19, 164. Purchased from Messrs. Rollin and Feuardent at the Londesborough Sale. From Sevington, Wiltshire.

BIBLIOGRAPHY   *BMASG*, 106.
Hawkins (1838), 303 and pl. 24.   Wilson and Blunt (1961), 121.

Found with nos. 67–71 and 73–9. For details of find, etc., see entry for no. 67.

Before 850. See above, pp. 28, 62, 63 and pl. xxx.

73. Silver blank for strap-end with a roughly shaped and faceted animal head at the terminal. The split end has been cut. The sides are of curved outline but the object is otherwise plain and undecorated.   Length: 4·5 cm.

Reg. no. 88, 7–19, 165. Purchased through Messrs. Rollin and Feuardent at the Londesborough Sale. From Sevington, Wiltshire.

BIBLIOGRAPHY   *BMASG*, 106.
Hawkins (1838), 303 and pl. 24.   Wilson and Blunt (1961), 121.

Found with nos. 67–72 and 74–9. For details of find, etc., see entry for no. 67.

Before 850. See above, pp. 28, 62, 63 and pl. xxx.

74. Silver blank for strap-end, with a roughly shaped faceted animal head at the terminal. The sides are of curved outline but the object is otherwise featureless.   Length: 4·2 cm.

Reg. no. 88, 7–19, 166. Purchased through Messrs. Rollin and Feuardent at the Londesborough Sale. From Sevington, Wiltshire.

BIBLIOGRAPHY   *BMASG*, 106.
Hawkins (1838), 303 and pl. 24.   Wilson and Blunt (1961), 121.

Found with nos. 67–73 and 75–9. For details of find, etc., see entry for no. 67.

Before 850. See above, pp. 28, 62, 63 and pl. xxx.

75. Fragment of bronze blank for strap-end. The fragment has been broken away at the terminal but the double scalloped and pierced split end remains. It is undecorated.
                                                    Length: 3·5 cm.

Reg. no. 88, 7–19, 167. Purchased through Messrs. Rollin and Feuardent at the Londesborough Sale. From Sevington, Wiltshire.

BIBLIOGRAPHY   *BMASG*, 106.
Hawkins (1838), 303.   Wilson and Blunt (1961), 121.

Found with nos. 67–74 and 76–9. For details of find, etc., see entry for no. 67.

Before 850. See above, pp. 28, 62 and pl. xxx.

76. Bronze ingot. Plain bronze ingot with split end and curved sides.   Length: 2·9 cm.

Reg. no. 88, 7–19, 168. Purchased through Messrs. Rollin and Feuardent at the Londesborough Sale. From Sevington, Wiltshire.

BIBLIOGRAPHY   *BMASG*, 106.
Hawkins (1838), 303.

Found with nos. 67–75 and 77–9. For details of find, etc., see entry for no. 67.

Before 850. See above, pp. 28, 62, 63 and pl. xxx.

77. Fragment of bronze blank for strap-end. The fragment, which is completely plain, has been bent and broken at its split end, part of which remains.   Length: 3·2 cm.

Reg. no. 88, 7–19, 169. Purchased through Messrs. Rollin and Feuardent at the Londesborough Sale. From Sevington, Wiltshire.

BIBLIOGRAPHY   *BMASG*, 106.
Hawkins (1838), 303.   Wilson and Blunt (1961), 121.

Found with nos. 67–76, 78 and 79. For details of find, etc., see entry for no. 67.

Before 850. See above, pp. 28, 62, 63 and pl. xxx.

78. Fragment of the split end of a silver blank for a strap-end. Plain and undecorated on either side. One of the leaves of the split end has broken away.   Length: 2·0 cm.

Reg. no. 88, 7–19, 170. Purchased through Messrs. Rollin and Feuardent at the Londesborough Sale. From Sevington, Wiltshire.

BIBLIOGRAPHY   *BMASG*, 106.
Hawkins (1838), 303 and pl. 24.   Wilson and Blunt (1961), 121.

Found with nos. 67–77 and 79. For details of find, etc., see entry for no. 67.

Before 850. See above, pp. 28, 62, 63.

79. Bronze buckle plate. The object consists of a single sheet of metal folded double. At the fold the sheet has been cut away to allow for the loop. The back of the plate expands gradually from this point, the rest forms the rectangular face of the buckle plate. It is decorated with a double incised linear border, embellished throughout its length with triangular punch marks which give each line a serrated edge. The plate is pierced twice for rivets to attach it to the belt, one of these, with a slightly domed head remains. A third circular hole in the centre of the reduced portion presumably carried the tongue of the buckle. These holes cut through the decoration. The back of the object is plain.

Length: 1·7 cm.

Reg. no. 88, 7–19, 171. Purchased through Messrs. Rollin and Feuardent, at the Londesborough Sale. From Sevington, Wiltshire.

Found with nos. 67–78. For details of find, etc., see entry for no. 67.

Before 850. See above, p. 53 and pl. xxx.

80. Iron scramasax, inlaid with copper, bronze, silver and niello. The cutting edge is straight and the straight back rises slightly from the tang to form an angle 11·5 cm. from the tip; from this point the back of the blade breaks away at an angle to form the tip. The tang is offset from the blade and decreases in width towards the, now rounded, tip. Above a median bar of ornament on one face are a series of inlaid panels. The bar is made up of a mosaic of rectangular plates of silver and copper and of lengths of twisted silver

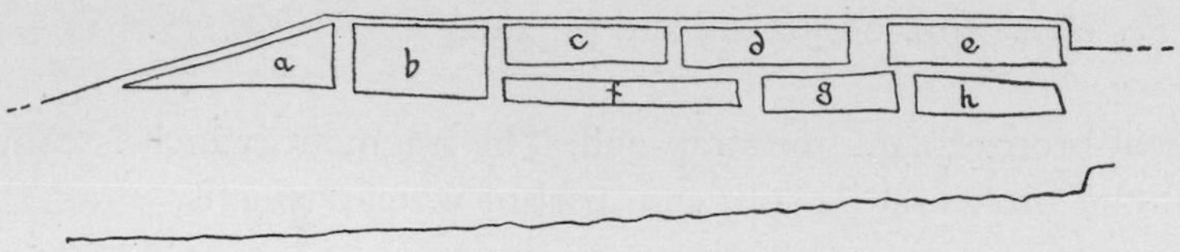

FIG. 33. Numeration of fields of no. 80.

and bronze wire to form a chequered pattern, which develops into a herring-bone design towards the tip. Below the bar are pendant triangles of silver. The area above the bar is divided up into fields (which are labelled in fig. 33) inlaid with nielloed silver and plain bronze plaques, two of which (*c* and *e*) are missing. Field *a* is triangular and contains a winged animal with its head in the top right-hand corner; it has a lemon-shaped eye and open mouth with emergent tongue; one foot is in the right-hand bottom corner and the other is in the centre of the field. The wing terminates in an acanthus frond, a series of nicks decorate its body, there are double nicks at its contours. In field *b* is a symmetrical plant motif with rather lush acanthus leaves (of which those in the centre are veined). In field *d* is a wavy, scroll motif with pointed leaves decorated with double nicks on their edges. In field *f* is inscribed: Σ. ⊑EBEREHT. In field *g* is inscribed MEĀH, this field is the only one not executed in silver and niello, it is of bronze and was apparently not nielloed. In field *h* (which is much worn) is a degenerate, animal motif; the body consists of a wavy line not dissimilar to the stem of the scroll in field *d*. The body has a series of double nicks and is double contoured in one place. The limbs are replaced by a ribbon ornament and the details of the head have been worn away. Each of these fields is separated from the next by a vertical inlaid strip of twisted silver and copper wire.

The other face bears a similar bar in the centre of the blade, save that the chequer pattern of silver and bronze plates is more regular and is split longitudinally by a band of twisted silver and copper wire. Another bar of similar pattern, without the pendant triangles, is inlaid below the back of the blade between the tang and the angle. The bar is formed of a chequer pattern of silver and bronze plates and twisted silver and bronze wire, bordered by two strands of twisted silver and copper wire, which are produced beyond the angle to link the upper bar with the lower bar. Between the two bars is an inscription with the base of the letters towards the back of the blade:

+BIORHTELMMEƿ◇RTE

it is inlaid with silver. Along the back edge of the blade is a long panel (bordered by a band of twisted silver and copper wire) of alternating silver and copper plates, much of which is now missing. This extends to the angle of the back, beyond which point is the outline of a triangle of inlaid silver and copper wire with a median vertical line.

Length: 32·2 cm.

Reg. no. 81, 6–23, 1. Given by E. Lloyd, Esq. From Sittingbourne, Kent.

BIBLIOGRAPHY
Stephens (1866–1901), iii, 160.
Evans (1873), 331–4 and pl. xii.
Payne (1893), 111–12 and pl. xxiv.
VCH Kent, i, 382–3.
BMASG, 95 f. and fig. 116.
Brøndsted (1924), 129 and fig. 106.

Kendrick (1934), 398 and fig. 3, A & B.
Jessup (1930), 237 and fig. 33, top.
Leclerq (1930), 2403–4 and fig. 7191, 5.
Himsworth (1953), 42 and fig. 12.
Waterman (1953), 60.
Wilson (1960a), 112, 216 and pl. 26.

Found while digging the foundations of a house, belonging to the donor, near the *Daily Chronicle* paper mills at Sittingbourne (according to Jessup (1930)). The address of the donor was the *Daily Chronicle* Office, Fleet Street, and this would seem to bear out Mr. Jessup's contention.

The Inscriptions can be translated 'Geberht owns me'; 'Biorthelm made me'. The meaning of the initial letter S is unclear.

Ninth/tenth century. See above. pp. 25, 38–43, 60, 72, 75, 80, 85, 86, 87 and pl. xxx.

81. Iron one-edged knife. The back of the blade is straight, forming an angle about two-thirds of the way along its length, from this point the back of the blade breaks away to form the tip. The cutting edge is curved, sagging considerably between point and hilt. Of the hilt only the pointed tang remains, emerging from the centre-top of the heel of the blade. A concave groove runs below the back of the blade on either face. The groove on the lower face is inlaid with silver to form a running spiral pattern between which are regularly sprouting leaves. The groove on the front face of the blade bears a series of panels inlaid with silver. The panel nearest the tip has a squared and a pointed end; from the pointed end, which is split, emerges a frond with three symmetrically placed lobes. Within the field, at the squared end, a pair of double oblique lines rise from each corner to form a triangular field. The outer pair of lines separate and turn away to form spirals. Within the triangular field so formed are two irregular lozenges. The details of this pattern are reserved in iron against the background formed by the silver inlaid plate. The next panel to the right is rectangular and contains a double herring-bone pattern made up of alternating inlaid silver and plain iron elements, the whole surrounded by a plain silver border. The silver elements of the herring-bone pattern are made up of lozenges formed of crossed wires hammered into the surface. The central field is also rectangular but is damaged in the middle. It is surrounded by a plain inlaid silver border and divided by a saltire; a silver acanthus frond fills the triangular fields so formed. The next field is also rectangular and contains, within the plain border, a double row of lozenges, the tips of which touch each other and the border. The next field is also rectangular and contains a complicated scrolled leaf ornament developing out of, and enclosed by, a central lozenge. The borders of the long sides of these rectangular fields are continuous and are joined by an upright line beyond the last described field. The object is in fine condition.

Length: 26·6 cm.

Reg. no. 1933, 5–10, 1. Given by O. Raphael, Esq. From Southwark, Surrey.

BIBLIOGRAPHY
The Antiquaries Journal, xiv (1934), 61 and pl. xi.   [Ward-Perkins] (1940), 51.

Found in Deadmans Place (now Park Street), 'just inside the line of the park wall of Winchester House', in September 1930.

Ninth century. See above, pp. 27, 33, 34, 38, 57, 60 and pl. XXXI.

82. Silver strap-end. Pendant between the two rivet-holes at the split end are three leaves in a sub-triangular field. At the terminal is an animal-head, seen from above in low relief. The head has oval ears with lunate openings and there is a circle on the forehead and a triangle on the snout. A cross divides the centre of the field, the long arms of which split to give a sloping side to each of the fields between them. The cross and its branches are beaded, as was originally the border of the field. Behind the head is a triangular field containing two leaves, while in each of the four fields between the arms of the cross is a degenerate animal motif, which has taken on foliate characteristics. The ornament is unclear owing to the worn and corroded condition of the surface. The back is plain and undecorated. The metal is very base.   Length: 5·0 cm.

Reg. no. 79, 12–22, 1. Given by Professor Arthur H. Church. From Stratton, near Cirencester, Gloucestershire.

BIBLIOGRAPHY   *BMASG*, 106 and fig. 131, 3.
Brøndsted (1924), 130.   Wilson and Blunt (1961), 121.

Ninth century. See above, pp. 28, 32, 62 and pl. XXX.

83. Silver disc brooch, dished and of irregular circumference. The border is composed of two bands; an outer one made up of adjacent crescents, each with triangular nicks inside and outside, the inner band being plain. Within this the field is divided up by four double-contoured, overlapping circles; the pointed ovals thus formed are repeated on the circumference of the two other quadrants of each circle to form a four-sided figure. At the joints and extremities of this geometrical construction are a series of nine dome-headed rivets, one of which is now missing. The domed heads are coarsely made, having been roughly hammered out from flat sheets of metal. The surface of the brooch is further divided up by two extended lines from the central bosses of each side of the square figure, to form a small sub-triangular field and two wing-shaped fields. The fields formed by these divisions are decorated with linear patterns. Each of the wing-shaped fields has an eye-shaped motif and is thus given a certain zoomorphic character, some of the fields could be interpreted as animal heads with long pointed jaws and short lines, to give roundness to the motif, and a simple line or pair of lines, to represent a mouth. In each of the pointed oval fields is a degenerate scroll ornament with short lines cut along one side at right angles to the scroll. The four major fields contain zoomorphic motifs. The field, top left, contains a pair of interlaced snakes, the uppermost snake

Superficies Convexa.

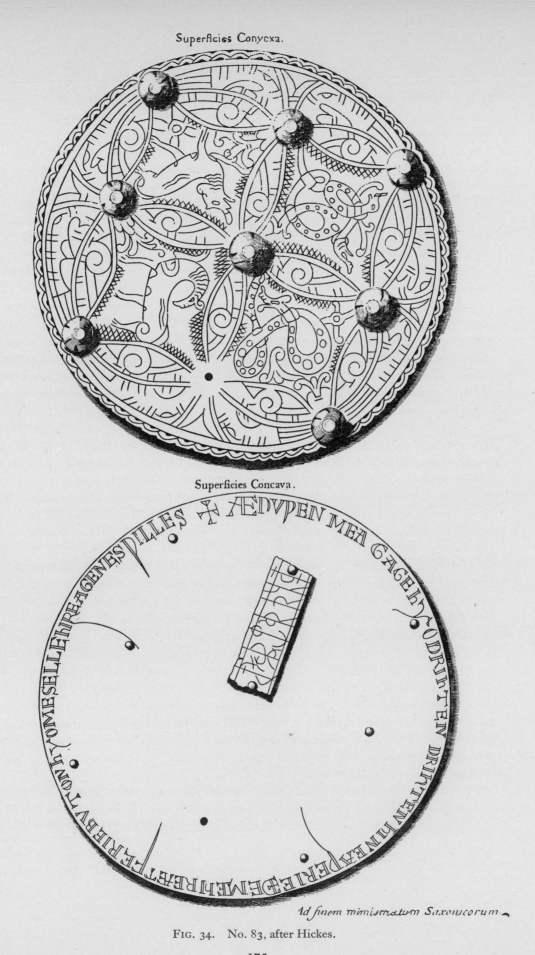

Superficies Concava.

FIG. 34.   No. 83, after Hickes.

175

having a head at either end of its body. The snout is slightly floriated and the eye consists in each case of a straight line with a convex curve below it, the mouths are open. The body is decorated with a number of irregular circles (scales ?) and a faintly scratched line gives it a double contour: at the point where the neck crosses the body it is interlaced with a ring. The second snake in the field has an amorphous head, an eye and a body decorated with roughly executed rings. The body is defined by a double contour executed in the same manner as the body of the other snake. Where the body crosses itself there are crude interlaced rings. At the top left, beneath the neck of the animal, is a loose tendril with scrolled ends. Where the snakes do not come up to the edge of the field, the field is filled out with a pattern of cross-hatching. The field, top right, contains a snake with an elaborate head in the bottom left-hand corner. The mouth is floriated with a suggestion of teeth; the bottom lip is scrolled. The ear is pear shaped and forms a continuous curve with the upper line of the jaw. The eye is almond-shaped. There are vestiges of an interlaced ring where neck and tail cross the body, and the body is decorated with roughly circular scale-like features. Filling in the background are two plant-like ornaments (one apparently a degenerate acanthus leaf) and a saltire, with scrolled terminals and an interlaced ring at the crossing. The edges of the field are hatched as before and a scratched line suggests double contouring of the snake. In the bottom left-hand corner is a quadruped with its rump bottom-right and its head top-right. The head of the animal has two faces, one at the front with open mouth, a pointed, bifurcated snout and teeth, and behind this, looking towards the rump, is a human elf-like head (with open mouth and small pointed nose, which forms the ear of the main animal—the almond-shaped eye is common to both faces. The animal has a mane, indicated by a number of short curved transverse lines. One foreleg is raised in front of the animal and it stands on the other, which is vertical. The first hind-leg occurs half way along the body and the other appears in the bottom right-hand corner. The tail curls between the leg. The body is decorated with a double wavy line and one or two nicks which indicate the hips of the animal. In the top left-hand corner is a *fleur-de-lys* shaped leaf ornament and between the legs of the animal is a rough knot with an interlacing ring at the centre. The ornament has a secondary, lightly drawn contour and the borders of the field, where they do not interfere with the animal, have a cross-hatched band. The animal in the bottom-right field is also a quadruped, the head and the neck, with its mane, made up of small wavy lines, bend backwards. The head is narrow and pointed, has a denticulated snout and an eye of plano-convex shape, with the straight line at the bottom. The ear forms a scroll above the eye but there is no mouth. The front leg rises in front of the body from a scrolled hip. The other three legs are vertical with a slight suggestion of a joint, but no feet. The hind hip is scrolled, but the others are merely suggested by curved lines. There is a double wavy line on the back. In the bottom left-hand corner is a frond of acanthus. The ornament has a secondary, lightly-drawn contour and is bordered by cross-hatched lines.

The back of the brooch retains part of the long supporting plate of the pin, the plate is broken at both ends, where the rivets fastened it. The strip is not complete and we must presume that the so-called 'runic' inscription continued beyond this point (the 'runes' are illustrated, pl. XXXII). Scratched on the rear surface, on either side of the strip, is a triquetra and round the rim is an inscription:

+ ÆDVÞEN MEAG AGEHYODRIHTEN DRIHTENHINEAÞERIEÐEMEHIRE
ÆTFERIEBVTONHYOMESELLEHIREAGENESÞILLES

Other scratches on the back appear to be accidental, save possibly for a triangle below the letters, HINEAÞ.   Diameter: varies between 14·9 and 16·4 cm.

Reg. no. 1951, 10–11, 1. Purchased from Mr. H. O'Conner. From Sutton, Isle of Ely, Cambridge-shire.

BIBLIOGRAPHY
Hickes (1705), iii, 187–8.
Camden (1772), i, 493.
Lewis (1840), 255.
Stephens (1866–1901), i, 289–93.
Stephens (1884), 218.
Black (1888–9), 340 and fig. 6.
Stephens (1894), 20.
Fox (1923), 300.
Smith (1925*b*), 137 and fig. 2.
VCH Cambridgeshire, i, 328.
Bennett (1950/1), 273.
Bruce-Mitford (1952*b*).
Bruce-Mitford (1956*a*), 193 ff., pls. xxviii and xxix, a and fig. 38.
Thompson (1956), 131 and pl. xxi, b.
Wilson (1958*c*), 170.
Thompson (1959), 280.
Wilson (1960*a*), 69, 162, 223 and pl. 78.
Wilson and Blunt (1961), 108.

The Brooch was turned up by the plough in 1694 in a lead casket with about a hundred silver coins of William the Conqueror, five heavy gold rings, a plain silver dish (or disc). Lewis (1840), 255, says it was found in 1634 with 'several coins and gold rings, and three silver plates, one of which had a curious inscription'. This need not be taken too seriously; Hickes's date and description are probably reliable. The piece, although never forgotten, was not rediscovered until 1951, when the British Museum acquired it from a Dublin dealer. Its history between these two dates is unknown; it is possible that it was in the possession of a member of the Howard family at some time.

Eleventh century. See above, pp. 3, 7, 31, 36, 48–50, 52, 80, 84, 86–90 and pls. XXXI and XXXII.

84. Bronze disc brooch. The brooch has a billeted border within which is a backward-looking animal with open mouth and a bump for an ear. The mane is shaggy and there are four

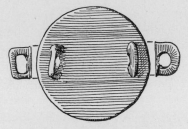

FIG. 35.   Back of no. 84. $\frac{1}{1}$.

strap-like legs, each terminating in three paws. The surface of the brooch is much worn. The back is plain, save for the catch-plate and loop of a (now missing) pin. The hook of the catch-plate is now closed, giving it the appearance of a loop.

Maximum diameter: 2·9 cm.

Reg. no. 54, 7–21, 1. Given by Mr. Plowright.[1] From Swaffham, Norfolk.

BIBLIOGRAPHY

Brøndsted (1924), 146.   *VCH Suffolk*, i, 348.

Ninth/tenth century. See above, pp. 36, 52 and pl. XXXII.

85. Gold finger-ring. Flat, plain hoop of gold. Against a pounced background is reserved the inscription:

The crosses in the inscription have expanding arms. The border is plain. The inside of the hoop is plain.   Diameter: 2·1 cm.

Ring Cat. no. 183. Found near Swindon, Wiltshire.

BIBLIOGRAPHY   *BMASG*, 116, fig. 146.

B.M. Ring Cat., 31.   Harder (1932).

As the object was never registered the details of its acquisition are not known. But it was apparently acquired in 1912.

Ninth century. See above, pp. 23, 27, 56, 75, 79, 83–84, 90, 178 and pl. XXXII.

86. Silver tag consisting of a hook with a flat plate behind it, which has a wide squared end with a pierced circular hole in each corner. The plate tapers gently to the upturned hook, which is of slightly oval section. It is undecorated.   Length: 2·7 cm.

Reg. no. 1946, 10–2, 1. Treasure Trove. From Tetney, Lincolnshire.

BIBLIOGRAPHY

Walker (1945), 81.

Found in May 1945, during deep ploughing, with a hoard of coins in a chalk container with no. 87. The coins are dated to *c.* 970.

Before 970. See above, pp. 7, 64 and pl. XXXII.

87. Another similar.   Length: 2·7 cm.

Reg. no. 1946, 10–2, 2. Treasure Trove. From Tetney, Lincolnshire.
Details as for no. 86.

Before 970. See above, pp. 7, 64 and pl. XXXII.

88. Pewter disc brooch, cast with a relief design on the face. The brooch is bordered by a band made up of two plain lines joined by closely spaced, hatched, oblique lines. Within the border is a design made up of a series of double-contoured, lentoid fields in the form

---

[1] I have been unable to trace the donor, whose initials and address are not recorded in the Register.

178

of a quatrefoil, which has been made into a squarish figure by the addition of two lentoid fields between the tip of each arm; where the fields join are a series of cast bosses. Five pellets can be seen in each of the four main fields, while a short curved line borders the

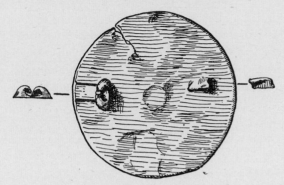

FIG. 36.   Back of no. 88. ⅟₁.

boss at the terminal of each leaf of the quatrefoil. The back contains the worn and fractured remains of a loop and catch-plate which have been soldered on. The brooch is warped and slightly torn.   Maximum diameter: 4·5 cm.

Reg. no. 93, 6–18, 111. Purchased from Messrs. Sotheby's through Messrs. Rollin and Feuardent. From the River Thames.

From the Bateman collection. The brooch was found in 1848 and the provenance was preserved on a MS. label detached in 1957. Bateman had a large number of antiquities from London and the provenance is presumably a London one. The legend 'N.I. 40' is painted in white ink on the back of the brooch.

Ninth/tenth century. See above, pp. 35, 36, 52 and pl. XXXII.

89. Iron stirrup-iron with a rectangular loop above a knop from which emerges the hoop. The hoop is of sub-triangular cross-section and merges into irregular hexagonal side plates below hollow bosses. The foot plate, which is fixed to these side plates, is broken, but was apparently a simple flat plate. Traces of an inlaid wire pattern can be seen on the side plates, while on one side of the hoop are traces of a running lozenge pattern, each lozenge separated by a double horizontal line. The surface of the iron was prepared for inlaying by cross-hatched engraving and the wire was beaten into the surface.

Height: 21·7 cm.

Reg. no. O.A. 295. Possibly from the River Thames.
The provenance depends on a label saying 'Thames' loosely associated with the object.

Tenth/eleventh century. See above, pp. 39, 62 and pl. XXXII.

90. Silver, parcel-gilt, chalice, which (as now reconstructed) consists of three elements, the bowl, the knop and the foot. The bowl was much shattered when recovered and is reconstructed on a modern copper form to which the twenty-one remaining fragments are soldered. A considerable portion of the bowl is missing but the shape of its

179

reconstruction is reasonable, for (a) there is sufficient depth surviving in the fragments to ascertain the curve and (b) the whole of the rim diameter survives. At one period the fragments were wired together and the holes made during this process can be seen, in pairs, along the line of the breaks. The peened rim of the bowl is flanged and of T-shaped cross-section. Round the rim, about 3 mm. from the top, is a series of rivet-holes in which riven shanks remain; owing to the damaged state of the bowl it is only possible to see eight of the shanks (one or two more may have been disturbed by the repairs). Some 4 mm. below the rim is a band of gilding some 3 mm. in width with a roughened surface at the top. Within this gilded band are the shanks of at least six rivets. The top

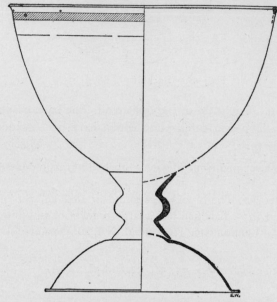

FIG. 37.   Section through no. 90. ½.

and inside of the rim are gilded. It is probably that the interior of the bowl was also gilded but the reconstruction has hidden the interior. 1·4 cm. below the rim, all round the cup, are traces of a scratched but regular line. There are traces of solder between this line and the gilded band. The bowl was hammered into shape, presumably by raising.

As at present reconstructed the central element of the chalice consists of a knop (pl. XXXIV). In elevation its shape appears as a double cone truncated in the centre by an oval: its section is shown in fig. 37. It is hammered out of a rough and heavy casting, presumably of tubular form; traces of radial blows in the constrictions would seem to indicate that the knop was finished externally by hammering and polishing. The interior of the knop is unpolished. The foot is complete and consists of a segment of a hammered hollow sphere with a top shaped to take the knop; this flattened portion contains three punched rivet-holes of slightly different diameter. The centre hole may have been enlarged slightly at the time of reconstruction. The bottom of the foot is turned over and then hammered flat to form a flange.   Reconstructed height: 12·6 cm.

Reg. no. 80, 4–10, 1, 2, & 3. Given by J. J. Rogers, Esq. From Trewhiddle, Cornwall.

BIBLIOGRAPHY
Rashleigh (1789), 187 and pl. viii, 1, 22 and 23.
Rashleigh (1794), 83–4 and pl. vii.
Davis Gilbert (1864), i, 49.
The Archaeological Journal, xii (1864), 184.
Rogers (1867), 292.
Rashleigh (1868), 138–9.
Proceedings of the Society of Antiquaries of London
   ser. 2, viii (1880), 313.
Smith (1904), 49–50 and fig.
VCH Cornwall, i, 375 and fig. 1.
Jackson (1911), i, 57 and fig. 75.
[O. M. Dalton] (1921), 68 and fig. 39.
Watts (1922), 13 and pl. 3, a.
BMASG, 99 and fig. 118.
Walker and Walker (1927), xiif.
Braun (1932), 72.
Hencken (1932), 262 and pl. yii.
Pfeilstücker (1936), 190.
Haseloff (1951), 12.
Talbot-Rice (1952), 227 and fig. 14.
Thompson (1956), 137 and pl. vi, d.
Oman (1957), 39 f. and pl. 1.
Wilson (1958c), 170.
Thompson (1959), 280–1.
Wilson (1960a), 65, 215 and pl. 17.
Wilson and Blunt (1961), *passim.*

Found in 1774 (with nos. 91–103) by tin-workers in a stream-work, 17 feet below ground surface at Trewhiddle, St. Austell, Cornwall. It was hidden in a heap of loose stones in an old mine-working. The hoard, which included a number of objects which are now lost and a silver penannular brooch of Hiberno-Saxon origin which is omitted from this catalogue,[1] was associated with a number of coins which date its deposition to *c.* 872–5. About 1806 the hoard passed into the hands of Canon Rogers of Penrose, whose son presented it to the British Museum in appreciation of the work for the national collections of the then Keeper of the Department of British and Medieval Antiquities and Ethnography, A. W. (later Sir Augustus) Franks.

Before 875. See above, pp. 54, 55, figs. 6 and 7 and pl. xxxiv.

91. Silver scourge: one strand of trichinopoly chainwork is doubled and the two strands so formed are held together by plaited loops of wire at five unequally spaced places. The chain terminates in a large loop, or knot, from which issue four slender pendant tails each terminating in a plaited knot. The whole is of silver. A bead, or toggle, 2·7 cm. in diam., made of blue glass with white veining, is attached to the end of the scourge by doubling it through the loop formed at the end.

Length of scourge (without bead): 56·5 cm.

Reg. no. 80, 4–10, 4. Given by J. J. Rogers, Esq. From Trewhiddle, Cornwall.

BIBLIOGRAPHY
Rashleigh (1789), 188 and pl. viii, 4.
The Archaeological Journal, xxi (1864), 184.
Rogers (1867), 292.
Rashleigh (1868), 138.
Proceedings of the Society of Antiquaries of London,
   Ser. 2, viii (1880), 313.
Smith (1904), 50.
VCH Cornwall, i, 376 and fig. 7.
BMASG, 99–100 and fig. 119.
Hencken (1932), 262 and pl. xii.
Thompson (1956), 137 and pl. xxii, ci.
Wilson (1960a), 65–66.
Wilson and Blunt (1961), *passim.*

Found with nos. 90 and 92–103. For details of find, etc., see entry for no. 90.

Before 875. See above, p. 59 and pl. xxxv.

[1] Wilson and Blunt (1961), pl. xxviii, b.

92. Silver pin with a hollow fourteen-sided head (1·9 cm. square). The pin passes through the bottom and top of this head. A carved, faceted stop fastens it below the head, while the pin is riveted over at the top and marked with a cross by a tracing tool. The fields at the top and bottom have stylised leaves engraved in each corner and inlaid with niello. The other fields are ornamented as set out below (fig. 38):

Lozenge-shaped field 1. The ornament in this field consists of a cross with pointed ends

FIG. 38. Ornament of no. 92. $\frac{1}{1}$.

and arms constructed of four concave lines. A square is constructed round the centre of the cross. The engraved lines are filled with niello. The centre of the cross is decorated with fine speckling, the rest of the field being plain.

Lozenge-shaped field 2 contains an angular animal with an eye in the left-hand corner; there is a notch behind the eye and the top of the jaw is notched; the bottom lip is curled. The head of the animal faces backwards, the front leg points along the bottom left-hand side and the hind leg stretches along the top right-hand side. The tongue of the animal crosses its body and forms an animal's head along the bottom right-hand side. There is a single notch in front of the eye, which is separated from the top of the head by an engraved line. The tongue and second animal head are slightly speckled. The ornament of the field is set against a nielloed background.

Lozenge-shaped field 3 contains trefoils growing swastika-wise out of a concave equal-sided figure. The central element is slightly speckled and the ornament is set against a nielloed background.

Lozenge-shaped field 4 contains exactly the same ornament as field 2, save that the head of the primary animal is at the apex of the lozenge and the whole pattern is twisted accordingly.

Triangular field 1 (*top*) contains a backward-looking animal with its head in the top left-hand corner and with its two-toed legs bent along the upper and right-hand sides. It has a lozenge-shaped ear and a pointed snout. It is set against a nielloed background. There is a small break in the metal across the hindquarters of the animal. *Triangular field* 2 (*top*) contains a plain, squarish triquetra knot set against a nielloed background.
Triangular field 3 (*top*) contains an animal similar to the animal in triangular field 1 (top) save that the head is in the lower corner. The ornament is set against a nielloed back-

ground. *Triangular field* 4 (*top*). Similar to triangular field 2 (top). *Triangular field* 1 (*bottom*). In this field the decoration is similar to that in triangular field 2 (top). *Triangular field* 2 (*bottom*) contains an animal of similar form to that in triangular field 1 (top), save that the top of the upper jaw is notched. The head is in the bottom right-hand corner. The background is nielloed. *Triangular field* 3 (*bottom*). In this field the decoration is similar to that in triangular field 2 (top). *Triangular field* 4 (*bottom*). An animal of similar form to that in triangular field 1 (top) has its head in the bottom right-hand corner. It is set against a nielloed background.

The pin is in three pieces and has been bent.   Length of pin: 19·3 cm.

Reg. no. 80, 4–10, 5 and 7. Given by J. J. Rogers, Esq. From Trewhiddle, Cornwall.

BIBLIOGRAPHY

Rashleigh (1789), 188 and pl. viii, 10 and 11.
The Archaeological Journal, xxi (1864), 184.
Rogers (1867), 292.
Rashleigh (1868), 138.
Smith (1904), 48 and figs. 3 and 4.
VCH Cornwall, i, 377 and fig. 6.
Shetelig (1909), 92 and fig. 16.
Jackson (1911), i, 57 and figs. 76 and 77.

BMASG, 100 and 120, 1.
Hencken (1932), 262 and fig. 49, 1.
Moss (1953*a*), 61.
Moss (1953*b*), 76.
Wilson (1955*a*), fig. 4.
Thompson (1956), pls. xxii, *c* 4 and xxiv, *a*, 6 and 7.
Wilson (1960*a*), pl. 63.
Wilson and Blunt (1961), *passim*.

Found with nos. 90, 91 and 93–103. For details of find, etc., see entry for no. 90.

Before 875. See above, pp. 24, 30, 59 and pl. XXXVI.

93. Silver box-like object in two pieces—sides and lid. The body of the box is rounded at one end and square at the other. The front of the box is divided into two rectangular fields with a rivet-hole at the centre top; both rectangles are divided by saltires and the whole is delineated and divided by beaded lines. In all but one of the triangular fields formed by the division is a foliate ornament; the one exception is that on the extreme left which has a small animal with its head in the bottom corner and its two legs along the opposite side. The ornament in all these fields is embellished by speckling. The square end of the box is plain, as is the back, save that in the centre, below the small hole, is a *cross moline*.

FIG. 39.   Ornament of no. 93. $\frac{3}{2}$.

The top has a central hole surrounded by a plain area and is bordered by a series of triangular chisel cuts. Inside the border, the top is divided by four arcs of a circle each touching the central area. In each of the four fields thus formed to surround the hole is a bifoliate motif. The arcs are beaded and divided in the middle by a plain billet. The outer

183

fields have more elaborate decoration: the top left-hand field has an animal's head with a zig-zagged, tadpole-like body and a foliate tail; there is a bump over the eye and the snout is rounded; traces of niello remain in the carving. The top right-hand field has two leaves, the bottom left-hand field has a triquetra with one elongated element, and the bottom right-hand field has two leaves with a curved zig-zag joining them. The whole ornament is speckled and was set against a nielloed background.

Length of lid: 2·6 cm.
Length of base: 2·8 cm.

Reg. no. 80, 4–10, 8 and 12. Given by J. J. Rogers, Esq. From Trewhiddle, Cornwall.

BIBLIOGRAPHY

Rashleigh (1789), 188 and pl. viii, 9 and 16.
Smith (1904), 51 and fig. 1 and 2.
VCH Cornwall, i, 376 and fig. 5.
Jackson (1911), i, 58 and fig. 81.
BMASG, 100 and fig. 120, 4.

Hencken (1932), 262 and fig. 49, 4.
Wilson (1955a), fig. 4.
Thompson (1956), pls. xxii, c 3 and xxiii, 3.
Wilson (1960a), pl. 63.
Wilson and Blunt (1961), *passim*.

Found with nos. 90–2 and 94–103. For details of find, etc. see entry for no. 90.

Before 875. See above, pp. 24, 30, 65 and pl. XXXVI.

94. Silver strip (repaired behind fields nos. 5 and 11 in modern times) with a straight top and an arcaded base. The strip is divided, between two plastic, terminal animal-heads, into eleven fields of sub-triangular shape each containing an engraved, originally nielloed, ornament. The triangles interlock, the apex of one alternating with the base of the next. The fields are divided by beaded lines and the top and bottom of the mount are delimited by a beaded border made up of square-cut billets. Inside these beaded lines each field is bordered by a thin, free-standing, unbroken line. Beyond the two plastic heads were, originally, two plain strips. One appears to have been broken off in antiquity and the second is bent downwards and broken at the rivet-hole (as though forced off its base). The mount is curved into a half circle of approx 10 cm. in internal diameter.

Description of the ornament of the fields from left to right; the straight edge is taken to be the top of the mount (numeration as in fig. 40):

FIG. 40.   Ornament of no. 94. Numeration from left to right. ⅔.

(1) The head of the animal is in the bottom of an irregular field: the animal is curved round a rivet-hole to the left of the field. The head, which looks into the bottom left-hand corner, has a square snout and a V-shaped mouth with a rounded ear; the body is sub-triangular, with an emphasised, muscular hip and a weak three-toed hind-leg. The front leg runs along the edge of the field behind the ear: it is club-shaped and has two nicks, suggestive of toes. The eye of the animal is attached to the back of the head by a short string-like feature. The body is speckled all over with small, triangular nicks formed with the point of the engraving tool.

(2) In this field is an animal with its head at the apex of an inverted triangle: the animal looks towards the apex. The head is of the same type as that in the first field, with the same eye but slightly different ear (the ear is extended and above a short constriction becomes a leaf). The body and the thigh are of a similar shape; but less angular. The front foot develops into a knot ornament attached to the bottom of the shoulder, but the back leg stretches in a normal way along the base of the triangle and has three toes. The animal is speckled all over. There is a suspicion of a foot below the chin.

(3) A triangular field with an arcaded base. In the centre of the field is a rivet-hole surrounded by a plain area, from which springs a ribbon which terminates in a small animal head. The head has an eye (filled with niello) and a mouth. Below the hole and not connected with the head are a series of pointed knots forming, at the join of the arcading, a small loop. The whole ornament, with the exception of the plain field surrounding the rivet-hole, is speckled.

(4) The animal in this field has a head facing towards the left in the top left-hand corner of the inverted triangle. The animal, which is speckled, is of a form similar to the others, with 'stringed' eye, an ear developing into a leaf, a sub-triangular body and a shaped hip. The two three-toed legs extend along the two shorter sides of the triangle and there is a short, stumpy tail.

(5) The plain area round the rivet-hole in this arcaded-based triangle almost touches the centre of the right-hand side. A speckled animal, looking upwards and back, is placed in the space below the rivet-hole. In detail it closely resembles the majority of the complete animals so far discussed, save that its tail is roughly and inaccurately interlaced and its front paw extends in a natural manner into the bottom left-hand corner of the field. The knot of the tail runs into the field surrounding the rivet-hole. The ear is less foliate than that in the previous field.

(6) In this field is a speckled animal with its head at the apex of an inverted triangle. The head, which looks towards the apex, is not drawn in as much detail as in the other fields; the eye has a rounded bump over it. The animal has a square snout and a long, trailing scrolled ear. The body is rather fuller than those of the other animals. The typical shaped hip develops into a three-toed hind-leg bent along the base of the triangle. Along the left-hand shorter side is a curved tail with a leaf-like terminal. The two-toed front leg extends in front of the animal into the top right-hand corner.

(7) This animal, which is speckled all over, is in the same position as the animal in field no. 5; it differs from that animal in that the head reaches up to the apex and the

tail is a three-element knot which does not run into the field round the rivet-hole. It has a slightly scrolled ear.

(8) In this inverted triangular field the head of the animal is placed in the top left-hand corner of the field and is backward-looking. In all details, save the ears, it is typical of the others on the mounting: the ear is in the form of a hook or loop. The body of the animal is speckled but the head is plain.

(9) In the centre of this triangular field with an arcaded base is a rivet-hole, surrounded by a plain area. Over this hole, with its head looking into the bottom left-hand corner, is an animal head with no body. In place of the body is a stem, with a regular loop (similar to that in the bottom of field 3) which retains a little niello, and two tendrils, which terminate in a leaf. Below the rivet-hole are three leaves, the two outer ones issuing from the central one and extending into the two corners of the field. These are connected by a broken line with the upper part of the field. The ornament is speckled all over.

(10) In the inverted triangle forming this field is an animal looking into the top right-hand corner, with niello surviving in the eye and between the toes of the hind-leg. The animal is of the usual shape but with a bump over the eye and no string-like motif; it has a scroll-like ear and stumpy tail. The animal is speckled all over.

(11) This field has a rivet-hole and, in the left-hand corner, a triquetra. This motif is not speckled.

At either end of the strip is a plastic, repoussé head of formalised appearance. This consists of two triangles touching at the apex where there are two round bosses, one on each side, representing the eyes. The centre of each triangle is filled with degenerate, pendant leaf ornament, the top one recognisable as a trefoil. The head on the right-hand side has a thin band of silver extending from its snout. This strip is slightly bent down at the end, where it is broken—there was a rivet-hole at the break. A similar strip has been broken from the other side.

In certain fields a number of small billets of silver are isolated by the engraver's tool and would stand up above the niello background (most of which has disappeared). A technical detail, worthy of mention, is that the speckling was started round the edge of the animals, perhaps in two lines; the remaining space then being speckled in a haphazard manner. It is not certain whether the speckling contained niello. The back of the mount is undecorated.   Length: 21·4 cm.

Reg. no. 80, 4–10, 9. Given by J. J. Rogers, Esq. From Trewhiddle, Cornwall.

BIBLIOGRAPHY
Rashleigh (1789), 188 and pl. viii, 6.
The Archaeological Journal, xxi (1864), 184.
Rogers (1867), 292.
Rashleigh (1868), 138.
Smith (1904), 51 and fig. 5.
VCH Cornwall, i, 376 and fig. 8.
Shetelig (1909), 92 and fig. 14.
Jackson (1911), i, 58 and fig. 78.

BMASG, 100 and fig. 120, 10.
Brøndsted (1924), 127 and fig. 104.
Hencken (1932), 262 and fig. 49, 10.
Kendrick (1938), 185 and pl. 78, 1.
MacDermott (1955), 84 and pl. xxxix, a.
Wilson (1955a), 111–12 and figs. 4 and 5.
Thompson (1956), pl. xxiii, 1.
Wilson (1960a), fig. 35 and pl. 63.
Wilson and Blunt (1961), *passim*.

Found with nos. 90–3 and 95–103. For details of find, etc., see entry for no. 90.

Before 875. See above, pp. 24, 30–33, 41, 42, 56, 57 and pls. XXXVI and XXXVII.

95. Another similar, but smaller, silver strip. It is divided in the same way, but has only seven fields and a diameter of curve of 9 cm.

Description of the animal ornament from left to right; the straight edge at the top (numeration as in fig. 41):

FIG. 41. Ornament of no. 95. Numeration from left to right. $\frac{3}{2}$.

(1) This field is delimited on one side by the plain area round the rivet-hole: in the bottom left-hand corner of the field is an animal head with square snout and a bump over the eye, a small ear and a body which degenerates into a foliate motif: the whole ornament is speckled.

(2) The field is in the shape of a triangle with arcaded base. In the field, with its beak towards the right-hand corner, is a hawk-like head with niello in the eye. This head is partially severed by two cuts one from above and one below; behind these cuts and at right angles to them are a series of four billets representing feathers. The ornament is speckled all over.

(3) This irregular field contains in the centre a rivet-hole with a plain surrounding area. A little way from the top left-hand corner is a small animal head, the animal quickly degenerating into a jumble of lines and interlace. A small leaf appears beneath the rivet-hole and a trefoil to the right. The whole ornament is speckled.

(4) This panel contains an irregular interlaced ribbon, the two ends of which terminate in leaves, the ornament is speckled throughout.

(5) This field is divided in two by the rivet-hole and its surrounding area. On the right-hand side there is a triquetra knot and on the left an animal with throat and lower jaw in a straight line along the upper edge; the head faces towards the right, having a slight point in front of its eye. In the top left-hand corner is a leg with a spread foot, other features are a shaped hip, a bent rear leg and a tail. Below the rivet-hole are two conjoined leaves. The ornament is speckled throughout.

(6) The field is approximately triangular in shape. In the bottom right-hand corner and facing into the corner is an animal head with a bump over the eye; the eye is nielloed. Two leaves emerge from the head. The ornament is speckled throughout.

(7) In this field is a figure-of-eight motif of semi-foliate character. There is the suspicion of an eyeless head in the middle of the left-hand side. The ornament is speckled throughout. A rivet-hole and its surrounding plain area forms one border of the field.

At either end of the mount is a repoussé head of similar form to those on the large mount, but with lozenge-shaped fields above the nostrils and two separate patterns in

187

the sub-triangular fields above the eyes. In that to the left is a pendant leaf decoration, while the right-hand one is divided by two touching segments of a circle. From the right-hand head leads a strip of silver, pierced at the end, a thinner strip emerges from the other end and terminates in a rivet-hole.

In certain fields a number of small billets of silver are isolated by the graver's tool and would stand up above the niello background (most of which has disappeared). An interesting technical detail is that the speckling is clearly seen to have started round the edge of the animal, perhaps in two lines; the remaining space being then speckled in a haphazard manner. It is not certain whether the speckling contained niello.

The back of the mount is undecorated. Length: 18·2 cm.

Reg. no. 80, 4–10, 10. Given by J. J. Rogers, Esq. From Trewhiddle, Cornwall.

BIBLIOGRAPHY
Rashleigh (1798), 188 and pl. viii, 7.
The Archaeological Journal, xxi (1864), 184.
Rogers (1867), 292.
Rashleigh (1868), 138.
Smith (1904), 51 and fig. 6.
VCH Cornwall, i, 376 and fig. 8.
Jackson (1911), i, 58 and fig. 79.
BMASG, 100 and fig. 120, 9.

Brøndsted (1924), 127 and fig. 104.
Hencken (1932), 262 and fig. 49, 9.
Kendrick (1938), 185 and pl. 78, 1.
MacDermott (1955), 84 and pl. 39, a.
Wilson (1955a), fig. 4.
Thompson (1956), pl. xxiii, 1.
Wilson (1960a), pl. 63.
Wilson and Blunt (1961), *passim*.

Found with nos. 90–4, 96–103. For details of find, etc., see entry for no. 90.

Before 875. See above, pp. 21, 24, 30, 31, 32, 33, 41, 42, 56, 57 and pls. XXXVI and XXXVII.

96. Silver strip, similar to the above, but hammered flat. It has only two fields of ornament, occupying no more than 5 cm. of the total length of the strip. The fields are on either side of a rivet-hole and there is no beaded division.

FIG. 42. Ornament of no. 96. ³⁄₂.

(1) The field, which is sub-rectangular with an arcaded base, contains a gentle foliate scroll with three leaves on either side of a curving stem with broadened terminals. Each leaf and the terminal have two nicks cut on the outer edge. In the left-hand bottom corner is a forked motif reminiscent of an animal head, this also has two short cuts in the thicker part.

(2) The field is of similar shape and an animal takes up the greater part of the area. The animal is upside down and the head is twisted round so that the snout is parallel with the top of the mount. There is a bump over the eye, a broken lower jaw and the suspicion of an ear. The animal has a tail and three legs, one of which penetrates the body, each with three toes. To the left of the panel is a tendril with a leaf, while to the right, between

the near front leg and the back leg, are two leaves on a single stem. The animal has a series of double cuts at various places to give the composition a sense of roundness.

The back of the mount is undecorated. Length: 12·2 cm.

Reg. no. 80, 4–10, 11. Given by J. J. Rogers, Esq. From Trewhiddle, Cornwall.

BIBLIOGRAPHY
Rashleigh (1789), 188 and pl. viii, 8.
Smith (1940), 51 and fig. 7.
VCH Cornwall, i, 376 and fig. 8.
Shetelig (1909), 92 and fig. 15.
Jackson (1911), i, 58 and fig. 80.
BMASG, 100 and fig. 120, 8.

Brøndsted (1924), 127 and fig. 104.
Hencken (1932), 262 and fig. 49, 8.
Wilson (1955a), fig. 4.
Thompson (1956), pl. xxiii, 2.
Wilson (1960a), pl. 63.
Wilson and Blunt (1961), *passim*.

Found with nos. 90–5 and 97–103. For details of find, etc., see entry for no. 90.

Before 875. See above, pp. 24, 30, 38, 56, 57 and pl. XXXVII.

97. Silver strap-end, the terminal of which is slightly faceted to give a suggestion of the animal-head usual in this position. The butt-end is split in the thickness of the metal and carries a single rivet. The long sides of the central field are defined by a beaded border. The field consists of a quadrilateral, the small side nearest the terminal being straight, the two long sides being convex, and the other short side concave. In the field (looking towards the split end) is a speckled animal. Its snout is square and the eye is separated from the head; the ear bends back on itself and two leaves grow out of the lower jaws. The body contracts to allow a shaped hip; the legs cross each other. The whole field was originally filled with niello. The back is plain.

FIG. 43. Ornament of no. 97. ¾.

Length: 3·0 cm.

Reg. no. 80, 4–10, 13. Given by J. J. Rogers, Esq. From Trewhiddle, Cornwall.

BIBLIOGRAPHY
VCH Cornwall, i, 377 and fig. 10.
BMASG, 100 and 120, 3.
Brøndsted (1924), 130 and fig. 107.
Hencken (1932), 262 and fig. 49, 3.

Wilson (1955a), fig. 4.
Thompson (1956), pl. xxiii, 3.
Wilson (1960a), pl. 63.
Wilson and Blunt (1961), *passim*.

Found with nos. 90–6 and 98–103. For details of find, etc., see entry for no. 90.

Before 875. See above, pp. 24, 28, 62 and pl. XXXVII.

98. Another similar. The strap-end is similar in detail to that just described, save only that the animal in the field has a slightly less chunky and angular appearance. The legs of the animal are set at right angles to each other. Length: 3·0 cm.

FIG. 44. Ornament of no. 98. ¾.

Reg. no. 80, 4–10, 14. Given by J. J. Rogers, Esq. From Trewhiddle, Cornwall.

BIBLIOGRAPHY
Rashleigh (1879), 188 and pl. viii, 15.
VCH Cornwall, i, 377.
Brøndsted (1924), 130.

Wilson (1955*a*), fig. 4.
Thompson (1956), pl. xxiii, 3.
Wilson (1960*a*), pl. 63.
Wilson and Blunt (1961), *passim*.

Found with nos. 90–7 and 99–103. For details of find, etc., see entry for no. 90.

Before 875. See above, pp. 24, 28, 62 and pl. XXXVII.

99. Cast silver strap-end with a single rivet-hole flanked by two nicks at the split end. The rivet is missing and part of the split end at the back has been broken away, but otherwise the object is complete. Fragments of leather remain inside the split end. The front of the strap-end has a midrib, the face sloping away from it on either side to the squared edges. The object narrows towards the rounded terminal at the same time decreasing in thickness. The back is flat, but slightly curved along the length. It is undecorated.

Length: 2·6 cm.

Reg. no. 80, 4–10, 15. Given by J. J. Rogers, Esq. From Trewhiddle, Cornwall.

BIBLIOGRAPHY
VCH Cornwall, i, 377.

Thompson (1956), pl. xxiv, *a* 4.
Wilson and Blunt (1961), *passim*.

Found with nos. 90–8 and 100–3. For details of find, etc., see entry for no. 90.

Before 875. See above, pp. 62, 63 and pl. XXXVII.

100. Another similar; the bottom of the split end is broken away, the marks inside indicate that the split was sawn. A plain silver rivet remains. Length: 2·5 cm.

Reg. no. 80, 4–10, 16. Given by J. J. Rogers, Esq. From Trewhiddle, Cornwall.

BIBLIOGRAPHY
Rashleigh (1789), 188 and pl. viii, 19.
VCH Cornwall, i, 377.

Thompson (1956), pl. xxiv, *a* 5.
Wilson and Blunt (1961), *passim*.

Found with nos. 90–9 and 101–3. For details of find, etc., see entry no. 90.

Before 875. See above, pp. 62, 64 and pl. XXXVII.

101. Belt-slide of silver, cast in the form of a rectangular loop. The upper portion, which is sloped away from a midrib, is in the shape of a lozenge with squared points (which are notched) on the broader edges. Length: 2·2 cm.

Reg. no. 80, 4–10, 17. Given by J. J. Rogers, Esq. From Trewhiddle, Cornwall.

BIBLIOGRAPHY
Rashleigh (1789), 188 and pl. viii, 18 and 20.
VCH Cornwall, i, 377.

Thompson (1956), pl. xxiv, *a*.
Wilson and Blunt (1961), *passim*.

Found with nos. 90–100, 102 and 103. For details of find, etc., see entry for no. 90.

Before 875. See above, pp. 52, 63 and pl. XXXVII.

102. Another similar. Length 2·2 cm.

Reg. no. 80, 4–10, 18. Given by J. J. Rogers, Esq. From Trewhiddle, Cornwall.

BIBLIOGRAPHY
VCH Cornwall, i, 377.
Thompson (1956), pl. xxiv, *a*.
Wilson and Blunt (1961), *passim*.

Found with nos. 90–101 and 103. For details of find, etc., see entry for no. 90.

Before 875. See above, pp. 52, 63 and pl. XXXVII.

103. Bronze buckle and plate; the buckle plate consists of a thin plain strip of bronze slightly pointed at one end, bent in two so that the pointed end projects slightly. Rivet-holes for a single rivet remain at the end away from the loop. The surface is pitted with corrosion and the plate is pierced in a number of places. The bend of the plate has a square cut in it, from which the buckle tongue originally emerged. The loop is semi-circular, with a straight bar which passes inside the bend of the buckle plate. The loop is semi-circular in section and a small nick is allowed for the tongue to be engaged. The tongue is missing. The whole is undecorated.   Length: 4·2 cm.

Reg. no. 80, 4–10, 19. Given by J. J. Rogers, Esq. From Trewhiddle, Cornwall.

BIBLIOGRAPHY
Rashleigh (1789), 188 and pl. viii, 17.
The Archaeological Journal, xxi (1864), 184.
VCH Cornwall, i, 377.
Thompson (1956), pl. xxiv, *a*, 1.
Wilson and Blunt (1961), *passim*.

Found with nos. 90–102. For details of find, etc., see entry for 90.

Before 875. See above p. 53 and pl. XXXVII.

104. Bronze circular seal matrix. On the obverse is a half-length bust of a man in profile. He is crowned with a fillet or diadem from which emerge two streamers. The folds of his robe can be seen on his right shoulder and he holds a sword with a D-shaped pommel and straight guard in his left hand, with its point upwards. The bust is surrounded by a border containing the legend +SIGILLVM ÆLFRICIXX, contained by a pair of incised lines. On the reverse is a conventional engraved design. Within a border is a hollow-sided lozenge defined by a double line and with a formalised acanthus design emerging from two corners. The design of these two acanthus leaves consists of an upstanding central element flanked by two long scrolled leaves. From a ring-and-dot, in the centre of the lozenge, emerges a cruciform motif which interlaces with the sides of the lozenge to produce a single, fan-shaped, acanthus-leaf beyond each side of the quadrilateral leaf. The remaining corners of the panel have apparently merely a collar and no produced acanthus ornament. The space here is largely taken up with solder and broken bronze in sunken fields.   Diameter: 4·3 cm.

Reg. no. 32, 5–12, 2. Given by H. Barnes, Esq. From Weeke, Hampshire.

BIBLIOGRAPHY
Barnes (1832), 359.
Madden (1856), 370.
Birch (1887), 2.
Proceedings of the Society of Antiquaries of London,
  2 series, xxiii (1910), 305.
VCH Hampshire, i, 397–8 and fig. 16.
BMASG, 110.
Brøndsted (1924), 255 and fig. 183.
Talbot Rice (1952), 235.
Tonnochy (1952), xviii, 2–3 and pl. i.

Found on 29 March 1832, by a labourer cutting away a bank on the Winchester/Stockbridge road, about three-quarters of a mile from the then boundary of Winchester in the parish of Weeke.

Late tenth century. See above, pp. 5, 43, 60, 79, 81–82 and pl. XXXVIII.

105. Gilt-bronze mount. In the centre of the mount is a circular hole surrounded by a plain field, which is in turn surrounded by a regular interlace chain pattern. The interlace is bordered by a circular band made up of three ridges. Outside this the mount takes the form of an octofoil made up of two triple-ridged bands, each of which makes four penannular loops before interlacing with the end of the other band. The four loose ends form small animal heads. The heads have a squared snout, an almond-shaped eye, a closed mouth and a curved cheek line. Each band interlaces with a circle equidistant between the inner circular band and the edge of the mount. The pattern forms two crosses with expanded arms and rounded terminals, set at an angle of 45° from each other. The space between the arms of these crosses and the large circle is left *à jour*. Rivet-holes occur in two arms of one of the crosses in the outer field—two corresponding arms, which are fragmentary, may have had similar holes. The fields defined by the bands are filled with irregular angular interlace. The object is fragmentary, being in sixteen pieces. The back is plain. Diameter: about 10·4 cm.

Reg. no. W. 27. On permanent loan from Mrs. Strickland. From Whitby Abbey, Yorkshire.

BIBLIOGRAPHY
Peers and Radford (1943), 52 and pl. xxvi, b.

Found during excavation or site clearance.

Eighth century. See above, pp. 10, 14, 15, 20, 21, 59 and pl. XXXVIII.

106. Another, similar. It appears to have been cast from the same mould. It is much damaged and the surface is corroded. Part of the central dome-headed boss remains and three of the arms of the crosses have rivet-holes. The back is plain.

Maximum surviving diameter: 10·0 cm.

Reg. no. W. 28. On permanent loan from Mrs. Strickland. From Whitby Abbey, Yorkshire.

BIBLIOGRAPHY
Peers and Radford (1943), 52.

Found during excavation or site clearance.

Eighth century. See above, pp. 10, 14, 15, 20, 21, 59 and pl. XXXVIII.

107. Bronze gilt octofoil openwork mount. In the middle of the decorated face is an empty setting surrounded by a panel of angular interlace. This panel is defined by a plain border. Outside this border are eight overlapping, almost complete, circles interlaced with a large circle centred on the empty setting. The large circle is made up of two plain bands flanking a faceted zig-zag band. The double contoured overlapping circles form two overlapping crosses, each with expanded terminals. The spaces between the arms of the two crosses are cut out above the large circle and four iron, dome-headed rivets were inserted in the space within the large circle, two of these survive. In the panels defined by the raised borders is angular chip carved interlace ornament; the interlace within the different fields varies in design; only rarely is there a repetition. Traces of gilt remain on the face. The back is plain and much corroded. It would seem from its colour that the object has been burnt. Maximum diameter: 9·0 cm.

Reg. no. W. 29. On permanent loan from Mrs. Strickland. From Whitby Abbey, Yorkshire.

BIBLIOGRAPHY
Burlington Fine Arts Club, Catalogue of an Exhibi-   A.D. 1), London 1930, 29 and pl. iii, A.36.
tion of art in the Dark Ages, (c. 400-1000   Peers and Radford (1943), 52 and pl. xxvi, a.

Found during excavation or site clearance.
To the back of this piece was adhering the filigree piece (no. 108).

Eighth century. See above, pp. 10, 14, 15, 59 and pl. xxxix.

108. Gold beaded-wire filigree collar with fragments of gold plate adhering to it.

Diameter: 1·1 cm.

Reg. no. W. 30. On permanent loan from Mrs. Strickland. From Whitby Abbey, Yorkshire.

BIBLIOGRAPHY
Peers and Radford (1943), 52.

Found during excavation or site clearance. Found adhering to the back of no. 107.

657–867. See above, pp. 15, 66 and pl. xxxix.

109. Silver roundel. The roundel is fragmentary and part is missing. The field is encircled by a beaded border, which is broken intentionally at one point by the remains of a broken off lug. The lug apparently had a square outline and a circular, central hole. Within the beaded border is a plain, linear border which encloses a backward-looking animal. The animal has a slightly upturned snout and a bump over the eye represents the forehead. The open mouth bites the upturned back legs. Rather far back on the head is an amorphous ear. The neck is collared by means of a double wavy band; the body, which has a series of double nicks at the edges, diminishes towards the hindquarters. The tail rises from a nick in the rump to form a scroll in front of the snout. The front leg is very short and vertical and has three nicks in the foot. One of the back legs bends at the hip, cuts through the body, the paw curling into the animal's open mouth. A second tail curled down below the hind-leg and formed a scroll above the front paw. The body of the animal is speckled all over with an oval punch. The engraved background apparently contained no niello. The back is covered with modern adhesive but is evidently plain.

Diameter: 1·6 cm.

Reg. no. W. 32. On permanent loan from Mrs. Strickland. From Whitby Abbey, Yorkshire.

BIBLIOGRAPHY
Peers and Radford (1943), 53, pl. xxvii, d and   Haseloff (1951), pl. 11, 3.
fig. 10, 8.

Found during excavation or site clearance.

Early ninth century. See above, pp. 25, 27, 33, 66 and pl. xxxix.

110. Bronze mount. Circular flat plate with central hole and two subsidiary secondary holes at the point where the border is broken away. The curve of the circle is broken at this point as part of the original design. Inside a double linear border is a cross with expanded arms, between which are triquetra knots. The back is plain.   Diameter: 2·2 cm.

Reg. no. W. 37. On permanent loan from Mrs. Strickland. From Whitby Abbey, Yorkshire.

BIBLIOGRAPHY

Peers and Radford (1943), 54, pl. xxvii, a and fig. 10, 16.

Found during excavation or site clearance.

Eighth century. See above, pp. 14, 66 and pl. xxxix.

III. Bronze fragment of sheet metal, showing portions of two panels divided by three engraved lines. The ornament in the panels is an irregular interlace made up of a series of short lines punched into the surface of the metal. The sheet is bent into a gentle curve.

Maximum surviving length: 3·0 cm.

Reg. no. W. 38. On permanent loan from Mrs. Strickland. From Whitby Abbey, Yorkshire.

BIBLIOGRAPHY

Peers and Radford (1943), 54, pl. xxvii, a and fig. 10, 7.

Found during excavations or site clearance.

Eighth century. See above, p. 66 and pl. xxxix.

112. Thin bronze plate. The plate is six-sided with four long sides of equal length and two short sides of equal length, which give it the shape of a truncated lozenge. The plate is divided into four by a cross with a single plaited chain in the centre. In each of the four fields so formed is an irregular, angular, ribbon-interlace ornament: the whole carried out in a series of engraved lines. The plate is dished, rising slightly on all sides from the edges to the central midrib. It is fragmentary and incomplete, being broken into seven pieces. Small holes at the ends of each panel of ornament (two of which survive) apparently carried the rivets that attached the plate to its base. The back is plain.

Surviving length: 6·3 cm.

Reg. no. W. 42. On permanent loan from Mrs. Strickland. From Whitby Abbey, Yorkshire.

BIBLIOGRAPHY

Peers and Radford (1943), 54, pl. xxvii, a and fig. 10, 2.

Found during excavation or site clearance

Eighth century. See above, p. 66 and pl. xxxix.

113. Thin silver cross applied to a slightly thicker bronze base. The arms of the cross have concave sides and expand so that originally they met at the tips to form a disc. The object is fragmentary and much buckled. The back is plain.   Diameter: 3·5 cm.

Reg. no. W. 48. On permanent loan from Mrs. Strickland. From Whitby Abbey, Yorkshire.

BIBLIOGRAPHY

Peers and Radford (1943), 55 and fig. 10, 6.

Found during excavation or site clearance.

Eighth/ninth century. See above, p. 55 and pl. xxxix.

114. Silver strap-end. At the terminal is an animal's head, seen from above in relief, with prominent eyes, triangular scrolled ears and a billeted trefoil motif on its forehead. At the split end is a dome-headed rivet in a sub-oval field. In the central field is an animal with an open mouth; it is collared and a line from the eye gives the impression that the eye and the top of the head are separated from the lower part. The ear is rounded. A two-element tendril issues from the lower jaw, one frond passing under the front leg. The front leg, which has a single nick at the paw, extends horizontally from the front of the body. The line of the back rises from the neck and falls again to the rump, the rear hip extending forward and the back leg rising and cutting through the body. The contour of the body is decorated with a series of double nicks. The tail forms a loop and is interlaced with a simple scroll. The whole animal is set against a background of niello. There is a beaded border on either side of the field above the terminal head of the strap-end. The back of the object is plain. Length: 4·0 cm.

Reg. no. W. 52. On permanent loan from Mrs. Strickland. From Whitby Abbey, Yorkshire.

BIBLIOGRAPHY
Peers and Radford (1943), 56, pl. xxvii, d and   Wilson and Blunt (1961), 121.
fig. 11, 2.

Found during excavation or site clearance.

Early ninth century. See above, pp. 27, 29, 62 and pl. xxxix.

115. Bronze strap-end. At the terminal is a formalised animal head in slight relief. The ears are oval with horseshoe shaped openings, the forehead is plain and the eyes are round. The snout is corroded away. The upper face at the split end was broken away in antiquity, when the original two bronze rivets were replaced by a single iron rivet. In the small central field is a backward-looking animal with squared snout, a long head and protruding ear, the foreleg is raised in front of the animal, while the hind-leg, which emerges from a shaped hip, is bent forward. Under the front hip is a plain billet of metal. Traces of the fan-shaped field, normally found in this position, can be seen towards the two rivets. Each foot of the animal has a nick representing a two-element paw. The back of the object is plain. Length: 3·8 cm.

Reg. no. W. 53. On permanent loan from Mrs. Strickland. From Whitby Abbey, Yorkshire.

BIBLIOGRAPHY
Peers and Radford (1943), 56, fig. 11, 6 and pl.   Wilson and Blunt (1961), 121.
xxvii, c, 36.

Found during excavation or site clearance.

Early ninth century. See above, pp. 27, 28, 62 and pl. xl.

116. Bronze strap-end. At the terminal is a plastic formalised animal head in relief seen from above. The ears are scrolled, meeting in a pear-shaped terminal in the centre, the eyes are round and the nose and eye ridges are deeply moulded. At the split end are two rivet-holes and pendant between them are three leaves. The central field is inlaid with niello, but it is much corroded and the design is difficult to interpret. It appears to contain an animal, but the details are unclear. The field is defined by a plain, nielloed, border. The back of the object is plain. Length: 4·1 cm.

Reg. no. W. 54. On permanent loan from Mrs. Strickland. From Whitby Abbey, Yorkshire.

BIBLIOGRAPHY
Peers and Radford (1943), 56, fig. 11, 10 and   Wilson and Blunt (1961), 121.
pl. xxviii, c, 38.

Found during excavation or site clearance.

Early ninth century. See above, pp. 27, 62 and pl. xl.

117. Bronze strap-end. At the terminal is a much corroded, plastic, formalised animal head. It has oval ears with lunate openings but the other features are obscure. At the split end between the two rivet-holes (one of which retains a rivet with a prominent flattened head) is a pendant trilobate leaf motif. The two outer leaves are plain but the central one is panelled. In the central field of the object is an animal with its head in the top right-hand corner, its outline inlaid in niello. At the nostril is a small fragment of niello the size of a pin-head. The ear is almond-shaped and panelled, while the eye is represented by a small blob of niello. The neck is apparently collared. The body of the animal forms a U-shaped curve and there are a series of nicks along the top of the back. The corroded nature of the surface has obscured the limbs of the animal. The back of the object is plain. Length: 5·0 cm.

Reg. no. W. 55. On permanent loan from Mrs. Strickland. From Whitby Abbey, Yorkshire.

BIBLIOGRAPHY
Peers and Radford (1943), 56 f., fig. 11, 1 and   Wilson and Blunt (1961), 121.
pl. xxv, cii, 39.

Found during excavation or site clearance.

Early ninth century. See above, pp. 27, 28, 62 and pl. xl.

118. Bronze strap-end. At the terminal is a plastic formalised animal head, badly corroded but evidently having lentoid eyes. The split end has two rivet-holes (the shank of one rivet survives), pendant between them is a field containing three formalised leaves. In the central field is an unintelligible linear ornament inlaid with slightly corroded niello. The same inlay occurs in the simple border of the field. The back of the object is plain. Length: 4·0 cm.

Reg. no. W. 56. On permanent loan from Mrs. Strickland. From Whitby Abbey, Yorkshire.

BIBLIOGRAPHY
Peers and Radford (1943), 57, fig. 11, 14 and   Wilson and Blunt (1961), 121.
pl. xxviii, c, 40.

Found during excavation or site clearance.

Early ninth century. See above, p. 62, and pl. xl.

119. Bronze strap-end. At the terminal is a formalised plastic animal head, very much corroded, with two shallow borings in the ears. Between and beneath the two rivet-holes (in which the shanks of the rivets survive) at the split end are three pendant, formalised leaves. In the central panel within the nielloed border is a formalised linear design inlaid with niello. The back is plain. Length: 3·2 cm.

Reg. no. W. 57. On permanent loan from Mrs. Strickland. From Whitby Abbey, Yorkshire.

BIBLIOGRAPHY
Peers and Radford (1943), 57, fig. 11, 9 and   Wilson and Blunt (1961), 121.
pl. xxviii, c, 41.

Found during excavation or site clearance.

Early ninth century. See above, p. 62 and pl. XL.

120. Bronze strap-end. At the terminal is a formalised animal head executed in low relief. The snout and eyes are much corroded but the ears remain and are of oval shape with inverted V-shaped openings. The split end is broken off, but the remains of two rivet-holes can be seen. The field between and below the rivet-holes evidently contained a foliate motif (the tips of two leaves remain). In the central field is a contorted animal with neck and body forming a loop with the head in the centre. The mouth is open and the animal has a looped ear with a pit-like terminal. The front leg extends below the head and it is possible that the back leg rises in front of the head—this supposition is based on the drawing published by Peers and Radford (1943), fig. 11, 12, for this area is now corroded. The body of the animal is decorated with a series of small punched or bored marks. The back of the object is plain. Length: 3·5 cm.

Reg. no. W. 58. On permanent loan from Mrs. Strickland. From Whitby Abbey, Yorkshire.

BIBLIOGRAPHY
Peers and Radford (1943), 57, fig. 11, 12 and   Wilson and Blunt (1961), 121.
pl. xxviii, c, 42.

Found during excavation or site clearance.
Peers and Radford (1943) drew the object in its original state before corrosion set in and show rounded eyes and two nostrils at the terminal, the latter are rather suspect, but the rest of their detail can probably be accepted.

Early ninth century. See above, pp. 27, 28, 62 and pl. XL.

121. Bronze strap-end (?). The terminal is spatulate and is cross ribbed. At the split end are two rivet-holes; one complete rivet and part of the shank of the other survives. Between the rivets and below them, in a fan-shaped field, are three formalised leaves. In the main field is an animal which is speckled all over. A central hole, made in antiquity breaks up the central field. The figure in this field is much damaged by this hole: it is square cut and appears to have a shaped hip, leg and tail at its hindquarters. The details of the front parts are rather nebulous. The back of the object is plain. Length: 3·4 cm.

Reg. no. W. 59. On permanent loan from Mrs. Strickland. From Whitby Abbey, Yorkshire.

BIBLIOGRAPHY
Peers and Radford (1943), 57, fig. 11, 7 and   Wilson and Blunt (1961), 121.
pl. xxviii, c, 43.

Found during excavation or site clearance.
It would seem that this object was adapted in antiquity as a book clasp.

Early ninth century. See above, pp. 27, 62 and pl. xl.

122. Bronze strap-end. The terminal is spatulate and ribbed at the top, the tip forms an animal head moulded in low relief, with the ears set above the ribbing on the main body of the strap-end. The ears are formed from scrolls. Above the ears is a row of square billets with a central dot, in the centre of the field is an inverted triangle. Below the two rivet-holes at the split end is a fan-shaped field containing three pendant leaves. The back of the object is plain.   Length: 4·6 cm.

Reg. no. W. 60. On permanent loan from Mrs. Strickland. From Whitby Abbey, Yorkshire.

BIBLIOGRAPHY
Peers and Radford (1943), 57, fig. 11, 4 and   Wilson and Blunt (1961), 121.
pl. xxviii, c, 44.

Found during excavation or site clearance.

Early ninth century. See above, pp. 27, 62 and pl. xl.

123. Bronze strap-end. Both terminal and split end are broken away; two secondary rivet-holes have been cut through the split end, but traces of the rivet-holes remain. The border is defined by engraved lines, each of which is interrupted by a triangular nick, which engages with the break between two opposed chevrons in the centre of the field. The chevrons are executed with two chisel cuts and are shallow towards the point. Traces of a similar chevron can be seen towards the split end. The back of the object is plain.
                Surviving length: 3·0 cm.

Reg. no. W. 61. On permanent loan from Mrs. Strickland. From Whitby Abbey, Yorkshire.

BIBLIOGRAPHY
Peers and Radford (1943), 58 and fig. 11, 3.   Wilson and Blunt (1961), 121.

Found during excavation or site clearance.

Early ninth century. See above, p. 62 and pl. xl.

124. Bronze strap-end. The terminal, which is of circular cross-section, is bar-like and ribbed. The split end is broken off. The central panel is filled with an engraved design based on short curves which touch and interlock with each other. The design is surrounded by an incised border. The back is plain.   Surviving length: 3·8 cm.

Reg. no. W. 62. On permanent loan from Mrs. Strickland. From Whitby Abbey, Yorkshire.

BIBLIOGRAPHY
Peers and Radford (1943), 58, fig. 11, 13, and   Wilson and Blunt (1961), 121.
pl. xxviii, c, 45.
Found during excavation or site clearance.
Early ninth century. See above, p. 62 and pl. XL.

125. Bronze strap-end. Similar to no. 124. The split end is also missing and the design less carefully executed. The object is buckled towards the split end.

Surviving length: 3·2 cm.

Reg. no. W. 63. On permanent loan from Mrs. Strickland. From Whitby Abbey, Yorkshire.

BIBLIOGRAPHY
Peers and Radford (1943), 58 and fig. 11, 11.   Wilson and Blunt (1961), 121.
Found during excavation or site clearance.
Early ninth century. See above, p. 62 and pl. XL.

126. Bronze strap-end. The terminal is bar-like and the split end is broken convexly. In the central field, defined by an incised border, two laterally placed rows of interlocking curved lines can be seen faintly. The object is much corroded. The back of the object is plain.   Surviving length: 4·0 cm.

Reg. no. W. 64. On permanent loan from Mrs. Strickland. From Whitby Abbey, Yorkshire.

BIBLIOGRAPHY
Peers and Radford (1943), 58 and fig. 11, 8.   Wilson and Blunt (1961), 121.
Found during excavation or site clearance.
Early ninth century. See above, p. 62 and pl. XL.

127. Bronze strap-end. The decoration of this long and pointed object has disappeared as a result of corrosion. Traces of the segmental field at the split end can still be seen.

Length: 4·0 cm.

Reg. no. W. 65. On permanent loan from Mrs. Strickland. From Whitby Abbey, Yorkshire.

BIBLIOGRAPHY
Wilson and Blunt (1961), 121.
Found during excavation or site clearance.
Early ninth century. See above, p. 62 and pl. XL.

128. Bronze strap-end. Much corroded, long, pointed strap-end, there are possibly traces of a formalised animal-head terminal. It is broken at the split end, which contained two rivets which are now missing. The centre of the strap-end contained a decorative panel, but this is now indistinguishable due to corrosion. The back is plain.

Surviving length: 4·0 cm.

Reg. no. W. 66. On permanent loan from Mrs. Strickland. From Whitby Abbey, Yorkshire.
Found during excavation or site clearance.
Early ninth century. See above, p. 62 and pl. XL.

129. Bronze strap-end. The object is much corroded, back and front, and no ornament is now visible. The terminal appears to have been a circular bar and the split end may have held two rivets, but both are broken away. Surviving length: 2·6 cm.

Reg. no. W. 67. On permanent loan from Mrs. Strickland. From Whitby Abbey, Yorkshire.

Found during excavation or site clearance.

Early ninth century. See above, p. 62 and pl. XL.

130. Bronze, lentoid bezel of a finger-ring with a small part of the hoop surviving. Within a plain, slightly hatched border is a contorted animal ornament. At one end of the field is an animal head with a squared snout, prominent forehead, elongated linear eye and squared prominent ear. Beneath the head is the front leg with a two-element paw: the back leg and tail are in the opposite corner. The animal is collared and a series of double nicks decorate the contours of the body. Rising from the rump is an animal head with its lower jaw nearest to the upper border. Above this jaw and along the border is a small foot-like element, this secondary head has a linear eye, a squared snout (with an open mouth) and a stubby ear. The edge of the bezel is much corroded and the border is fractured in places. The inside of the ring is plain.

FIG. 45. Ornament of no. 130. $\frac{1}{1}$.

Length: 2·3 cm.

Reg. no. W. 73. On permanent loan from Mrs. Strickland. From Whitby Abbey, Yorkshire.

BIBLIOGRAPHY
Peers and Radford (1943), 58 and fig. 12, 5.

Found during excavation or site clearance.

Early ninth century. See above, pp. 27, 56 and pl. XL.

131. Bronze pin, or stylus, with sub-triangular head to which is applied a silver repoussé plate. The plate has a beaded border which encloses a symmetrical interlace ribbon ornament. On the shaft of the pin are five mouldings, each divided into three cords. Each of the parts of the sections of the shaft so formed has a slight entasis.

Length: 13·9 cm.

Reg. no. W. 334. On permanent loan from Mrs. Strickland. From Whitby Abbey, Yorkshire.

BIBLIOGRAPHY
Burlington Fine Arts Club. Catalogue of an exhibition of art in the Dark Ages (c. 400–1000 A.D.), London 1930, 29.

Peers and Radford (1943), 64, fig. 15, 7 and pl. xxvii, c.
Wilson (1961), 211.

Found during excavation or site clearance.

Eighth century. See above, p. 63 and pl. XL.

132. Bronze key. The shank and loop only survive. The loop contains an openwork saltire with ring and dot ornament on the loop at the end of each arm and at the crossing. The ornament is repeated back and front. Length: 5·0 cm.

Reg. no. W. 362. On permanent loan from Mrs. Strickland. From Whitby Abbey, Yorkshire.

BIBLIOGRAPHY

Peers and Radford (1943), 66, and fig. 17, 3. Almgren (1955), 11, 106, fig. 6.

Found during excavation or site clearance.

Eighth/ninth century. See above, p. 57 and pl. XL.

133. Iron stirrup-iron, inlaid with copper. It has a square loop (with flanged vertical sides) to take the stirrup leather, the lower portion of the loop is decorated (on one side only) with four transverse lines of copper wire. An oval knop separates this loop from the hoop; the knop was originally plated, back and front, with a square of copper: the plating has almost completely disappeared from the back of the object. The main hoop of the stirrup-iron above the foot plate is of sub-triangular form, the triangle having long sides which curve sharply to the knop at the top. It is of sub-triangular cross section above a pair of hollow, hemi-spherical bosses near the base of the triangle. From this point the side elements become plates which curve concavely to a sub-rectangular base. The foot plate is convex and is supported internally by a twisted iron bar. The bosses are plated in the same way as the knop, while all the other outer surfaces were decorated with a running spiral ornament. The ornament of the side plates consists of a tree-like feature on either side of a central stem. The copper wire in which this ornament is executed is worn away in places. The surface of the metal was prepared for inlaying by incised cross-hatching; the wire being beaten into the keyed surface.   Height: 31·8 cm.

Reg. no. 58, 11–16, 6. Given by the [Royal] Archaeological Institute. From the bed of the River Witham, near Lincoln.

Tenth/eleventh century. See above, pp. 39, 62 and pl. XLI.

134. Pewter circular brooch. The face has a small raised boss in the centre of a lozenge with concave sides. This is surrounded by a border made up of three beaded lines, which

alternate with two plain lines. The back of the brooch is plain but the iron pin, the pewter hinge and the pewter catch-plate survive. The ornament is all raised and has been cast. The metal has been confirmed by laboratory examination as a tin/lead alloy.

Maximum diameter: 3·8 cm.

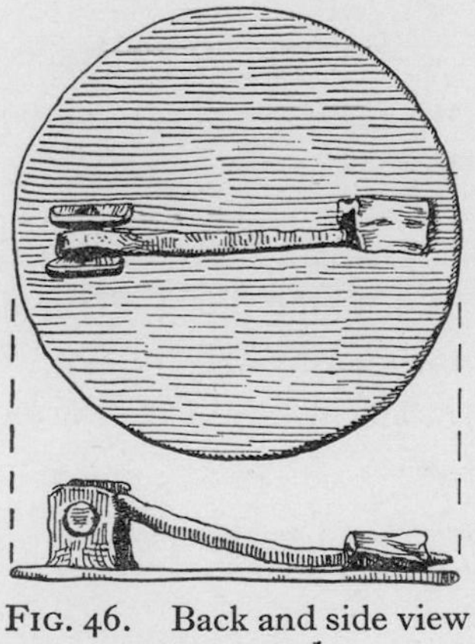

Reg. no. 76, 2–12, 27. Purchased from the Rev. Canon William Greenwell, F.R.S., F.S.A. From York.

BIBLIOGRAPHY

The Proceedings of the Society of Antiquaries of London, xxii (1908), 66 and pl. facing p. 63, no. 3.

FIG. 46. Back and side view of no. 138. ⅟₁.

Tenth century. See above, p. 52 and pl. XLII.

135. Bronze strap-end. The split end is scalloped and contains two rivets. The terminal is an animal's head seen from above, narrowing to a neck which is flanked by elongated, curved ears separated from the main body of the strap-end by pointed oval openings.

The head has prominent eyes; the two nostrils being indicated by small borings. The head is panelled with shallow incised lines, which were originally inlaid with niello. In the field behind the head is an interlaced pattern which is difficult to interpret (but which appears to have certain zoomorphic characteristics) above a small panel filled with small circles. The interlace ornament is inlaid with niello most of which is missing. The back is plain. Length: 4·5 cm.

Reg. no. 79, 12–9, 2090. Given by the Rev. Canon William Greenwell, F.R.S., F.S.A. From York.

BIBLIOGRAPHY
Brøndsted (1924), 131.
BMASG, fig. 131, 4.
Gilbert (1954), fig. 24.
Wilson and Blunt (1961), 121.

The British Museum Research Laboratory has examined the inlay in this specimen and submitted the following report: 'a silvery inlay of low resistance containing silver, copper, gold, tin and lead. This inlay is now completely metallic . . . it may originally have been niello.'

Tenth century. See above, pp. 29, 62 and pl. XLII.

136. Bronze strap-end. There are two rivet-holes at the split end and below them, in a rectangular field, is an inverted V-shaped motif. A plastic animal head forms the terminal: it has oval ears with lunate openings and small pointed eyes. In the central field two, touching, billeted cords of a circle divide the field; the four areas thus delimited are filled with scratched and hatched ornament. An incised line is inscribed along the long sides of the central field. The back is featureless. A fragment is broken from one corner of the left-hand rivet-hole at the top-back. Length: 4·5 cm.

Reg. no. 73, 6–2, 64. Purchased from Mrs. Ruth Faulkner, from Youlgreave, Derbyshire.

BIBLIOGRAPHY
Brøndsted (1924), 132 *n.*
Wilson and Blunt (1961), 121.
Found in a mine at Youlgreave probably with nos. 137-139.
From the collection of J. F. Lucas, of Ashbourne, Derby.
Ninth century. See above, pp. 28, 62 and pl. XLII.

137. Bronze strap-end. There are two rivet-holes at the split end and, pendant between them, three leaves in a fan-shaped field. In the centre of the strap-end is a long panel, defined by a beaded border, containing a regular ribbon-interlace pattern inlaid with niello. At the terminal is a formalised animal head, seen from above, with oval ears with lunate openings. The snout is much worn. The back of the object is plain. Length: 4·2 cm.

Reg. no. 73, 6–2, 66. Purchased from Mrs. Ruth Faulkner. From Youlgreave, Derbyshire.
Details as for no. 136.
The niello inlay was examined in the British Museum Research Laboratory who submitted the following report concerning it (18 April 1957): 'A black inlay of high resistance containing silver and copper, gold, tin and lead. From its appearance and high resistance this niello seems to resemble the "acanthite" niello as found in the Fuller brooch and described by Moss in *Conservation*, Vol. I, No. 2.'

Ninth century. See above, pp. 28, 62 and pl. XLII.

138. Bronze strap-end. It has a straight split end with two rivet-holes (one retaining the shank of the rivet); it is much worn and corroded. There are three pendant leaves in the fan-shaped field below the rivet-holes and an indistinct animal head can just be seen at the terminal: the ears are scrolled and the eyes are hollowed out. The central field, which has a beaded border, contains a regular interlace pattern made up of a dotted ribbon. The back is plain and undecorated. Length: 4·6 cm.

Reg. no. 73, 6–2, 67. Purchased from Mrs. Ruth Faulkner. From Youlgreave, Derbyshire. Details as for no. 136.
Ninth century. See above, pp. 27, 28, 62 and pl. XLII.

139. Fragment of bronze strap-end. The split end is missing; only the central panel and the terminal remain. The terminal is formed as an animal head, seen from above, in low relief. The forehead and snout are made up of opposed triangles and the eyes are pointed ovals, the ears are square, with an engraved border. The central field is made up of two rows of interlocking engraved 'V's' with a triangle at each end. The long edges of the central field are bevelled down to a slightly offset border. The back is plain.
Length: 2·5 cm.

Reg. no. 73, 6–2, 68. Purchased from Mrs. Ruth Faulkner. From Youlgreave, Derbyshire. Details as for no. 136.
Ninth century. See above, pp. 28, 62 and pl. XLII.

140. Bronze key. The lozenge-shaped bow is filled with an openwork linear cross, with a central pierced hole. A large and very worn suspension loop is set at right-angles to the bow at the top of the lozenge. The oval shank is hollow and the rectangular tongue has a central hole and forked, upturned terminal. Length: 7·8 cm.

Reg. no. 36, 9–1, 140. Purchased from Mrs. Lang. No recorded provenance.

BIBLIOGRAPHY
Almgren, (1955). 106, and Tab. II: F/7.
Ninth/eleventh century. See above p. 57 and pl. XLII.

141. Bronze openwork mount. From a protruding animal head, modelled in relief with triangular ears, emerges the snake-like body of a quadruped which forms a spiral loop, so that the mount has the shape of a circle with a single projection. From a front, spiral hip, immediately behind the head, emerges a straight leg which clutches one of the ribbons with which the animal interlaces. This is the only limb (although there is a back hip in the centre of the mount, which apparently produced a tendril-like tail). The main ribbon, which interlaces with the animal, starts on the right-hand side of the neck and runs into the centre of the field, giving off tendrils along its length. The back of the rounded portion of the mount is concave and plain, while behind the small head is the shank of a rivet which was cast in one piece with the mount. Part of the edge is broken away from the design on the right-hand side. The mount is much worn.
Length: 4·6 cm.

Reg. no. 62, 3–21, 7. Presented by Sir A. W. Franks, K.C.B. No recorded provenance.

BIBLIOGRAPHY
Shetelig (1909), 100 and fig. 26.
Åberg (1941), fig. 20, 9.
Kendrick (1949), 116 and fig. 19, *b*.

This object has been given an Irish provenance by Shetelig and Kendrick. There is no apparent reason for this since Franks's own entry in the register reads 'Origin unknown (bought many years since of Falcke, Bond St.).' In the 'Book of Presents to the British Museum', all the objects given by Franks in March 1862 are said to have been found in London. It would seem safer, however, to accept Franks's own registration of the object.

Eleventh century. See above, pp. 48, 51 and pl. XLII.

142. Pewter circular brooch. The face is ornamented in a cast technique with a degenerate imitation of a coin. In the centre of the brooch is a human bust facing right. The shoulders of the bust are draped and the border of a cloak or cuirass is represented by means of a ladder-like effect in relief. Round the head is the retrograde inscription: CONV TIV +. Each letter has a pronounced serif; the break is filled with a series of three trident-like features. This central panel is surrounded by a raised herring-bone border which is in turn surrounded by a beaded border, which is broken in one place. A small hole has been punched, secondarily, at the top of the brooch. On the back is a loop and a catch plate. The catch-plate has been bent down and the loop perhaps replaces an earlier hinge structure of which traces remain. The metal has been confirmed by laboratory examination as a tin/lead alloy. Diameter: 6·0 cm.

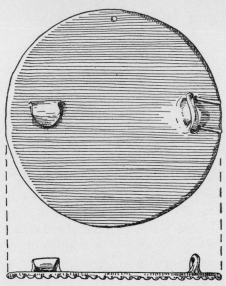

FIG. 47.   Back and side view of no. 142. ¼.

Reg. no. 62, 7–1, 19. Purchased, through G. Eastwood, Esq., from the Nightingale Sale. No recorded provenance.

BIBLIOGRAPHY
Proceedings of the Numismatic Society (25 April 1844), 28.

Tenth century. See above, pp. 35, 36 and pl. XLII.

143. Bronze fragment of a thin, engraved, sheet-metal panel—originally gilded on the decorated face, the gilding only survives in the light incisions of the graving tool. The fragment forms the end of a narrow rectangular panel. Within a plain, incised border a symmetrical foliate pattern is reserved against a cross-hatched background. Taking the complete end as the bottom of the panel: two ribbon-like scrolls extend from the corners of the broken side and form a pair of loops (linked by a ring) which, having looped, join and rise to form a scroll, flanked by a series of pendant scrolled leaves and fleshy tendrils—the longest leaf crosses the downward stroke of the loop. From the bottom of each loop a fleshy tendril emerges to form a loop with itself in the corner of the plate. The ring, which joins the two main loops, extends below them to produce two fleshy leaves, which spread out along the base of the mount. A lentoid ornament extends downwards from the joint of the two loops. Many of the main ribbons and leaves are decorated with a series of pairs of parallel incisions. The whole pattern is executed in shallow engraving. Wit h i the loops are four rivet-holes, pierced at random. The plate is slightly buckled and the back is plain. Maximum width: 2·9 cm.

Reg. no. 62, 7–7, 62. Given by Mrs. Martin Atkins. No recorded provenance.

BIBLIOGRAPHY
Proceedings of the Society of Antiquaries of London, Brøndsted (1924), 295.
xxvi (1914), 71 and fig. 13.   Shetelig (1941), iv, 59.

A provenance of 'probably from Berkshire' has been given in the past to this piece. There is no evidence for this attribution.

Tenth/eleventh century. See above, pp. 57, 50, 66 and pl. XLII.

144. Bronze strap-end. The strap-end is bent and slightly pitted with corrosion. Pendant between the two rivet-holes is a plant with four leaves arranged fan-wise. At the terminal is an animal head seen from above; on the snout (which is slightly faceted) is a cross patee, while a feather pattern of scratched lines can be seen on the forehead. The ears are oval and have lunate openings. The ornament in the central field, which is defined by a plain border, consists of two pairs of symmetrically opposed animals whose bodies and limbs degenerate into symmetrical interlace. At the top of the field, on either side, is an animal head with rounded crown, beaded eye and squared, short snout, open mouth and the suspicion of a tongue. Below and behind each of these heads is a smaller edition of the same head, the lower jaw of which crosses the neck of the larger animal and the lower jaw of its opposite number in the centre of the field, where it is surrounded by a heart-shaped ribbon. The amorphous bodies of these animals degenerate into interlace. The background is hatched in a basketry pattern. The back of the object is plain and the remains of an iron rivet can be seen in one of the rivet-holes. Length: 4·8 cm.

Reg. no. 96, 4–11, 164. Presented by Sir A. W. Franks, K.C.B. No recorded provenance.

BIBLIOGRAPHY
Wilson and Blunt (1961), 121.

Ninth century. See above, pp. 27, 62 and pl. XLII.

145. Gold finger-ring. Flat hoop of gold, slightly squashed and now almost oval in shape, the beaded border is badly worn. An inscription inlaid with niello reads:

The stops in between the letters are executed with the corner of a chisel. The inside of the hoop is plain. Maximum diameter: 2·8 cm.

Reg. no. AF 459. *Ring Cat.* No. 182. Bequeathed by Sir A. W. Franks, K.C.B. No recorded provenance.

BIBLIOGRAPHY
British Museum, Alfred the Great Millenary Exhibition, London 1901, 14.

B.M. Ring Cat., 30 and pl. ii, 182.
BMASG, 116.
Oman (1931), fig. B, 15.

Ninth century. See above, pp. 23, 27, 56, 80, 89, 90 and pl. XLII.

146. Gold finger-ring. On either side of the emerald bezel are the head, shoulders and front legs of an animal. The head is club-shaped, with two shallow circular borings for eyes.

FIG. 48.   Ornament of No. 146. $\frac{1}{1}$.

The legs lie alongside the head and touch each other on either side of the bezel. The bodies of the animals degenerate from the pronounced shoulders. A pair of wings and legs bear no relationship to the bodies of the animals. The ring is much worn and has been filed and cut about; it has been squashed slightly out of shape. The inside of the hoop is plain.   Diameter: 2·6 cm.

Reg. no. AF 492. *Ring Cat.* No. 167. Bequeathed by Sir A. W. Franks, K.C.B. No recorded provenance.

BIBLIOGRAPHY
B.M. Ring Cat., 26 and pl. i, 168.

Ninth century. See above, p. 56 and pl. XLII.

147. Cast, gilt-bronze, handled and spouted vessel. Below the slightly everted rim the sides of the vessel develop in a straight line to a rounded belly and a constriction above the foot. The constriction is ringed by a plain moulding; the foot expands from this moulding and is decorated with a border of contiguous crescents against a reserved roughened background. The concave underside of the foot is also gilded. The spout rises at one side and takes the form of an animal head with engraved lentoid eyes, mane, lips and throat. A spiral develops on either side of the mane. Below the belly of the spout is a double contoured triangle with a roughened centre. The spout is balanced by a serpentine handle which emerges from an animal head behind the broken hinge of the (now missing) lid. The handle is in the form of a snake and curls to one side below the point where it joins the belly of the vessel; it has been badly cut about and battered. The rest of the surface of the vessel is covered with a series of reliefs arranged in two sets of five on each side of the jug, two under the lip and three on the belly. The reliefs take the form of two adorsed birds, the raised mouths of which bite towards the downward-bent tendrils of a bifurcated stem which is placed between them. Above and between the two tendrils is a triangular feature crowned with a granule. Separating each set of adjoining reliefs, and above them, is a cat-like mask with lentoid eyes and small upturned ears. A similar much-worn mask appears beneath the loop of the handle. Above the spout is a further stamp, consisting of a winged beast with down-turned reversed head, the open mouth gripping its own tail.

The inside of the vessel is gilt and a small blow-hole pierces the side of the vessel in one of the animal figures.   Height: 7·2 cm.

Reg. no. AF 3175. Bequeathed by Sir A. W. Franks, K.C.B. No recorded provenance.

BIBLIOGRAPHY

Fairholt (1857), pl. xxi, 4.

Kendrick (1938c).

Kendrick (1949), 41 and pl. xxxvi, 3.

Talbot Rice (1952), 234 and pl. 90 b.

H. Swarzenski (1954), 49 and pl. 65, 149.

Arbman (1958), 190.

The object was at one time in the Londesborough collection (see Fairholt (1857)). It is probable that Franks bought it from that collection after the death of Lord Londesborough.

A letter from Dr. H. J. Plenderleith, the Keeper of the Research Laboratory at the British Museum (31 July 1936) reads '. . . it is a *cire perdue* casting in one piece covered with a wash of copper and then gilt. . . . I believe the tooling around (the) foot rim has been added after casting. . . .'

Tenth century. See above, pp. 43, 44, 46, 50, 57 and pl. XLIII.

148. Bronze cast strap-end with plain flat back. Six rivet-holes at the butt-end are bored in a plain rectangular field which is set at a slightly lower level than the main decorated surface. The rivet-holes are countersunk. The field of decoration is rectangular with a curved terminal. The border at the butt-end is high but elsewhere it is worn; it appears to be undecorated. Cast in low relief on the main field, amid tendrils of acanthus spreading from three central lobes (in the form of cat's heads with small stubby ears, but now much worn), are at the top a pair of backward-looking birds of naturalistic form. Below them are a pair of birds with sharply everted heads and legs touching the central stem. Their tails are produced below the tendril to the bottom of the field. The creatures are much worn but traces of wings can be seen. From the lowest of the three central cat-heads emerges a long expanding, round-ended, panelled tongue.   Length: 6·6 cm.

Reg. no. 1903, 6–23, 95. Purchased from Messrs. Rollin and Feuardent. No recorded provenance.

BIBLIOGRAPHY

Kendrick (1938c), 380 and pl. 74, 1.   Kendrick (1949), 41.

Kendrick[1] supposes that this piece came from London because it was bought with a number of other medieval objects of which some have a London provenance. There is no evidence for this identification. It came from the Cecil Brent Collection (sold at Messrs. Sotheby's, December, 1902) and is drawn in *Brent MS. 2*, fol. 68 r, no. 4 (Department of British and Medieval Antiquities, British Museum). Brent had a large collection of material from London—but he also had objects from Kent and elsewhere.

Tenth century. See above, pp. 43, 47, 62 and pl. XLIII.

149. Bronze rhomboid pendant with suspension loop (much worn) in centre of upper edge. The design, which appears to be cast, is surrounded by a raised border decorated with a lightly raised ladder-like pattern. Raised above the slightly sunken central field is a

---

[1] (1938c), 380 and (1949), 41.

triquetra knot of regular interlace, which occupies the whole field of ornament and is flanked by two small, spiral hooks issuing from the topmost, shorter, border. The back is plain.

Length of base: 2·8 cm.

Reg. no. 1903, 6–23, 97. Purchased from Messrs. Rollin and Feuardent. No recorded provenance. It came from the Cecil Brent Collection (sold at Messrs. Sotheby's, December, 1902).

Tenth century. See above, p. 59 and pl. XLIII.

150. Bronze weight. The weight is circular; on the face, surrounded by a plain border, is a quadruped against a carved background. It has a rounded ear, angular snout and a pear-shaped eye. One forefoot is raised forward and the other leg is straight, issuing from a thigh indicated by two incised lines. The hind-quarters are well shaped and both hind legs bend slightly forward, a tail runs down behind. Above the animal is a tendril decoration with an element of interlace. To fill out the empty spaces of the field are three round billets. The back and sides are plain.

Weight 68·7 gm., 1061 grains. Diameter 3·6 cm.

Reg. no. 1926, 10–20, 1. Given by L. A. Lawrence, Esq., F.S.A. No recorded provenance.

Ninth/tenth century. See above, p. 65 and pl. XLIII.

151. Bronze disc. The disc is slightly damaged and part of one side is missing but the full pattern can be restored. In the centre of the field is a circular sunken field enclosed by a 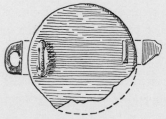 concave-sided figure the four corners of which are produced to form a loose knot. Each knot is double contoured. The whole pattern is surrounded by a plain border and the background has been carved away. The back is undecorated. A lug survives at one side and a stump in the same plane, at the other side, is possibly the remains of another lug.

Diameter: 2·9 cm.

FIG. 49. Back of no. 151. ¼.

Reg. no. 1942, 10–8, 17. Given by the Christy Trustees. No recorded provenance.

BIBLIOGRAPHY
Evison (1957), 220.

Purchased at Lord Grantley's sale (lot 65) (Messrs. Glendenings', 9 September 1942). Said to be from Kent, but the provenances of objects in the Grantley collection are questionable (cf. nos. 51–4) and it is for that reason included with the unprovenanced objects.

Eleventh century. See above, pp. 48, 52 and pl. XLIII.

152. Silver disc-brooch, dished and decorated on the convex surface with inlaid gold and niello ornament. The basic design is formed of a hollow-sided, cruciform figure (de-limited by a beaded border), with terminals in the form of animal masks seen from above, all within a quatrefoil field (partly delimited by a beaded border). The divisions of the lobes of the quatrefoil interlock with the spaces between the arms of the cross, and at these points are other animal masks. In the spaces between the lobes of the quatrefoil,

208

and in the centre, are dome-headed rivets, surrounded by a beaded wire collar. The disc has a triple border: the outermost is beaded, the second consists of a band of alternate lozenges and pellets and the third of an inlaid gold band, which has been speckled with the corner of an engraving tool after being placed in position: the speckling is not con-

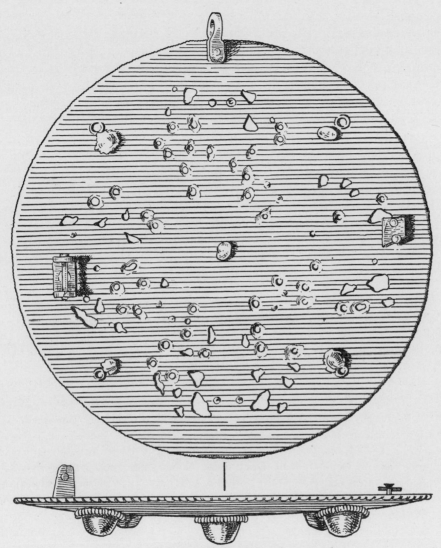

FIG. 50. Back and side views of no. 152. $\frac{1}{1}$.

fined to the gold band; it also occurs on the immediately surrounding silver. Within the fields round the bosses, and in the centre of the cruciform figure, is a scale pattern carried out by means of a series of inlaid gold plates, enclosed by a line inlaid with niello: most of the niello is now missing, but the keying is visible. The animal masks consist of a central hour-glass shape in inlaid gold, surrounded originally by a nielloed border, which forms the snout and forehead of the animal. This is surrounded by a plain silver border. In the space provided by the constriction are the eye sockets—in some of which survive blue glass cabochon eyes; the eyes are surrounded by crescent borders. The ears are shaped like scrolled pears. The inlaid gold plates are speckled, as are all the other gold plates on the brooch. In the fields between the cross and the quatrefoil are a series of small animals, divided from each other on one side by a beaded border and on the other side by the animal heads. The animals are carved in openwork and their bodies are inlaid with speckled gold plates. Each animal looks backwards and has a collar round its neck, its eye is represented by a small circular socket with no surviving filling. In the treatment of the heads, tails and the legs there is some variety: in one or two cases the mouth is indicated open, occasionally it is not indicated at all. Some of the heads have a relatively flat top with a pointed snout, others have a rounded skull and square snout. The tails either curl forward and meet the back under the chin or follow the line of the border. The legs are sometimes slightly elongated with double-nicked paws.

The back is plain save only for the rivets and a few nicks which are apparently proving marks. At the top is a loop attached by a single rivet, this may be original or secondary. Also on the back are a square hinge-plate and spindle, which carried the (now missing) pin, it is attached to the brooch by rivets which are riveted over on the face of the brooch. The catch-plate is broken but a fragment remains attached by two rivets (fig. 50).

Maximum diameter: 11·2 cm.

Reg. no. 1949, 7–2, 1. Purchased from Mrs. Strickland. No recorded provenance.

BIBLIOGRAPHY

Sotheby's Sale Catalogue, 9th May, 1949; lot 128, pls. iii–iv.

Bruce-Mitford (1952c), 75 and pl. xxx.

Moss (1953a), 61.

Moss (1953b), 76.

Wilson (1955a), 116 and fig. 6.

Bruce-Mitford (1956a), 190 ff., fig. 37 and pl. xxvi.

Wilson (1960a), 221 and pl. 64.

Dunning and Evison (1961), 141, 143, 144, 148 and 151.

Wilson and Blunt (1961), 94 and 105.

The object is known as the Strickland brooch. The brooch, which had been purchased by an American collector after a sale at Sotheby's (see sale catalogue cited above), was refused an export licence and was bought by the Museum (which was the underbidder). It formed part of a collection sold by Mrs. Strickland, then of Boynton Hall, Bridlington, Yorks, and, although unprovenanced, most probably formed part of the collection of the Yorkshire antiquary, Sir William Strickland (1753-1834), who collected widely in a number of fields. It has sometimes been assumed that it is of Yorkshire provenance, Wilson (1955a) and Bruce-Mitford (1956a), but there is no evidence for this.

The brooch is sufficiently authenticated by its history, but physical tests, carried out in the British Museum Research Laboratory, have proved beyond doubt that the brooch is not a forgery. The report of the Research Laboratory reads:

I have examined the silver brooch with care and it seems to me to be original. The metal (gold and silver), the niello, the blue glass eye inlays, and the method of construction (punch and chisel work) all seem to me to be in keeping. I consider the marks of wear to be old. The hanging ring is obviously later, and the brooch has been cleaned with rouge, not recently. I feel that there are grounds for assigning it considerable antiquity, apart from the ornament, and this being so it is probably authentic.

Subsequently the niello was examined and proved to be of the early type used before the eleventh century.[1]

Ninth century. See above, pp. 3, 16, 22 27, 31–34, 40, 52 and pl. XLIII.

153. Silver and niello disc brooch. The face is dished and is divided into two fields of orna-ment, a central circular panel and a broad border. The circular panel has a centrally

FIG. 51.   Section through no. 153.

placed, convex-sided, lozenge-shaped field containing a three-quarter-length human figure. The corners of this field touch the border of the circular panel thus delimiting four smaller fields, each of which contains a full-length human figure. The main lines bordering and dividing the surface of the brooch are finely billeted and a line produced from each corner of the central field divides the border into four. At the intersections of these lines and at the border of the central panel are slightly dome-headed rivets. Another similar rivet occurs in the centre of the brooch. In each of the four divisions of the border are four roundels containing various ornamental features: in each quadrant is a bird, an animal, a human figure and a semi-geometric floral ornament. The roundels in the border are defined by openwork sub-triangles. The ornament has been fully described by Bruce-Mitford[2] and in the shortened description published here I use his

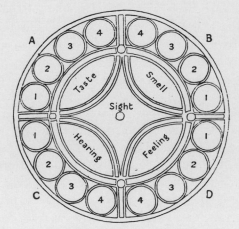

FIG. 52.   The division of the fields of no. 153.

numeration of the fields (fig. 52). *Roundel A*1 contains a bird with open mouth which bites the leaf-like terminal of a scroll which crosses its body. The head is in the bottom of the field, balancing a five-clawed foot in the opposite side of the field. The body, wing and tails are broken up into sections. *Roundel A*2 contains a floriated circle with a central

[1] Moss (1953*a*), 61.   [2] (1955), 173–7.

circular billet. *Roundel A3* contains a backward-looking animal with the head twisted so that the underside of the jaw and the back of the neck lie along the top of the roundel. The body and legs are naturalistic in shape and proportion and the tail forms a loop under the hind-leg and through the body. There are nicks beneath the chin and on the rump and two pairs of single lines cross the body completely. The animal has a mane. The eye is formed as a round dot with a curved eyebrow. *A4* contains the bust and shoulders of a human figure. The face is highly formalised and symmetrical. Eyebrows and nose are one continuous line, the eyes are represented as dots and the mouth has a downward twist. The ears are loop-like and stick out below the hair, which is parted centrally. The dress has a collar and central border and the arms appear to be emerging from the breasts. On either side of the head is a double V of foliage. *B1* is similar to field *A1* with slight variations, and field *B2* is similar to *A2*, except that the internal terminals of the petals are formed of a semi-circle and not a scalloped edge. The animal in field *B3* is similar, in general design, to that in field *A3*, but the mane has become more formalised and the tail has lost its character and become obscure. Field *A4* and *B4* are similar in all respects. *C1* contains an ornamental motif made up of interlocking scrolled curves set in a cruciform pattern within a quartered circle: in the angle of each arm of the cross which divides the circle is a round billet. *C2* contains an animal which is basically backward-looking, its long neck, collared below the head, expands towards the body which has a well-defined front hip and leg. The body tails off and is bitten across the belly by the jaws of the animal, after which it degenerates into an interlace pattern which spreads through the lower half of the field. The head is of similar shape to the heads of the other animals on the brooch with squarish snout and rounded cranium, the eye consisting of a dot surmounted by a curved line as eyebrow. The ear is of pointed oval shape. There is a V-shaped incision on the back of the animal and a double line crosses the body of the animal, between the front hip and the belly. *C3* contains an animal with downward-bent and twisted head, which bites in towards the foot. The eye consists of a dot with curved eyebrow, the mouth is open and a tongue can be seen. The body and the wing are panelled, the feathering of tail and wings being formalised. Behind the bird is a complicated scroll feature. The human bust in *C4* is similar to that in *A4* and *B4*. *D1* contains an animal whose head turns and bites across its body. Its head is similar to the other animals' heads on the brooch and the neck curves to join the body in a V-shaped cut. The paws are indicated by double nicks. Nicks occur in front of the small pendant tail and on the hind hip. Various leaf and billet patterns fill the rest of the field. Field *D2* contains a flower-like design, each petal being composed of an elongated petal. In the centre is a small ring. The bird in field *D3* is similar to that in *B3* save that it is slightly less cramped and the leaf in the mouth has become a scroll, the bird's body is panelled in the same way as that in *C3*. *D4* contains a human bust similar to the others in the roundels of this zone, save that there is a break at the bottom of the nose and no ridge on the upper lip.

In the central zone there are five human figures. To the top left is a man, in profile, with his arm bent and his right hand in his mouth. He has a small nose and a distorted pendant ear but a very prominent almond-shaped eye with a dot in the centre. His hair is made up of irregular billets as though representing curly hair. The other hand clutches a tendril. On his feet are shoes which appear to have a tongue and are either braided or tied at the ankle. He wears a tunic belted at the waist and apparently wears a long-sleeved bolero-like garment over it. Under his right arm is a triquetra and the spaces between his limbs, and between the borders of the field and his body, are filled with foliate motifs and dots. He faces outwards. The male figure (top-right) also faces outwards. His hands are tucked behind his back. His head is in profile, his chin is well defined and his eye consists of a dot with a curved eyebrow. In dress and in all other respects he is similar to the first figure. The background of the field is filled with scrolls and interlace. In the bottom-left field is a man depicted three-quarter face looking inwards. One leg is bent behind his thigh and one hand is also raised, as though to his ear, with the palm outwards. he is dressed in a similar manner to the other figures. His hair is parted in the middle and is straight, his features are delineated in a formal manner with lines and dots, his ear is small and slightly pendulous. The background is filled with leaves and scrolls. The figure, bottom-right, has one hand laid upon the other, his arm crosses the body and obscures the waist, his dress is similar to that of the other figures on the brooch. The face, which looks inwards, is in three-quarters profile and is closely related to the one in the bottom left. The legs are slightly bent. The three-quarter-length figure in the central panel is full-face with round, wide, open eyes with the pupil represented as a central dot; the eyes, nose and lip ridge are represented by a single line; above the eyes are two up-curved lines perhaps intended as eyebrows; the hair is straight and parted in the middle. He carries in each hand, at chest level, a horn from which spring four long foliate features, each leaf of which has a double nick. The topmost leaf has a pointed terminal. The figure wears a coat and on the tunic (which shows at the opening of the coat) is a cross and a series of small curved nicks. Above the head is a three-element foliate motif. On either side of the head is a small scrolled leaf and a triquetra. The whole background and engraving of the ornamental fields are filled with niello: the niello is keyed into the brooch by means of a roughening carried out, presumably, with a graver or chisel. This feature can be seen in a number of places where the niello is missing. The back of the brooch is plain, the riveting on the back is simple in the case of the top, bottom and centre rivets, the terminals of the rivets to the left and right consist of square billets which perhaps held the pin. The surface of the brooch has been kept polished and the niello which fills the background and the engraved lines has been preserved in pristine condition.   Diameter: 11·4 cm.

Reg. no. 1952, 4–4, 1. Part gift from Capt. A. W. F. Fuller. No recorded provenance.

BIBLIOGRAPHY
The Antiquary, xlix, new series vi (1910), 268–9.
Clapham (1930), 130 and note.
Bruce-Mitford (1952c).
Moss (1953a), 61.
Moss (1953b), 76.

Bruce-Mitford (1956a), 173 ff., figs. 34, b and 35 and pl. xx.
Wilson (1960a), 145, 222 and pl. 65.
Dunning and Evison (1961), 143.
Wilson and Blunt (1961), 97 and 105.

The object is named (after the part donor) the Fuller brooch.

The brooch's history (as recounted by Bruce-Mitford) is that it was bought from a London bric-à-brac dealer by an unnamed man who did not know its history, he passed it to Sir Charles Robinson who published it in *The Antiquary*. A few years later Mr. E. Hockliffe, the son-in-law of Sir Charles Robinson, offered the brooch as a loan to the Ashmolean Museum, Oxford. E. T. Leeds, then an assistant at the museum, persuaded the then keeper D. G. Hogarth to accept the loan. On the advice of the then keeper of British and Medieval Antiquities at the British Museum (Sir Hercules Read, P.S.A.) and his assistant keeper (R. A. Smith) the brooch was pronounced a fake and withdrawn from exhibition with the approval of the Ashmolean Museum's technical specialist, W. H. Young. The brooch was eventually purchased by Capt. A. W. F. Fuller and, apart from occasional mentions (e.g. by Sir Alfred Clapham), was not thought of seriously until the Strickland brooch (no. 152) was brought to the British Museum. On the advice of Sir Thomas Kendrick the Fuller brooch was traced by Mr. Bruce-Mitford and after laboratory examination it was acquired by the British Museum.

The persistent view that it was a fake was quashed by a preliminary report on the brooch by the Keeper of the Research Laboratory, Dr. Plenderleith, who wrote as follows:

> The brooch has been so cleaned and burnished on the obverse as at first glance to appear to be modern, but the reverse suggests that it has a history. Here the metal is seen as base silver, which has been in contact with leather (? pigskin) and this has left a black imprint of the pore structure. There are traces of copper carbonate in a mineralised condition (malacite) arising from the segregation of the copper constituent of the silver. One can deduce that the metal is in the brilliant crystalline condition which is characteristic of silver of some considerable age by the fractures to be seen where a small triangular piece is missing near the top. It may well be that the two small holes in this part of the brooch were bored at a later date in its history, when the silver was already brittle, and that this was done so that the object could be suspended as an ornament. The tooling is all craftwork carried out with primitive implements in a free-hand manner: and under slight magnification it can be seen that there is no mechanical regularity anywhere. Such technical evidence as this object affords is, therefore, in my view entirely in favour of its antiquity.
>
> Signed: H. J. Plenderleith.[1]

Subsequently an analysis of the niello of the brooch was made by Dr. A. A. Moss in the course of a general investigation into the composition of niello.[2] He found the niello to consist mainly of silver sulphide, a type of niello that went out of use in the eleventh century. As Dr. Moss's researches were not concluded until 1953 it precludes the possibility that a forger had sufficient knowledge of the materials involved to make this brooch before 1910, and presumably earlier, for the brooch came to the Museum in a wooden leather-covered case, apparently made to fit the brooch in the seventeenth or eighteenth century. Mr. Leeds' and Sir Alfred Clapham's faith in the authenticity of this object were thus justified. It seems unlikely that this brooch had even been buried.

Bruce-Mitford suggests that the human figures on the brooch represent the five senses:

	Taste		Smell	
		Sight		
	Hearing		Touch	

Ninth century. See Appendix, p. 91–98 *and* pp. 3, 21, 25, 27, 30, 31, 40, 52 and pl. XLIV, *above.*

154. Silver engraved rectangular plate from a house-shaped casket. Within a billeted border are three wheel crosses, each enclosing between its arms a triquetra interlace pattern:

[1] Letter in the Department of British and Medieval Antiquities, British Museum.   [2] *Studies in Conservation*, vol. ii, 179.

in the gores between the outer circles and that in the centre are four similar triquetras, while inside the border, at each corner, a few chisel marks perhaps represent incipient interlace patterns. The rings of the wheel, the triquetras in the outer crosses and the two horizontal arms of the cross to the right, are left plain, all the other elements of the ornament on the plate have a billeted midrib. The two plain arms of the right-hand cross are bordered by billeted lines. In the centre of each cross is a hole, that in the centre being surrounded by what appears to be an incurving collar; these three holes are cut-away bosses. The plate has had a great deal of secondary attention: the edges have been clipped, part of the border in the bottom right-hand corner is missing and it has been pierced with nail holes some twenty-four times. The back of the plate is plain.

Length: 12·6 cm.

Reg. no. 1954, 12–1, 1. Purchased from K. J. Hewett, Esq. No recorded provenance.

BIBLIOGRAPHY
Wilson (1955*b*).
Wilson (1956*c*).

Arbman (1956), 110 and fig. 13.
Wilson (1960*a*), 162, 215, fig. 38 and pl. 18.

This object is a fragment of the same casket as no. 155. When purchased by the Museum this plate and no. 155 were mounted on a piece of nineteenth-century velvet in a Morland frame. Examination in the Research Laboratory of the Museum showed that no trace of niello survives in the plate.

Early tenth century. See above, pp. 38, 41, 42, 49, 53 and pl. xliv.

155. Silver engraved rhomboid plate from a house-shaped casket. The face is divided by a saltire, undecorated save for a billeted midrib, and bounded by a billeted border. The roughly cut edges are chamfered. Five holes are pierced in the saltire, one in the centre and the other at the extremities, each is surrounded by a plain undecorated area, in one case lightly defined by means of a scratched line. In the lowest field is a degenerate interlace ornament surmounted by a scratched human mask. Part of the interlace in this field bears triangular speckling. In the three other panels are tortuously interlaced animals

FIG. 53.   Ornament of no. 155. $\frac{1}{1}$.

(fig. 53). In the left-hand field the animal's head with its large ring and dot eye is in the bottom-left of the field. The head has become floriated and the neck is crossed by one

215

of the limbs and encircled by an interlacing ring. The double-contoured body is sub-triangular and covered with triangular speckling. The limbs, some of which are speckled, are crudely and complicatedly interlaced. The head of the animal in the right-hand field is in the bottom right-hand corner and has a large ring-and-dot eye, a toothed mouth and a slightly domed forehead. The double contoured body is roughly quadrangular and is speckled. A few of the limbs and the neck are also speckled. The neck is crossed by one of the limbs and surrounded by an interlaced ring. One of the hind-legs is well defined, but the other legs are crudely interlaced. The animal in the topmost field has a long, pointed, speckled head in the right-hand corner. Its saw-like teeth are indicated, as is the ring-and-dot eye. The neck is again crossed by a leg and ringed. The double contoured body is sub-triangular in shape and one of the hind-legs is clearly defined. The body and certain limbs are speckled. Below the belly of the beast appears a short billeted line. The engraving was filled in with niello of which some remains. The plate has been secondarily pierced seven times and the shanks of the two secondary iron pins remain in their holes. The back of the plate is plain.   Maximum length: 12·1 cm.

Reg. no. 1954, 12–1, 2. Purchased from K. J. Hewett, Esq. No recorded provenance.

Bibliography and history as for no. 154.

This object is a fragment of the same casket as no. 154. The niello in the engraving was examined by the British Museum Research Laboratory and the following report was submitted:

'The niello was tested by the three tests detailed by Moss (1953). These tests indicated that the niello is a non-fusible type (acanthite), which was used before the introduction of fusible mixed sulphide in about the eleventh century.'

Early tenth century. See above, pp. 38, 41, 42, 49, 53 and pl. XLIV.

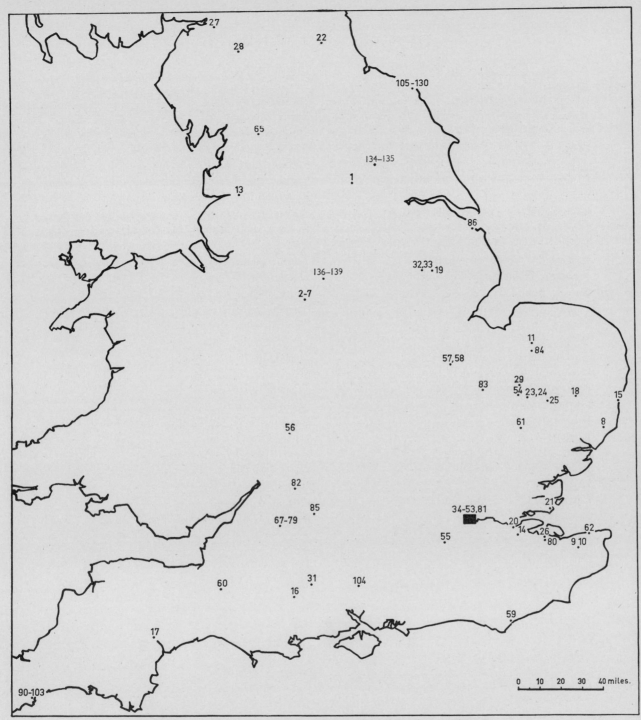

Fig. 54. Find spots of the objects listed in the catalogue.

DONORS AND VENDORS

RECONCILIATION OF REGISTRATION AND CATALOGUE NUMBERS

Registration	Cat.	Registration	Cat.	Registration	Cat.	Registration	Cat.
22,12–14,1	18	76,2–12,27	134	1904,6–23,4	42	AF 492	146
29,11,14,1	31	79,12–9,2090	135	1908,10–5,1	11	AF 3175	147
32,5–12,2	104	79,12–22,1	82	1909,5–18,25	46	O.A.21	28
33,1–1,1	14	80,4–10,1,2,3	90	1912,7–23,2	22	O.A.294	15
36,9–1,140	140	80,4–10,4	91	1925,1–14,1	2	O.A.295	89
37,3–28,1	44	80,4–10,5,7	92	1925,1–14,2	3	Sl.64	30
39,3–19,1	20	80,4–10,8,12	93	1925,1–14,3	4	Sl.396	62
41,7–11,456	13	80,4–10,9	94	1925,2–17,1	5	W.27	105
47,2–7,1	63	80,4–10,10	95	1925,2–17,2	6	W.28	106
48,10–21,1	32	80,4–10,11	96	1925,2–17,3	7	W.29	107
50,7–1,1088	38	80,4–10,13	97	1925,11–18,1	16	W.30	108
52,3–25,2	37	80,4–10,14	98	1926,10–20,1	150	W.32	109
54,4–24,1	35	80,4–10,15	99	1926,11–16,1	23	W.37	110
54,7–21,1	84	80,4–10,16	100	1926,11–16,2	24	W.38	111
54,12–27,66	8	80,4–10,17	101	1927,11–16,1	9	W.42	112
55,11–15,1	57	80,4–10,18	102	1927,12–12,23	25	W.48	113
56,7–1,1087	40	80,4–10,19	103	1931,12–15,1	59	W.52	114
56,7–1,1413	43	80,8–2,163	12	1933,5–10,1	81	W.53	115
56,7–1,1462	47	81,6–23,1	80	1938,3–2,1	29	W.54	116
56,7–1,1466	48	83,12–13,579	26	1942,10–8,4	51	W.55	117
56,7–1,1468	39	88,7–19,98	67	1942,10–8,5	52	W.56	118
56,7–1,1473	49	88,7–19,99	68	1942,10–8,6	53	W.57	119
56,7–1,1474	34	88,7–19,161	69	1942,10–8,11	54	W.58	120
57,6–23,1	36	88,7–19,162	70	1942,10–8,17	151	W.59	121
58,11–16,4	19	88,7–19,163	71	1944,3–1,1	65	W.60	122
58,11–16,6	133	88,7–19,164	72	1946,10–2,1	86	W.61	123
59,1–22,12	50	88,7–19,165	73	1946,10–2,2	87	W.62	124
62,3–21,6	58	88,7–19,166	74	1949,7–2,1	152	W.63	125
62,3–21,7	141	88,7–19,167	75	1951,2–6,1	64	W.64	126
62,7–1,19	142	88,7–19,168	76	1951,10–11,1	83	W.65	127
62,7–7,62	143	88,7–19,169	77	1952,4–4,1	153	W.66	128
62,7–28,1	66	88,7–19,170	78	1954,12–1,1	154	W.67	129
67,3–20,20	33	88,7–19,171	79	1954,12–1,2	155	W.73	130
69,6–10,1	45	92,11–4,15	21	1955,10–2,1	55	W.334	131
73,6–2,64	136	93,6–18,111	88	1955,12–1,1	61	W.362	132
73,6–2,66	137	93,7–15,1	41	1959,2–10,1	10		
73,6–2,67	138	96,4–11,164	144	1960,7–1,1	56	Ring Cat. 183	85
73,6–2,68	139	1903,6–23,95	148	AF 458	1	Ring Cat. 184	27
75,6–17,15	17	1903,6–23,97	149	AF 459	145	Loan	60

BIBLIOGRAPHY

Åberg, N. (1921): 'Stil III och jellingestil', *Fornvännen*, xvi, 63–82.

Åberg, N. (1923): *Die Goten und Langobarden in Italien*, Uppsala.

Åberg, N. (1941): *Keltiska och orientaliska stilinflytelser i vikingatidens nordiska konst*, Stockholm (*Kungl. Vitterhets historie och Antikvitets Akademiens handlingar*, 46:4).

Acland, J. E. (1928): 'Sword of the Viking Period', *The Antiquaries Journal*, viii, 361–2.

Adamson, J. (1834): 'Account of the Discovery at Hexham, in the County of Northumberland of a brass vessel containing a number of Anglo-Saxon coins called Stycas', *Archaeologia*, xxv (1834), 279–310.

Agrell, S. (1927): *Runornas talmystik och des antika förebild*, Lund.

Agrell, S. (1931): *Senantik mysterireligion och nordisk runmagi*, Stockholm.

Agrell, S. (1931/2): 'Die spätantike Alphabet-mystik und die Runenreihe', *K. Humanistiska Vetenskap Samfundets i Lund, Årsberättelse*, 155–210.

Almgren, B. (1955): *Bronsnycklar och Djurorna-mentik*, Uppsala.

Altheim, F. (1948): *Literatur und Gesellschaft im ausgehenden Altertum*, i, Halle.

Ålund, E. (1904): *Runorna i Norden*, Stockholm.

Anderson, J. (1883): *Scotland in Pagan Times: the Iron Age*, Edinburgh.

Ångström, M. (1937): *Studies in Old English MSS., with special reference to the delabialisation of* y̆ (ŭ+i) *to* ĭ Uppsala.

Arbman, H. (1936): 'En kammargrav från vikingatiden vid Långtora, Uppland', *Fornvännen*, xxxi, 89–98.

Arbman, H. (1937): *Schweden und das Karolingische Reich*, Stockholm.

Arbman, H. (1940–3): *Birka I*, Stockholm.

Arbman, H. (1956): 'The Skabersjö Brooch and some Danish Mounts', *Meddelanden från Lunds Universitets Historiska Museum*, 93–113.

Arbman, H. (1958): 'Die Kremsmünsterer Leuchter', *Meddelanden från Lunds Universitets Historiska Museum*, 170–92.

Arbman, H. and Stenberger, M. (1935): *Vikingar i Västerled*, Stockholm.

Armstrong, A. M., *et al.* (1950–2): *The Place-Names of Cumberland* (*English Place-Name Society*, xx–xxii), Cambridge.

Arntz, H. (1935): *Handbuch der Runenkunde*, Halle/Saale (*Sammlung kurzer Grammatiken germanischer Dialekte, B*, 3).

Arntz, H. (1938): *Die Runenschrift, ihre Ge-schichte und ihre Denkmäler*, Halle.

Arntz, H. and Zeiss, H. (1939): *Die einheimischen Runendenkmäler des Festlandes*, Leipzig.

Arntz, H. (1944*a*): *Handbuch der Runenkunde*, (2nd Ed.) Halle/Saale.

Arntz, H. (1944*b*): 'Runen und Runennamen', *Anglia*, lxviii, 172–250.

Arwidsson, G. (1942): *Vendelstile*, Uppsala.

Bæksted, A. (1943): *Runerne, deres Historie og Brug*, København.

Bæksted, A. (1952): *Målruner og Troldruner. Runemagiske studier*, København.

Baesecke, G. (1940): *Vor- und Frühgeschichte des deutschen Schrifttums*, i, Halle.

Baldwin Brown, G. (1903–37): *The Arts in Early England*, London.

Baldwin Brown, G. (1913–14): 'An Early Spoon found in Kent', *The Burlington Magazine*, xxiv, 99–100.

Barnes, H. (1832): 'Account of the discovery of the Matrix of an Anglo-Saxon Seal', *Archaeologia*, xxiv, 359–61.

Battiscombe, C. F. (*ed.*) (1956): *The Relics of St. Cuthbert*, Durham.

Baum, J. (1937): *La sculpture figurale en Europe à l'époque mérovingienne*, Paris.

Baye, J. de (1889): *Industrie anglo-saxonne*, Paris.

Baye, J. de (1893): *The Industrial Arts of the Anglo-Saxons*, London.

Bennet-Clarke, M. A. (1954): 'Excavation at Middle Brook Street, Winchester, 1953', *Proceedings of the Hampshire Field Club and Archaeological Society*, xviii, 315 24.

Bennett, J. A. W. (1950–1): 'The Beginnings of Runic Studies in England', *Saga Book of the*

Viking Society for Northern Research, xiii, 269–83.

Birch, W. de G. (1885–93): *Cartularium Saxonicum*, London.

Birch, W. de G. (1887): *Catalogue of Seals in the Department of Manuscripts in the British Museum*, i, London.

Björkman, E. (1920): *Studien über die Eigennamen im Beowulf*. Halle a. S. (*Studien zur englischen Philologie*, 58).

Black, G. F. (1881–9): 'Notice of two Sculptured Stones at Kirk Andreas . . . with notices of other bind-rune inscriptions', *Proceedings of the Society of Antiquaries of Scotland*, xxiii, 332–43.

Blair, P. H. (1956): *An Introduction to Anglo-Saxon England*, Cambridge.

Blindheim, C. (1953): *Kaupang*, Oslo.

Blindheim, C. (1960): 'Kaupangundersøkelsen etter 10 år', *Viking* xxiv, 43–68.

Blunt, C. E. (1961): 'The Coinage of Offa', *Anglo-Saxon Coins* (ed. R. H. M. Dolley), London, 39–62.

BMASG: British Museum, A Guide to the Anglo-Saxon . . . Antiquities . . , London, 1923.

B. M. Ring Cat.: Catalogue of the Finger Rings, Early Christian, Byzantine, Teutonic, Medieval and Later . . . in the Museum, London (British Museum) 1912 (by O. M. Dalton).

Bøe, J. (1932): 'An Anglo-Saxon bronze mount from Norway', *The Antiquaries Journal*, xii, 440–442.

Boinet, A. (1913): *La miniature carolingienne*, Paris.

Bork, F. (1929): 'Runenstudien', *Archiv für Schreib- und Buchwesen*, iii, 67–81.

Brade-Birks, S. G. (1953): *Teach Yourself Archaeology*, London.

Brassington, W. S.: *Historic Worcestershire*, Birmingham . . ./London *n.d.*

Braun, J. (1932): *Das christliche Altargerät in seinem Sein und in seiner Entwicklung*, München.

Brodeur, A. G. (1932): *The Riddle of the Runes*, Berkeley.

Brøgger, A. W. (1921): *Ertog og øre*, Kristiania, *Videnskapsselskapets Skrifter II. Hist.-Filos. Klasse*, No. 3.

Brøgger, A. W. (1920–1): 'Rolvsøyætten', *Bergens Museums Aarbok*.

Brøndsted, J. (1920): 'Nordisk og fremmed Ornamentik i Vikingetiden, med særligt Henblik paa Stiludviklingen i England,' *Aarbøger for nordisk Oldkyndighed og Historie*, 162–282.

Brøndsted, J. (1924): *Early English Ornament*, London/Copenhagen.

Brøndsted, J. (1936): 'Danish Inhumation Graves of the Viking Age. A Survey', *Acta Archaeologica*, vii, 81–228.

B(rooke), G. C. (1924): 'Beeston Tor Find of Anglo-Saxon Coins', *Numismatic Chronicle*, 5 ser., iv, 322–5.

Brooke, G. C. (1950): *English Coins from the Seventh Century to the Present Day*, (3 ed.) London.

Bruce-Mitford, R. L. S. (1952a): 'A Late Saxon disk-brooch and sword-pommel', *British Museum Quarterly*, xv, 74–75.

Bruce-Mitford, R. L. S. (1952b): 'A late-Saxon disk-brooch from the Isle of Ely', *British Museum Quarterly*, xvii, 15–16.

Bruce-Mitford, R. L. S. (1952c): 'The Fuller Brooch', *British Museum Quarterly*, xvii, 75–76.

Bruce-Mitford, R. L. S. (1952/3): 'A bronze strap-end of *c.* A.D. 900 from Souldern, Oxon.', *Oxoniensia*, xvii/xviii, 236.

Bruce-Mitford, R. L. S. (1953): 'Some recent results of the application of laboratory techniques to antiquities of the Anglo-Saxon period in Britain', *Congrès International des Sciences Préhistoriques et Protohistoriques. Actes de la IIIe Session, Zurich 1650*, Zurich, 321–323.

Bruce-Mitford, R. L. S. (1956a): 'Late Saxon Disk-Brooches', *Dark-Age Britain*, (ed. D. B. Harden), London, 171–201.

Bruce-Mitford, R. L. S. (1956b): *The Sutton Hoo Ship-burial. A Provisional Guide*, 5th impression, London (British Museum).

Buck, C. D. (1919–20): 'An ABC inscribed in Old English Runes', *Modern Philology*, xvii, 219–224.

Bugge, S. (1908): 'Das Runendenkmal von Britsum in Friesland', *Zeitschrift für deutsche Philologie*, xl, 174–184.

Bugge, S. and Olsen, M. (1891–1924): *Norges Indskrifter med de ældre Runer*, Christiania.

Bu'lock, J. D. (1960): 'The Celtic, Saxon and Scandinavian Settlement at Meols in Wirral', *Transactions of the Historic Society of Lancashire and Cheshire*, cxii, 1–28

Butcher, S. (1955): 'Interim Report on Excavations in St. George's Street, Winchester',

Proceedings of the Hampshire Field Club and Archaeological Society, xix, 1–11.

Butler, V. J. (1961): 'The metrology of the late Anglo-Saxon Penny: the reigns of Æthelræd II and Cnut', *Anglo-Saxon Coins* (ed. R. H. M. Dolley), London, 195–214.

Cabrol, F. (1907–53): *Dictionnaire d'archéologie chrétienne et de liturgie*, Paris.

Cahen, M., Olsen, M. and Osieczkowska, C. (1930): 'L'inscription runique du coffret de Mortain', *Collection Linguistique*, xxxii, 1–66.

Callander, J. G. (1932/3): 'A Collection of pre-historic relics from Stevenston Sands, Ayrshire, and other objects in the National Museum', *Proceedings of the Society of Antiquaries of Scotland*, lxvii, 26–34.

Campbell, A. (1959): *Old English Grammar*, Oxford.

Camden, W. (1772): *Britannia*, 2nd ed. (E. Thompson), London.

Camden, W. (1806): *Britannia*, 3 ed. London.

Chadwick, H. M. (1899): 'Studies in Old English', *Transactions of the Cambridge Philological Society*, iv, 85–265.

Chaillu, P. B. du (1889): *The Viking Age*, i, London.

Chamot, M. (1930): *English Medieval Enamels*, London.

Christiansson, H. (1959): *Sydskandinavisk stil*, Uppsala.

Clapham, A. W. (1923): 'Six early carved stones from South Kyme Church, Lincolnshire', *The Antiquaries Journal*, iii, 118–21.

Clapham, A. W. (1928): 'The Carved Stones at Breedon on the Hill, Leicestershire, and their position in the history of English Art', *Archaeologia*, lxxvii, 219–238.

Clapham, A. W. (1930): *English Romanesque Architecture before the Conquest*, Oxford.

Clarke, R. R. (1960): *East Anglia*, London.

Clemoes, P. A. M. (1952): *Liturgical Influence on punctuation in late Old English and early Middle English Manuscripts*, Cambridge. (Occasional papers of the Department of Anglo-Saxon, I.)

Cochet (1859): *Le tombeau de Childéric 1er*, Paris.

Cockayne, T. O. (1864–6): *Leechdoms, Wortcunning, and Starcraft of Early England*, London (*Rolls Series*, 35).

Collingwood, W. G. (1906): 'Late and Magic Runes in Cumberland', *Transactions of the Cumberland and Westmorland Antiquarian and Archaeological Society*, new series vi, 305–12.

Collingwood, W. G. (1911): 'A Rune-inscribed Anglian Cross-shaft at Urswick Church', *Ibid.*, new series xi, 462–8.

Collingwood, W. G. (1915): 'Anglian and Anglo-Danish Sculpture in the West Riding', *Yorkshire Archaeological Journal*, xxiii, 129–299.

Collingwood, W. G. (1927): *Northumbrian Crosses of the pre-Norman Age*, London.

Cowen, J. D. (1934): 'A Catalogue of Objects of the Viking period in the Tullie House Museum, Carlisle', *Transactions of the Cumberland and Westmorland Antiquarian and Archaeological Society*, new series, xxxiv, 166–187.

Cowen, J. D. (1935): 'A 9th–10th century Bronze Mounting from York', *Saga Book of the Viking Society for Northern Research*, xi, 125–128.

Cuming, H. S. (1863): 'On Ancient Nielli', *Journal of the British Archaeological Association*, 213–18.

Cuming, H. S. (1868): 'On a Runic Epigraph found in the Thames', *Journal of the British Archaeological Association*, xxiv, 178–182.

Curle, A. O. (1923–4): 'A note on four silver spoons and a fillet of gold found in the nunnery at Iona . . .', *Proceedings of the Society of Antiquaries of Scotland*, lviii, 102–11.

Dahl, I. (1938): *Substantival Inflexion in early Old English: Vocalic Stems*, Lund. (*Lund Studies in English*, vii).

Dalton, O. M. (1909): *Catalogue of the Ivory Carvings of the Christian Era . . . in . . . the British Museum*, London.

Dalton, O. M. (1912): See *B.M. Ring Cat.*

Dalton, O. M. (1921): *British Museum Guide to the Early Christian and Byzantine Antiquities*, London.

Dalton, O. M. and Tonnochy, A. B. (1924): *British Museum: Guide to the Medieval Antiquities and Objects of Later Date*, London.

Daunt, M. (1939): 'Old English Sound-Changes reconsidered in relation to Scribal Tradition and Practice', *Transactions of the Philological Society*, 108–37.

Davies, D. S. (1926): 'Pre-conquest carved stones in Lincolnshire', *The Archaeological Journal*, lxxxiii, 1–20.

Davies J. (1672): *The ancient rites . . . of Durham*, London.

Davis, C. E. (*n.d.*): *The Saxon Cross found in Bath, July 1898*, Bath.

Derolez, R. (1954): *Runica manuscripta: the English Tradition (Rijksuniversiteit te Gent Werken uitgegeven door de Faculteit van de Wijsbegeerte en Letteren*, cxviii).

Dickins, B. (1932): 'A System of Transliteration for Old English Runic Inscriptions', *Leeds Studies in English*, i, 15–19.

Dickins, B. (1935): 'Runic Rings and Old English Charms', *Archiv für das Studium der neueren Sprachen*, clxvii, 252.

Dickins, B. (1938): 'The Sandwich Runic Inscription *Ræhæbul*', *Beiträge zur Runenkunde und nordischen Sprachwissenschaft. Gustav Neckel zum 60. Geburtstag (ed.* K. H. Schlottig), Leipzig, 83–85.

Dickins, B. (1956): 'The Inscriptions upon the Coffin', *The Relics of St. Cuthbert (ed.* C. F. Battiscombe), Durham, 305–7.

Dickins, B. and Ross, A. S. C. (1940): 'The Alnmouth Cross', *Journal of English and Germanic Philology*, xxxix, 169–178.

Dietrich, F. (1867): 'Drei altheidnische Segensformeln', *Zeitschrift für deutsches Alterthum*, xiii, 193–217.

Dietrich, F. (1869): 'Funf northumbrische Runensprüche', *Zeitschrift für deutsches Alterthum*, xiv, 104–123.

Digby Wyatt, M. (1852): *Metalwork and its Artistic Design*, London.

Dinklage, K. (1955): 'Karolingischen Schmuck aus dem Speyer und Wormsgau', *Pfälzer Heimat*, 1–4 and 41–6.

Dobbie, E. V. K. (1942): *The Anglo-Saxon Minor Poems*, New York. (*The Anglo-Saxon Poetic Records*, vi.)

Dolley, R. H. M. (1957): 'A Spanish Dirhem found in England', *The Numismatic Chronicle*, 6th series, xvii, 242–3.

Dolley, R. H. M. (1958): 'Three forgotten English finds of pence of Æthelred II', *The Numismatic Chronicle*, 6th ser., xviii, 97–107.

Dolley, R. H. M. and Metcalf, D. M. (1961): 'The Reform of the English Coinage under Eadgar', *Anglo-Saxon Coins (ed.* Dolley, R. H. M.), London, 136–68.

Dolley, R. H. M. and Scaare, K. (1961): 'The Coinage of Æthelwulf, King of the West Saxons, 839–58', *Anglo-Saxon Coins (ed.* Dolley, R. H. M.), London, 63–76.

Dolley, R. H. M. and Strudwick, J. S. (1955): 'The Provenances of the Anglo-Saxon coins recorded in the two volumes of the British Museum catalogue', *British Numismatic Journal*, xxviii, 26–59.

Dornseiff, F. (1922): *Das Alphabet in Mystik und Magie*, Leipzig/Berlin. (*ΣTOIXEIA*, vii).

Douce, F. (1827): 'Dissertation on the Runic Jasper Ring belonging to George Cumberland Esq. of Bristol', *Archaeologia*, xxi, 119–37.

Dugdale, W. (1846): *Monasticon Anglicanum*, ii, London.

Dunning, G. C. and Evison, V. I. (1961): 'The Palace of Westminster Sword', *Archaeologia*, xcviii, 123–58.

Earle, J. and Plummer, C. (1897): *Two of the Saxon Chronicles Parallel*, Oxford.

Ekwall, E. (1960): *The Concise Oxford Dictionary of English Place-Names*, 4th ed., Oxford.

Elbern, V. H. (*ed.*) (1956): *Werdendes Abendland an Rhein und Ruhr*, Essen.

Eldjárn, K. (1956): *Kuml og haugfé, úr heiðnum sið á Íslandi*, Reykjavík.

Elgee, F. & H. W. (1933): *The Archaeology of Yorkshire*, London.

Elliott, R. W. V. (1957): 'Runes, Yews, and Magic', *Speculum*, xxxii, 250–61.

Elliott, R. W. V. (1959*a*): *Runes, an Introduction*, Manchester.

Elliott, R. W. V. (1959*b*): 'Two Neglected English Runic Inscriptions: Gildon [*sic*] and Overchurch', *Mélanges de linguistique et de philologie, Fernand Mossé in Memoriam*, Paris, 140–7.

Evans, J. (1873): 'Note on an Anglo-Saxon knife found in Kent, bearing an inscription', *Archaeologia*, xliv, 331–4.

Evans, J. (1887): 'Notes on a Danish sword-hilt found near Wallingford', *Archaeologia*, l, 534–6.

Evans, J. (1892): 'An Archaeological Survey of Hertfordshire', *Archaeologia*, liii, 245–62.

Evison, V. I. (1957): 'A Group of Late Saxon Brooches', *The Antiquaries Journal*, xxxvii, 220–2.

Fairholt, F. W. (1847): 'Remarks on Ancient Fibulae', *Journal of the British Archaeological Association*, ii, 309–15.

Fairholt, F. W. (1857): *Miscellanea Graphica*, London.

Falke, O. v. and Meyer, E. (1935): *Romanische Leuchter und Gefässe, Giessgefässe der Gotik*, Berlin.

Farrer, J. (1862): *Maes-Howe. Notice of Runic Inscriptions discovered during recent Excavations in the Orkneys, n.p.*

Feilitzen, O. v. (1937): *The Pre-Conquest Personal Names of Domesday Book*, Uppsala. (*Nomina Germanica*, iii.)

Ferguson, R. S. (1893): 'An Archaeological Survey of Cumberland and Westmorland,' *Archaeologia*, liii, 485–538.

Fink, A. (1957): 'Zum Gandersheimer Runenkästchen', *Karolingische und Ottonische Kunst. Werden. Wesen. Wirkung*, Wiesbaden, 277–81.

Fleury, C. R. de (1883–9): *La Messe*, Paris.

Fleury, M. and France-Lanord, A. (1961): 'Les Bijoux mérovingiens d'Arnegonde', *Art de France*, i, 7–18.

Forbes, M. D. and Dickins, B. (1914): 'The Inscriptions on the Ruthwell and Bewcastle Crosses and the Bridekirk Font', *The Burlington Magazine*, 25–9.

Förstemann, E. (1900): *Altdeutsches Namenbuch*, i, *Personennamen*, 2 ed., Bonn.

Fowler, J. T. (1870): 'An Account of the Anglo-Saxon Ring discovered near Driffield, Yorks., now in the possession of the Rev. Geo. Welby, Barrowby, Grantham'. *Report of the Proceedings of the Geological and Polytechnical Society of the West Riding of Yorkshire*, 157–61.

Fowler, J. T. (1880): 'An account of excavations made on the site of the Chapter-house of Durham Cathedral in 1874', *Archaeologia*, xlv, 385–404.

Fowler, J. T. (ed.) (1903): *The Rites of Durham*, Durham. (*Surtees Society*, cvii).

Fox, C. (1923): *The Archaeology of the Cambridge Region*, Cambridge.

Franks, A. W. (1876): 'On a Ring with a Runic Inscription', *Archaeologia*, xliv, 481–2.

Friesen, O. v. (1918/19): 'Runenschrift', *Reallexikon der germanischen Altertumskunde*, iv (ed. J. Hoops), Strassburg, 5–51.

Friesen, O. v. (1929): 'Runes', *Encyclopædia Britannica*, 14th ed., vol. xix.

Friesen, O. v. (1933): *Runorna*, Stockholm, (*Nordisk Kultur*, vi).

Friesen, O. v. (1936): 'Rune', *Enciclopedia Italiana*, Rome, xxx, 241–3.

Friis-Johansen, K. (1912): 'Sølvskatten fra Terslev', *Aarbøger for Nordisk Oldkyndighed og Historie*, 189–263.

Gardner, J. W. (1955): Saxon finds from Lansdown, Bath, *The Archaeological News Letter*, v, 252.

Gericke, B. (1934): *Die Flexion des Personalpronomens der 3. Person im Spätags.*, Leipzig. (Palaestra, 193.)

Gilbert, D. (1864): *Parochial History of Cornwall*, Truro.

Gilbert, E. (1954): 'Deerhurst Priory Church Revisited', *Transactions of the Bristol and Gloucestershire Archaeological Society*, lxxiii, 73–114.

Goddard, E. H. (1898–9): 'On fragments of a Saxon Cross Shaft, found at Minety and a Saxon Silver Ornament from Cricklade', *Wiltshire Archaeological Magazine*, xxx, 230–2.

Goldschmidt, A. (1926): *Die Elfenbeinskulpturen aus der romanischen Zeit*, iv, Berlin.

Gorsleben, R. J. (1930): *Hoch-Zeit der Menschheit*, Leipzig.

Gosse, E. (1911): 'Runes, Runic Language and Inscriptions', *Encyclopædia Britannica*, 11th ed., vol. xxiii.

Green, A. R. (1928): 'Anglo-Saxon Sundials', *The Antiquaries Journal*, viii, 489–516.

Grieg, S. (1929): 'Vikingetidens Skattefund', *Oslo Universitetets Oldsaksamlings Skrifter*, ii, 177–311.

Grienberger, T. v. (1898): 'Beiträge zur Runenlehre', *Arkiv för nordisk filologi*, xiv, 101–36.

Grienberger, T. v. (1913): 'The Thames Fitting', *Zeitschrift für deutsche Philologie*, xlv, 47–55.

Grierson, P. (1958): *Sylloge of Coins of the British Isles, Fitzwilliam Museum, Cambridge*, i, London.

Griffith, G. (1786): 'Account of Coins &c. found in digging up the Foundations of some old Houses near the Church of St. Mary Hill', *Archaeologia*, iv, 356–62.

Grimes, W. F. (1956): 'Excavations in the City of London', *Recent Archaeological Excavations in Britain* (ed. R. L. S. Bruce-Mitford), London.

Grove, L. R. A. (1938): 'Five Viking Period Swords', *The Antiquaries Journal*, xviii, 251–7

Grueber, H. A. and Keary, C. F. (1893): *A Catalogue of English Coins in the British Museum. Anglo-Saxon Series*, ii, London.

Gurney, H. (1824): 'Observations on the Seal of

Ethilwald Bishop of Dunwich, lately discovered at Eye, in Suffolk', *Archaeologia*, xx, 479–83.

Haddan, A. W. and Stubbs, W. (1869–73): *Councils and Ecclesiastical Documents relating to Great Britain and Ireland*, Oxford.

Hagen, A. and Liestøl, A. (1947): 'Storhedder', *Viking*, xi, 141–233.

Haigh, D. H. (1861): *The Conquest of Britain by the Saxons*, London.

Haigh, D. H. (1870): 'The Runic Monuments of Northumbria', *Proceedings of the Geological and Polytechnical Society of the West Riding of Yorkshire*, 178–271.

Haigh, D. H. (1872): 'Notes in illustration of the Runic Monuments of Kent', *Archaeologia Cantiana*, viii, 164–270.

Haigh, D. H. (1873): 'Yorkshire Runic Monuments', *Yorkshire Archaeological Journal*, ii, 252–88.

Hammarström, M. (1930): 'Om runskriftens härkomst', *Studier i nordisk filologi*, xx, part I.

Hamper, W. (1821): 'The Runic inscription on the Font at Bridekirk considered and a new Interpretation proposed', *Archaeologia*, xix, 379–82.

Hamper, W. (1827): 'Observations on a Gold Ring with a Runic Inscription, in the possession of . . . the Earl of Aberdeen . . .', *Archaeologia*, xxi, 25–30.

Harder, H. (1931): 'Eine angelsächsische Runeninschrift', *Archiv für das Studium der neueren Sprachen*, clx, 87–9.

Harder, H. (1932): 'Eine angelsächsische Ring-Inschrift', *Archiv für das Studium der neueren Sprachen*, clxi, 37–9.

Harder, H. (1935): 'Beiträge zur Schriftgestalt in lateinischen Inschriften der Germanenreiche', *Archiv für das Studium der neueren Sprachen*, clxviii, 18–24.

Harder, H. (1936): 'Die Inschriften angelsächsischer Runenringe', *Archiv für das Studium der neueren Sprachen*, clxix, 224–8.

Harder, H. (1938): 'Die Formverschiebung der Runen', *Archiv für das Studium der neueren Sprachen*, clxxiii, 145–51.

Haseloff, G. (1950): 'An Anglo-Saxon Openwork Mount from Whitby Abbey', *The Antiquaries Journal*, xxx, 170–4.

Haseloff, G. (1951): *Der Tassilokelch*, München.

Haseloff, G. (1958): 'Fragments of a Hanging-Bowl from Bekesbourne, Kent, and some Ornamental Problems', *Medieval Archaeology*, ii, 72–103.

Hawkins, E. (1838): 'An Account of some Saxon Pennies and other articles, found at Sevington, North Wilts'., *Archaeologia*, xxvii, 301–5.

Hawkins, E. (1840/41): 'On some Saxon Coins discovered near Gravesend in 1838', *Numismatic Chronicle*, iii, 14–34.

Hawkins, E. (1841): *Silver Coins of England*, London.

Hawkins, E. (1842–3): 'An Account of Coins and Treasure found in Cuerdale', *Numismatic Chronicle*, v, 1–48 and 53–104.

Hawkins, E. (1847): 'An Account of Coins and Treasure found in Cuerdale', *The Archaeological Journal*, iv, 111–30 and 189–99.

Head, J. F. (1955): *Early Man in South Buckinghamshire*, Bristol.

Hedley, A. (1822): 'An Essay towards ascertaining the etymology of the names of places in the county of Northumberland', *Archaeologia Aeliana*, i, 242–62.

Hempl, G. (1903–4): 'Hickes's Additions to the Runic Poem', *Modern Philology*, i, 135–42.

Hencken, H. (1932): *The Archaeology of Cornwall and Scilly*, London.

Hencken, H. (1950): 'Lagore Crannog', *Proceedings of the Royal Irish Academy*, liii, Section C.

Henry, F. (1940): *Irish Art in the Early Christian Period*, London.

Hickes, G. (1705): *Linguarum Vetterum Septentrionalium. Thesaurus*, Oxford.

Himsworth, J. B. (1953): *The Story of Cutlery*, London.

Hodgkin, R. H. (1952): *A History of the Anglo-Saxons*, 3rd edition, Oxford.

Holmboe, C. A. (1835): *En Merkværdig Samling av Smykker, for Størstedelen av Guld og Mynter fra 8de og 9de Aarhundrede fundne i August Maaned 1834 paa Gaarden Hoen i Egers Prestegjeld i Agershus Stift i Norge*, Kristiania.

Holmqvist, W. (1951): 'Viking Art in the Eleventh Century', *Acta Archaeologica*, xxii, 1–56.

Holmqvist, W. (1959): 'The Syllöda Silver Pin—an English Element in the Art of the Viking Age', *Suomen Museo*, 34–63.

How, G. E. P. and How J. P. (1952): *English and Scottish Silver Spoons*, i, London.

Howarth, E. (1899): *Catalogue of the Bateman Collection of Antiquities in the Sheffield Public Museum*, London.

Hume, A. (1863): *Ancient Meols*, London.

Jackson, C. J. (1893): 'The Spoon and its history; its form, material and development, more particularly in England', *Archaeologia*, liii, 107–46.

Jackson, C. J. (1911): *History of English Plate*, London.

Jacobsen, L., Moltke, E., *et al.* (1941–2): *Danmarks Runeindskrifter*, København.

James, M. R. (1912): *A Descriptive Catalogue of the Manuscripts in the Library of Corpus Christi College, Cambridge*, Cambridge.

Jankuhn, H. (1937): *Haithabu: Eine germanische Stadt der Frühzeit*, Neumünster.

Jankuhn, H. (1943): *Die Ausgrabungen in Haithabu* (1937–9), Berlin.

Janson, H. W. (1952): *Apes and Ape-lore in the Middle Ages and the Renaissance*, London.

Jantzen, H. (1947): *Ottonische Kunst*, München.

Jefferson, S. (1840): *The History and Antiquities of Cumberland*, Carlisle.

Jenny, W. (n.d.): 'Das Sogenannte Rupertus-Kreuz in Bischofshofen', *Arte del primo millenio* (*Atti de 2 convegno per lo studio dell'arte dell'alto medio evo Pavia* 1950), Turin, 383 ff.

Jenny, W. A. v. and Volbach W. F. (1933): *Germanischer Schmuck des frühen Mittelalters*, Berlin.

Jessup, R. (F.) (1930): *The Archaeology of Kent*, London.

Jessup, R. (F.) (1950): *Anglo-Saxon Jewellery*, London.

Johannson, A. (1933): 'Evarix und jór', *Arkiv för nordisk filologi*, 3. ser., v. 234–58.

Jones, W. (1876): *Finger-Ring Lore: Historical, Legendary, Anecdotal*, London.

Jungandreas, W. (1936): 'Zur Runenreihe', *Zeitschrift für deutsche Philologie*, lxi.

Keary, C. F. (1884): 'A hoard of Anglo-Saxon Coins found in Rome and described by Sig. de Rossi', *Numismatic Chronicle*, 3rd ser., iv, 225–55.

Keary, C. F. (1887): *A Catalogue of English Coins in the British Museum, Anglo-Saxon Series*, i, London.

Kemble, J. M. (1840): 'On Anglo-Saxon Runes', *Archaeologia*, xxviii, 327–72.

Kendrick, T. D. (1930): *A History of the Vikings*, London.

Kendrick, T. D. (1933a): 'Viking Period Anti-quities in England', *The South-Eastern Naturalist and Antiquary*, 42–9.

Kendrick, T. D. (1933b): 'Polychrome Jewellery in Kent', *Antiquity*, vii, 429–52.

Kendrick, T. D. (1934): 'Some types of ornamentation on Late Saxon and Viking Period Weapons in England', *Eurasia Septentrionalis Antiqua*, ix, 292–8.

Kendrick, T. D. (1938a): *Anglo-Saxon Art to A.D. 900*, London.

Kendrick, T. D. (1938b): 'Flambard's Crozier', *The Antiquaries Journal*, xviii, 236–42.

Kendrick, T. D. (1938c): 'An Anglo-Saxon Cruet', *The Antiquaries Journal*, xviii, 377–81.

Kendrick, T. D. (1941a): 'A late Saxon hanging-bowl', *The Antiquaries Journal*, xxi, 161–2.

Kendrick, T. D. (1941b): 'The Viking Taste in Pre-Conquest England', *Antiquity*, xv, 125–41.

Kendrick, T. D. (1949): *Late Saxon and Viking Art*, London.

Kendrick, T. D. *et al.* (1960): *Evangeliorum Quattuor Codex Lindisfarnensis*, Oltun et Lausanna.

Kent, J. P. C. (1961): 'From Roman Britain to Saxon England', *Anglo-Saxon Coins* (*ed.* R. H. M. Dolley), London, 1–22.

Ker, N. R. (1957): *Catalogue of Manuscripts containing Anglo-Saxon*, Oxford.

Kermode, P. M. C. (1907): *Manx Crosses*, London.

Kessler, P. T. (1932): 'Schlüssel aus spät-merowingisch-karolingischer Zeit', *Mainzer Zeitschrift*, xxvii.

King, R. J. (1876): 'Runes and Runic Stones', *Fraser's Magazine*, new series, xiii, 247–57.

Kirk, J. (1948): *The Alfred and Minster Lovel Jewels*, Oxford.

Kitson Clark, M. (1941a): 'Late Saxon pin-heads from Roos, East Yorkshire and South Ferriby, Lincolnshire . . .', *Proceedings of the Leeds Philosophical and Literary Society* (*Literary and Historical Section*), v, 333–8.

Kitson Clark, M. (1941b): 'Bracelet and Toilet Set, from Burton Fields Gravel Pit', *Proceedings of the Leeds Philosophical and Literary Society* (*Literary and Historical Section*), v, 339–43.

Knudsen, G., Kristensen, M. *et al.* (1936–): *Danmarks gamle Personnavne*, København.

Krapp, G. P. and Dobbie, E. V. K. (1936): *The Exeter Book*, London, New York. (*The Anglo-Saxon Poetic Records*, iii).

Krause, W. (1932): 'Eine altgermanische Bezeichnung des Pferdes und der Runenstein von Möjebro', *Arkiv för nordisk filologi*, 3rd series iv, 156–73.

Krause, W. (1937): *Runeninschriften im älteren Futhark*, Halle/Saale.

Krause, W. (1943): *Was man in Runen ritzte*, 2nd ed., Halle/Saale.

Kummer, S. A. (1932): *Heilige Runenmacht*, Hamburg.

Laborde, M. de (1857): *Notice des emaux du Louvre*, Paris.

Laking, G. F. (1920): *A Record of European Armour and Arms through Seven Centuries*, i, London.

Lasko, P. (1956): 'The comb of St. Cuthbert', *The Relics of St. Cuthbert* (ed. C. F. Battiscombe), Durham, 336–55.

Lavrsen, J. (1960): 'Brandstrup, En ryttergrav fra 10. århundrede', *Kuml*, 90–105.

Leclerq, H. (1930): *Dictionnaire d'archéologie chrétienne et de liturgie* (ed. Cabrol/Leclerq), ix, 2éme partie, Paris.

Leeds, E. T. (1911): 'Notes on Examples of Late Anglo-Saxon Metal Work', *University of Liverpool: Annals of Archaeology and Anthropology*, iv, 1–10.

Leeds, E. T. (1936): *Early Anglo-Saxon Art and Archaeology*, Oxford.

Lewis, C. S. (1936): *The Allegory of Love*, Oxford.

Lewis, S. (1840): *A Topographical Dictionary of England*, 4th ed., iv, London.

Liljegren, J. G. (1833): *Run-Urkunder*, Stockholm.

Lind, E. H. (1905–15): *Norsk-isländska Dopnamn och fingerade Namn från Medeltiden*, Uppsala/Leipzig.

Lindqvist, S. (1931): 'Yngre Vikingastilar', *Nordisk Kultur, Kunst* (ed. H. Shetelig), Oslo, 144–179.

Logeman, H. (1891): *L'inscription anglo-saxonne du reliquaire de la Vraie Croix au trésor de l'église des SS. Michel-et-Gudule à Bruxelles*, Bruxelles (*Mémoires couronnés . . . publiés par l'Académie Royale . . . de Belgique*, xlv).

Lowe, E. A. (1934–): *Codices Latini Antiquiores*, Oxford.

Lowe, E. A. (1958): 'A Key to Bede's Scriptorium', *Scriptorium*, xii, 182–90.

Luick, K. (1914–): *Historische Grammatik der englischen Sprache*, Leipzig.

Lysons, D. and S. (1816): *Magna Britannia*, iv, London.

MacDermott, M. (1955): 'The Kells Crozier', *Archaeologia*, xcvi, 59–113.

Madden, F. (1856): 'Remarks on the Anglo-Saxon Charters granted to the Abbey of St. Denis in France and on the Seals attached to them', *The Archaeological Journal*, xiii, 355–71.

Magnusen, F. (1820): 'Forsøg til Forklaring over en Runeindskrift paa en i Engelland i Aaret 1818 funden Guldring . . .', *Antiqvarisk Annaler*, iii, 339–51.

Magnusen, F. (1822): 'De Annulo aureo Runicis Characteribus signato, nuper in Anglia invento, et pluribus ejusdem generis', *Archaeologia Aeliana*, i, 136–41.

Mahr, A. (1932): *Christian Art in Ancient Ireland*, i, Dublin (see also Raftery (1941)).

Maryon, H. (1950): 'A Sword of the Viking Period from the River Witham', *The Antiquaries Journal*, xxx, 175–79.

Maurice, J. (1911): *Numismatique constantinienne* ii, Paris.

Maxwell, H. (1912–13): 'Notes on a hoard of personal ornaments, implements, and Anglo-Saxon and Northumbrian coins from Talnotrie, Kircudbrightshire', *Proceedings of the Society of Antiquaries of Scotland*, xlvii, 12–16.

Meroney, H. (1945): 'Irish in the Old English Charms', *Speculum*, xx, 172–182.

Messerer, W. (1952): *Der Bamberger Domschatz*, München.

Meyer, E. (1929): 'Ein frühmittelalterlicher Bucheinband aus Enger I.W. im Schlossmuseum', *Berliner Museum, Berichte aus den preussischen Kunstsammlungen*, i, 71–5.

Millar, E. G. (1926): *English Illuminated Manuscripts from the Xth to the XIIth Century*, Paris/Bruxelles.

Mitchell, H. P. (1923): 'Flotsam of later Anglo-Saxon Art, I', *The Burlington Magazine*, xlii, 63–72.

Moe, O. H. (1955): 'Urnes and the British Isles', *Acta Archaeologia*, xxvi, 1–30.

Montgomerie, D. M. (1947): 'Old Sarum', *The Archaeological Journal*, civ, 129–39.

Moss, A. A. (1953a): 'Niello', *Studies in Conservation*, i, 49–62.

Moss, A. A. (1953b): 'Niello', *The Antiquaries Journal*, xxxiii, 75–7.

Müller, S. (1880): 'Dyreornamentiken i Norden', *Aarbøger for nordisk Oldkyndighed og Historie*, 185–403.

Müller, S. (1881): *Die Thierornamentik in Norden*, Hamburg.

Müller, S. (1898): *Nordische Altertumskunde*, ii, Strassburg.

Mütherich, F. (1955): 'An illustration of the five senses in Medieval Art', *Journal of the Warburg and Courtauld Institutes*, xviii, 140–1.

Neckel, G. (1938): 'Die Runen', *Acta Philologica Scandinavica*, xii, 102–15.

Nerman, B. (1959): 'The dating of the runic-inscribed scramasax from the Thames', *The Antiquaries Journal*, xxxix, 289–90.

Nesbitt, A. and Thompson, E. M. (1883): 'Two Memoirs of the "Evangelia Quatuor" once belonging to the Abbey of Lindau . . .', *Vetusta Monumenta*, vi, pls. xlvii, xlviii.

Newton, W. H. (1851–4): 'Inscribed Runic Ring', *Proceedings of the Society of Antiquaries of Scotland*, i, 22–5.

Noreen, A. (1923): *Altisländische und altnorwegische Grammatik*, 4th ed., Halle a. S. (*Sammlung kurzer Grammatiken germanischer Dialekte*, iv, 1).

Nørlund, P. (1935): 'En doppeltske i sølvfundet fra Ribe, Østermark, nedlagt 1247', *Aarbøger for nordisk Oldkyndighed og Historie*, 117–28.

Oakeshott, R. E. (1951): 'An "Ingelri" sword in the British Museum', *The Antiquaries Journal*, xxxi, 69–71.

Olsen, M. (1932): 'Kingigtórsoak-stenen og sproget i de grønlandske Runeinnskrifter', *Norsk Tidsskrift for Sprogvidenskap*, v, 189–257.

Olsen, M. *et al.* (1941–): *Norges innskrifter med de yngre runer*, Oslo.

O'Dell, A. C. *et al.* (1959): 'The St. Ninian's Isle Silver Hoard', *Antiquity*, xxxiii, 241–68.

O'Dell, A. C. (1960): *The St. Ninian's Isle Treasure*, Edinburgh/London.

Oman, C. C. (1930): *Catalogue of Rings*, London (Victoria and Albert Museum).

Oman, C. C. (1931): 'Anglo-Saxon Finger-Rings', *Apollo*, xiv, 104–8.

Oman, C. C. (1957): *English Church Plate 597–1830*, London.

Page, R. I. (1959): 'Language and Dating in OE Inscriptions', *Anglia*, lxxvii, 385–406.

Page, R. I. (1960): 'The Bewcastle Cross', *Nottingham Medieval Studies*, iv, 36–57.

Page, R. I. (1962a): 'The Finding of the Bramham Moor Runic Ring', *Notes and Queries*, 450–52.

Page, R. I. (1962b): 'A Note on the Transliteration of Old English Runic Inscriptions'. *English Studies*, xliii, 484–90.

Paor, M. and L. de (1958): *Early Christian Ireland*, London.

Paues, A. C. (1907): 'Runes and Manuscripts', *Cambridge History of English Literature*, i, 7–18.

Paues, A. C. (1911): 'The Name of the Letter ʒ', *Modern Language Review*, vi, 441–54.

Payne, G. (1893): *Collectanea Cantiana*, London.

Peers, C. R. (1923-4): 'The Inscribed and Sculptured Stones of Lindisfarne', *Archaeologia*, lxxiv, 255–70.

Peers, C. R. and Radford, C. A. R. (1943): 'The Saxon Monastery of Whitby', *Archaeologia*, lxxxix, 27–88.

Pegge, S. (1786): 'Illustration of a gold enamelled Ring, supposed to have been the Property of Alhstan Bishop of Sherburne . . .', *Archaeologia*, iv, 47–68.

Petersen, J. (1919): *De Norske Vikingesverd, en typologisk-kronologisk studie over Vikingetidens vaaben*, Kristiania. (*Videnskapsselskapets Skrifter, ii, Hist. Filos. Klasse*, No. I).

Petersen, J. (1928): *Vikingetidens Smykker*, Stavanger.

Petersen, J. (1951): *Vikingetidens Redskaper*, Oslo (*Det Norske Videnskaps-Akademi i Oslo Skrifter, ii, Hist. Filos. Klasse. No. 4*).

Petrie, H. and Sharpe, J. (1848): *Monumenta Historica Britannica*, London.

Pfeilstücker, S. (1936): *Spätantikes und Germanisches Kunstgut in der Frühangelsächsischen Kunst*, Berlin.

Philip, A. J. (1954): *A History of Gravesend*, Wraysbury.

Pijoán, J. (1942): *Summa Artis*, viii, Madrid.

Ploss, E. (1958): 'Der Inschriftentypus "N. N. me fecit" und seine geschichtliche Entwicklung bis ins Mittelalter', *Zeitschrift für deutsche Philologie*, lxxvii, 25–46.

Potratz, H. (1943-8): 'Die Goldene Halskette von Isenbüttel', *IPEK*, xvii, 77–103.

Potter, C. (1889): 'Leather, Bronze, Pewter, &c., Ornaments, from the Cheshire shore', *Transactions of the Historic Society of Lancashire and Cheshire*, xli, 195–202.

Potts, R. U. (1925): 'A Saxon Burial Cross found in St. Austin's Abbey,' *Archaeologia Cantiana* xxxvii, 211–3.

Powicke, F. M. (*ed.*) (1939): *Handbook of British Chronology*, London (*Royal Historical Society Guides and Handbooks*, ii).

Radford, C. A. R. (1940): 'Small bronzes from St. Augustine's Abbey, Canterbury', *The Antiquaries Journal*, xx, 506–8.

Radford, C. A. R. (1955): 'Two Scottish Shrines —Jedburgh and St. Andrews', *The Archaeological Journal*, cxii, 43–60.

Radford, C. A. R. and Donaldson G. (1957): *Whithorn and Kirkmadrine, Wigtownshire*, Edinburgh.

Raftery, J. (1941): *Christian Art in Ancient Ireland*, ii, Dublin (see also Mahr (1932)).

Raine, J. (1852): *A brief historical account of the episcopal castle, or palace, of Auckland*, Durham.

Rand, E. K. (1929): *A Survey of the Manuscripts of Tours*, Cambridge (Mass.).

Rankin, J. W. (1921): 'Rhythm and Rime before the Norman Conquest', *Publications of the Modern Language Association of America*, xxxvi, 401–28.

Rashleigh, J. (1868): 'An Account of Anglo-Saxon Coins and Gold and Silver Ornaments found at Trewhiddle, near St. Austell, Cornwall, A.D. 1774', *Numismatic Chronicle*, new series, viii, 137–57.

Rashleigh, P. (1789): 'Account of Antiquities discovered in Cornwall, 1774', *Archaeologia*, ix, 187–90.

Rashleigh, P. (1794): 'Farther Account of Antiquities discovered in Cornwall, 1774', *Archaeologia*, xi, 83–4.

Rask, R. K. (1838): *Samlede Afhandlinger*, iii, København, (a letter reprinted from *The Foreign Review*, 1828, 259–62).

Read, C. H. (1887): 'On an iron sword of Scandinavian type found in London, now in the British Museum; and a bronze stirrup of the same period found near Romsey in Hampshire, in the possession of Philip B. Davis Cook Esq.', *Archaeologia*, l, 530–3.

Reaney, P. H. (1943): *The Place-Names of Cambridgeshire and the Isle of Ely*, Cambridge (*English Place-Name Society*, xix).

Redin, M. (1919): *Studies on Uncompounded Personal Names in Old English*, Uppsala (*Uppsala universitets Årsskrift* 1919, *Filosofi,*

Språkvetenskap och Historiska Vetenskaper, 2).

Reichardt, K. (1936): *Runenkunde*, Jena.

Reichardt, K. (1938): 'Schrift', *Germanische Altertumskunde* (*ed.* H. Schneider, München), 431–59.

Reiss, B. (1936): *Runenkunde*, Leipzig.

Richardson, K. M. (1959): 'Excavations in Hungate, York', *The Archaeological Journal*, cxvi, 51–114.

Riegl, A. (1923): *Die spätrömische Kunstindustrie*, ii, Wien.

Ring Cat. See *B.M. Ring Cat.*

Roach Smith, C. (1850): *The Antiquities of Richborough, Reculver and Lymne*, London.

Roach Smith, C. (1854): *Catalogue of the Museum of London. Antiquities collected by, and the property of, Charles Roach Smith*, London.

Roach Smith, C. (1859): *Illustrations of Roman London*, London.

Robertson, A. J. (1956): *Anglo-Saxon Charters*, 2nd ed., Cambridge.

Roes, A. (1958): 'A strap-end in the Yorkshire Museum and its continental counterparts', *The Antiquaries Journal*, xxxviii, 94–6.

Rogers, J. J. (1867): 'Saxon Silver Ornaments and Coins found at Trewhiddle, near St. Austell: A.D. 1774', *Journal of the Royal Institution of Cornwall*, ii 292–305.

Romilly Allen, J. (1903): *The Early Christian Monuments of Scotland*, Edinburgh.

Romilly Allen, J. (1904*a*): 'Anglo-Saxon pins found at Lincoln', *The Reliquary and Illustrated Archaeologist*, new series, x, 52–53.

Romilly Allen, J. (1904*b*): 'A carved bone of the Viking Age', *The Reliquary and Illustrated Archaeologist*, new series, x, 270–5.

Romilly Allen, J. (1906): 'The Thurible of Godric', *The Reliquary and Illustrated Archaeologist*, new series, xii, 50–3.

Rosenberg, M. (1921): *Geschichte der Goldschmiedekunst, Zellenschmeltz*, iii, Berlin.

Rouse, E. C. and Baker A. (1955): 'The Wall-paintings at Longthorpe Tower, nr. Peterborough', *Archaeologia*, xcvi, 1–58.

Ruding, R. (1817): *Annals of the Coinage of Britain*, 1st ed., i, London.

Rydbeck, M. (1931–2): 'Skånska praktsvärd från Vikingatiden', *Meddelanden från Lunds universitets historiska museum*, 38–47.

Rygh, O. (1885): *Norske Oldsager*, Christiania.

Salzmann, L. F. (1912): 'Excavations at Selsey, 1911', *Sussex Archaeological Collections*, lv, 56–62.

San Quentino, G. d. (1849): 'Monete del xe dell' xi secolo nei duitorni di Roma nel 1843', *Memorie della Reale Academia della Scienze di Torino*, ser. ii, ix–x, 1–115.

Saxl, F. (1927): *Verzeichnis astrologischer und mythologischer illustrierter Handschriften des lateinischen Mittelalters, ii, Die Handschriften der Bibliothek in Wien*, Heidelberg.

Scherer, C. (1931): *Die Braunschweiger Elfenbeinsammlung*, Leipzig.

Schetelig, H. See Shetelig H.

Schlunk, H. (1950): 'The Crosses of Oviedo', *The Art Bulletin*, xxxii, 91–114.

Schmid, W. M. (1893): *Eine Goldschmiedschule in Regensburg um das Jahr 1000*, München.

Schnitzler, H. (1957): *Rheinische Schatzkammer*, Tafelband, Düsseldorf.

Schönaich-Carolath, I. v. (1924): *Runeudenkmäler*, Mülhausen (Thüringen).

Schramm, P. E. (1954): *Herrschaftszeichen und Staatssymbolik*, i, Stuttgart.

Schramm, G. (1957): 'Namenschatz und Dichtersprache', *Zeitschrift für vergleichende Sprachforschungen*, Ergänzungshefte, nr. 15.

Scott, F. S. (1956): 'The Hildithryth Stone and the other Hartlepool Name-stones', *Archaeologia Aeliana*, 4th Ser., xxxiv, 196–212.

Seaby, W. A. (1950): 'Late Dark Age Finds from the Cherwell and Ray, 1876–86', *Oxoniensia*, xv, 29–43.

Searle, W. G. (1897): *Onomasticon Anglo-Saxonicum*, Cambridge.

Sephton, J. (1895/6): 'On some Runic Remains', *Proceedings of the Literary and Philosophical Society of Liverpool*, 183–210.

Shetelig, H. (1909): 'Urnesgruppen', *Foreningen til norske Fortidsmindesmærkers Bevaring, Aarsberetning*, 75–107.

Shetelig, H. (1930): 'Runeskriftens Kilder. En orientering i de nyere synsmåter', *Bergens Museums Årbok*, 1–17.

Shetelig, H. (ed.) (1931): *Kunst*, Oslo/Stockholm/København. (*Nordisk Kultur*, xxvii).

Shetelig, H. (ed.) (1940): *Viking Antiquities in Great Britain and Ireland*, parts i–v, Oslo.

Shetelig, H. (1948): 'The Norse style of ornamentation in the Viking Settlements', *Acta Archaeologica*, xix, 69–113.

Shetelig, H. (ed.) (1954): *Viking Antiquities in Great Britain and Ireland*, part vi, Oslo.

Shetelig, H. and Falk, H. (1937): *Scandinavian Archaeology*, Oxford.

Shore, T. W. (1906): *Origin of the Anglo-Saxon Race*, London.

Shortt, W. T. P. (*n.d.*): *Sylva Antiqua Iscana*, Exeter.

Sierke, S. (1939): *Kannten die vorchristlichen Germanen Runenzauber?* Königsberg/Berlin.

Sievers, E. (1896–1901): *Runen und Runeninschriften*, 2nd ed., Strassburg.

Sievers, E. and Brunner, K. (1951): *Altenglische Grammatik*, 2nd ed., Halle a.S. (*Sammlung kurzer Grammatiken germanischer Dialekte*, A, 3).

Simms, R. S. (1932): 'Medieval Spoon from Pevensey Castle', *The Antiquaries Journal*, xii, 73–4.

Sisam, K. (1953): 'Anglo-Saxon Royal Genealogies', *Proceedings of the British Academy*, xxxix, 287–348.

Sjøvold, T. (1951): 'A bronze ornament of Western European origin found in Northern Norway', *Antiquity*, xxv, 127–30.

Skeat, W. W. (1881): *Ælfric's Lives of Saints, being a set of sermons on saints' days formerly observed by the English Church*, London.

Skeat, W. W. (1887): *The Gospel according to St. Matthew in Anglo-Saxon, Northumbrian and Old Mercian Versions*, Cambridge.

Skinner, F. G. and Bruce-Mitford, R. L. S. (1940): 'A Celtic Balance-beam of the Christian Period', *The Antiquaries Journal*, xx, 87–102.

Smith, A. H. (1935): *The Parker Chronicle 832–900*, London.

Smith, H. C. (1908): *Jewellery*, London.

Smith, R. A. (1904): 'Some Anglo-Saxon Silver Ornaments found at Trewhiddle, Cornwall in 1774', *Proceedings of the Society of Antiquaries of London*, 2nd series, xx, 47–55.

Smith, R. A. (1913): 'The Evolution of the Hand-pin in Great Britain and Ireland', *Opuscula Archaeologica Oscari Montelio Septuagenario . . .*, Holmiae, 281–9.

Smith, R. A. (1914): 'Irish Brooches of Five Centuries', *Archaeologia*, lxv, 223–50.

Smith, R. A. (1923): 'Early Anglo-Saxon Weights', *The Antiquaries Journal*, iii, 122–9.

Smith, R. A.: *British Museum Guide to Anglo-Saxon Antiquities*, London, 1923, Referred to as *BMASG*.

Smith, R. A. (1925*a*): 'Examples of Anglian Art', *Archaeologia*, lxxiv, 233–54.

Smith, R. A. (1925*b*): 'The Beeston Tor Hoard', *The Antiquaries Journal*, v, 135–40.

Starkie Gardner, J. (1894): *Some Minor Arts.*

Stenberger, M. (1947–58): *Die Schatzfunde Gotlands der Wikingerzeit*, Lund/Stockholm.

Stenberger, M. (1958): 'Traditionsbundenhet i vikingatida gotländsk brakteatkonst', *Tor*, iv, 113–133.

Stephens, G. (1866–1901): *The Old-Northern Runic Monuments of Scandinavia and England . . .*, London/København.

Stephens, G. (1884): *Handbook of the Old-Northern Runic Monuments of Scandinavia and England*, London/Copenhagen.

Stephens, G. (1894): *The Runes, whence came they*, London/København.

Stevenson, J. (1847): *Libellus de vita et miraculis S. Godrici, Heremitæ de Finchale*, London/Edinburgh. (*Surtees Society*, xx).

Stevenson, R. B. K. (1955): 'Pictish Art', *The Problem of the Picts* (ed. F. T. Wainwright), Edinburgh, 97–128.

Stevenson, W. H. (1904), *Asser's Life of King Alfred together with the Annals of Saint Neots, erroneously ascribed to Asser*, Oxford.

Stollenmeyer, P. (1949): 'Der Tassilokelch', *Der Professoren Festschrift zum 400 jährigen Bestande des öffentlichen Obergymnasiums der Benediktiner zu Kremsmünster.*

Stolz, W. (1908). *Der Vokalismus der betonen Silben in der altnordhumbrischen Interlinearversion der Lindisfarner Evangelien*, Bonn.

Stone, L. (1955): *Sculpture in Britain: the Middle Ages*, Harmondsworth.

Storms, G. (1948): *Anglo-Saxon Magic*, The Hague.

Ström, H. (1939): *Old English Personal Names in Bede's History, an etymological-phonological investigation*, Lund, (*Lund Studies in English*, viii).

Strömberg, M. (1953): 'Eine silbertauschierte Eisenaxt im Historischen Museum zu Lund', *Meddelanden från Lunds Universitets Historiska Museum*, 264–73.

Strömberg, M. (1961): *Untersuchungen zur jüngeren Eisenzeit in Schonen*, Lund.

Sutherland, C. H. V. (1948): *Anglo-Saxon Gold Coinage in the Light of the Crondall Hoard*, London.

Swarzenski, G. (1954), 'An Early Anglo-Irish portable shrine', *Bulletin of the Museum of Fine Arts*, Boston, lii, 50–62.

Swarzenski, H. (1954), *Monuments of Romanesque Art*, London.

Sweet, H. (1885): *The Oldest English Texts*, London (*Early English Text Society*, 83).

Talbot Rice, D. (1952): *English Art, 871–1100*, Oxford.

Tanner, L. E. (1954): 'The Quest for the Cross of St. Edward the Confessor', *Journal of the British Archaeological Association*, 3rd ser., xvii, 1–10.

Taylor, I. (1879): *Greeks and Goths. A Study on the Runes*, London.

Taylor, I. (1890): 'The Order of the Letters in the Runic Futhork', *Academy*, xxxviii, 505–6.

Taylour, C. (1688): *A true and perfect narrative of the strange and unexpected finding of the crucifix and gold-chain of that pious prince, St. Edward, the King and Confessor . . .*, London.

Thompson, J. D. A. (1956): *Inventory of British Coin Hoards*, London.

Thompson, J. D. A. (1959): 'Some additions and corrections to J. D. A. Thompson, *Inventory of British Coin Hoards*: A Recension', *Medieval Archaeology*, iii, 280–2.

Thorpe, B. (1844–46): *Homilies of the Anglo-Saxon Church*, Oxford.

Tonnochy, A. B. (1932): 'A Romanesque Censer-cover in the British Museum', *Archaeological Journal*, 89, 1–16.

Tonnochy, A. B. (1937): 'The Censer in the Middle Ages', *Journal of the British Archaeological Association*, 3rd series, ii, 47–62.

Tonnochy, A. B. (1952): *Catalogue of British Seal-Dies in the British Museum*, London.

VCH: *Victoria History of the Counties of England*, London.

Velge, H. (1925): *La collégiale des saints Michel et Gudule à Bruxelles.* Bruxelles.

Vigfusson, G. and York Powell, F. (1868): *An Icelandic Prose Reader*, Oxford.

Vleeskruyer, R. (1953): *The Life of St. Chad, an Old English Homily*, Amsterdam.

Vulliamy, C. E. (1930): *The Archaeology of Middlesex and London*, London.

Walker, J. (1945): 'A hoard of Anglo-Saxon coins from Tetney, Lincolnshire', *Numismatic Chronicle*, series vi, V, 81–95.

Walker, J. W. and M. I. (1927): *The Church Plate of Berkshire, n.p.*

Ward Perkins, J. B. (1939): 'A Medieval Spoon in the Guildhall Museum, London', *The Antiquaries Journal*, xix, 313–16.

Ward Perkins, J. B. (1940): *Medieval Catalogue, (London Museum Catalogues: vii)* London.

Waterman, D. M. (1951): 'A gold ring found at Malton in 1774', *The Antiquaries Journal*, xxxi, 192.

Waterman, D. M. (1953): 'Notes on two early medieval swords found in Ulster', *Ulster Journal of Archaeology*, xvi, 59–62.

Waterman, D. M. (1959): 'Late Saxon, Viking and Early Medieval Finds from York', *Archaeologia*, xcvii, 59–105.

Waterton, E. (1862): 'On Niello', *The Archaeological Journal*, xix, 323–39.

Watts, W. W. (1922): *Catalogue of the Chalices and other Communion Vessels [in the Victoria and Albert Museum]*, London.

Weber, E. (1941): *Kleine Runenkunde*, Berlin.

Weigall, A. (1927): *Wanderings in Anglo-Saxon Britain*, London.

Werner, J. (1959): 'Frühkarolingische Silberohrringe von Rastede (Oldenburg)', *Germania*, xxxvii, 179–92.

Westell, W. P. (1935): 'Bronze objects found in Hertfordshire', *The Antiquaries Journal*, xv, 349–51.

Wheeler, R. E. M. (1927): *London and the Vikings (London Museum Catalogues: i)*, London.

Wheeler, R. E. M. (1935): *London and the Saxons (London Museum Catalogues: vi)*, London.

Whitelock, D. (1930): *Anglo-Saxon Wills*, Cambridge.

Whitelock, D. (1952): *The Beginnings of English Society*, Harmondsworth.

Wideen, H. (1955): *Västsvenska Vikingatidsstudier*, Göteborg.

Williams, I (1905): 'A Grammatical Investigation of the Old Kentish Glosses', *Bonner Beiträge zur Anglistik*, xix, 92–166.

Willis, B. (1727): *A Survey of the Cathedrals*, i, London.

Wilson, D. (1863): *The Archaeology and Prehistoric Annals of Scotland*, 2nd edition, Edinburgh.

Wilson, D. M. (1955a): 'An Early Viking Age Grave from Källby, Lund', *Meddelanden från Lunds Universitets Historiska Museum*, 105–26.

Wilson, D. M. (1955b): 'Two Silver Plates from an Anglo-Saxon Casket', *The British Museum Quarterly*, xx, 47–50.

Wilson, D. M. (1955c): 'An Irish mounting in the National Museum, Copenhagen', *Acta Archaeologica*, xxvi, 163–72.

Wilson, D. M. (1956a): 'A bronze mounting from Oxshott Wood, Surrey', *The Antiquaries Journal*, xxxvi, 70–71.

Wilson, D. M. (1956b): 'The Poslingford Ring', *The British Museum Quarterly*, xx, 90–2.

Wilson, D. M. (1956c): 'Two Plates from a Late Saxon Casket', *The Antiquaries Journal*, xxxvi, 31–9.

Wilson, D. M. (1957): 'An Enamelled Disc-Brooch', *The British Museum Quarterly*, xxi, 52–4.

Wilson, D. M. (1958a): 'A group of penannular brooches of the Viking period', *Árbók hins íslenzka fornleifafélags, fylgirit*, 95–100.

Wilson, D. M. (1958b): 'An Early Carolingian Finger-ring', *British Museum Quarterly*, xxi, 80–1.

Wilson, D. M. (1958c): 'Some Archaeological Additions and Corrections to J. D. A. Thompson, *Inventory of British Coin Hoards*', *Medieval Archaeology*, ii, 169–71.

Wilson, D. M. (1959a): 'Almgren and Chronology', *Medieval Archaeology*, iii, 112–19.

Wilson, D. M. (1959b): 'A Group of Anglo-Saxon Amulet Rings', *The Anglo-Saxons (ed. P. Clemoes)*, Cambridge, 159–70.

Wilson, D. M. (1960a): *The Anglo-Saxons*, London.

Wilson, D. M. (1960b): 'An Anglo-Saxon Ivory Comb', *The British Museum Quarterly*, xxiii, 17–19.

Wilson, D. M. (1960c): 'The King's School, Canterbury, disc brooch', *Medieval Archaeology*, iv, 16–28.

Wilson, D. M. (1960d): 'Irsk-britisk import i Lejre', *Nationalmuseets Arbejdsmark*, 36–7.

Wilson, D. M. (1960e): 'The Fejø cup', *Acta Archaeologica*, xxxi, 147–73.

Wilson, D. M. (1961): 'An Anglo-Saxon Bookbinding at Fulda (Codex Bonifatianus 1)', *The Antiquaries Journal*, xli, 199–217.

Wilson, D. M. and Blunt, C. E. (1961): 'The Trewhiddle Hoard', *Archaeologia*, 98, 75–122.

Wilson, D. M. and Hurst, J. G. (1958): 'Medieval Britain in 1957', *Medieval Archaeology*, ii, 183–213.

Wimmer, L. F. A. (1874): 'Runeskriftens Oprindelse og Udvikling i Norden', *Aarbøger for nordisk Oldkyndighed og Historie*, 1–270.

Wimmer, L. F. A. (1887): *Die Runenschrift*, Berlin.

Winckelmann, M. (1953): 'Archäologische Untersuchungen unter den Pfarrkirche zu Vreden', *Westfalen*, xxxi, 304–19.

Winkelmann, E. (1883): *Geschichte der Angelsächsen bis zum Tode König Alfreds*, Berlin.

Wormald, F. (1945): 'Decorated Initials in English MSS. from A.D. 900–1100', *Archaeologia*, xci, 107–35.

Wormald, F. (1952): *English Drawings of the Tenth and Eleventh Centuries*, London.

Wormald, F. (1959): *The Benedictional of St. Ethelwold*, London.

Wright, T. (1865): 'Account of Anglo-Saxon Jewellery, etc. found at Seamer in the East Riding of Yorkshire', *Journal of the British Archaeological Association*, 329–32.

W[right], T. and Halliwell, J. O. (1841–3): *Reliquiae Antiquae. Scraps from ancient manuscripts illustrating . . . the English language*, London.

Zarnecki, G. (1951): *English Romanesque Sculpture*, 1066–1140, London.

Zarnecki, G. (1957): *English Romanesque Lead Sculpture*, London.

Zimmermann, E. H. (1918): *Vorkarolingische Miniaturen*, Berlin.

Zupitza, J. (1877): 'Kentische Glossen des neunten Jahrhunderts', *Zeitschrift für deutsches Alterthum und deutsche Litteratur*, xxi, 1–59.

INDEX VERBORUM

This is a complete Index Verborum of the sixteen texts examined in Appendix A. The actual forms found in the inscriptions are used as head-words. OE words are parsed, save for nouns in the nom. sg. The order of letters is alphabetical: Æ is treated as a separate letter after A, Ð appears after S, Þ in place of W. Doubtful readings or identifications are preceded by a question mark. References are to pages in Appendix A.

A

AG, AGE, see AH

AGENES, *adj.* (*gen. sg. n.*), own, Sutton, Isle of Ely, brooch, 86–7

agROf, *st. v.* (*VI*) (*3. sg. pret. ind.*), engrave, Lancashire ring, 75

AH, *pret.-pres. v.* (*3. sg. pres. ind.*), own, Cuxton brooch, 84; Lancashire ring, 75; Sittingbourne scramasax, 86; AG, Sutton, Isle of Ely, brooch, 86–7; ? ΛH, *Eawen* finger-ring, 89–90; AGE, (*3. sg. pres. subj.*), Sutton, Isle of Ely, brooch, 86–7

AÞERIE, *w. v.* (*I*) (*3. sg. pres. subj.*), curse, Sutton, Isle of Ely, brooch, 86–7

Æ

æDRED, *m. a-stem*, pers. name, Lancashire ring, 75–7

ÆDVÞEN, *f. jō-stem* (*=Ædwynn*) or *i-stem* (*=Ædwen*), pers. name, Sutton, Isle of Ely, brooch, 86–8

ÆLFGIVV, *f. ō-stem*, pers. name, Cuxton brooch, 84

ÆLFRICI, Latinised *m.*, pers. name, Ælfric seal-die, 81–2

'ærkriufltkriuriþonglæſtæpontol', amuletic formula, Greymoor Hill ring, 73–5

ÆTFERIE, *w. v.* (*I*) (*3. sg. pres. subj.*), take away, Sutton, Isle of Ely, brooch, 86–7

B

'bêagnoþ', *m. a-stem*, pers. name, Thames scramasax, 69, 72–3

BIORHTELM, *m. a-stem*, pers. name, Sittingbourne scramasax, 86

BVREDRVÐ, *f. i-stem*, pers. name, Bvredrvð finger-ring, 83–4

BVTON, *conj.*, unless, Sutton, Isle of Ely, brooch, 86–7

C

? CES, *st. v.* (*II*) (*3. sg. pret. ind.*), choose, *Eawen* finger-ring, 89–90

? CES, for *Cristes, m. a-stem* (*gen. sg.*), Christ, *Eawen* finger-ring, 89–90

D

DRIHTEN, *m. a-stem*, Lord, Sutton, Isle of Ely, brooch (2 x), 86–7

E

EAnRED, *m. a-stem*, pers. name, Lancashire ring, 75

EAÐELSVIÐ, *f. ō-stem*, pers. name, Æthelswith finger-ring, 82–3

? EAÞEN, *f. i-stem*, pers. name, *Eawen* finger-ring, 89–90

EOFRI[.], *m.*, pers. name, Exeter sword-pommel, 84–5

EP. ‾, for *episcopi*, Æthelwald seal-die, 80

ETH/ELVVLF, *m. a-stem*, pers. name, Æthelwulf's finger-ring, 82

EÐILVVALDI, Latinised *m.*, pers. name, Æthelwald seal-die, 80–1

F

FE[C], for *fecit*, Exeter sword-pommel, 85

'fuþorcgwhnijʒpxſtbeŋdlmœaæyêa', the OE twenty-eight letter *fuþorc* in a slightly garbled form, Thames scramasax, 69–73

G

GODRIC, *m. a-stem*, pers. name, Pershore censer-cover, 84

H

HINE, *pron.* (*acc. sg. m.*), he; HYO (*nom. sg. f.*); HYO (*acc. sg. f.*); HIRE (*gen. sg. f.*); HIRE (*dat. sg. f.*), Sutton, Isle of Ely, brooch, 86–8

235

L

LEUTLRIL, CGerm. *m.*, pers. name, Lincoln sword, 90

M

ME, *pron.* (*acc. sg.*), I, me, Cuxton brooch, 84; Pershore censer-cover, 84; Sittingbourne scramasax (2 x), 86; Sutton, Isle of Ely, brooch (3 x), 86–7; ?MIE, *Eawen* finger-ring, 89–90; MEC, Lancashire ring (2 x), 75

ME, Latin *pron.*, Exeter sword-pommel, 85

P

? PETRVS, pers. name, *Eawen* finger-ring, 89–90

R

REGNA, or REGI/NA, Æthelswith finger-ring, 82

R/X, for *rex*, Æthelwulf's finger-ring, 82

S

? S, for *sanctus*, *Eawen* finger-ring, 89–90

'sbe/rædht3bcaie/rh/ad/æbs', cryptic text, perhaps amuletic, Thames mount, 77–9

SELLE, *w. v.* (*I*) (*3. sg. pres. subj.*), give, Sutton, Isle of Ely, brooch, 86–7

S⟨I⟩GEBEREHT, *m. a-stem*, pers. name, Sittingbourne scramasax, 86

SIGILLVM, Ælfric seal-die, 81; SII͞, Æthelwald seal-die, 80

? SPETRVS·STANCES, for *spiritus sancte*, *Eawen* finger-ring, 89–90

? STAN, *m. a-stem*, stone, rock, *Eawen* finger-ring, 89–90

? STANCES, for *sancte*, *Eawen* finger-ring, 89–90

Ð

ÐE, *pron.*, who, Sutton, Isle of Ely, brooch, 86–7

Þ

ÞILLES, *n. ja-stem* (*gen. sg.*), will, Sutton, Isle of Ely, brooch, 86–7

ÞORTE, *w. v.* (*I*) (*3. sg. pret. ind.*), make, Sittingbourne scramasax, 86; ÞVORHT⟨E⟩, Pershore censer-cover, 84, 88

236

GENERAL INDEX

238

PLATE XI

1

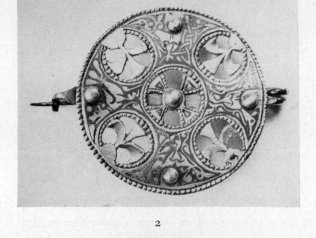

2

4

3

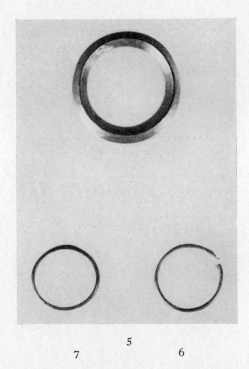

7   5   6

8

All scale $\frac{1}{1}$.

PLATE
XII

9. Scale ⅟₁.

PLATE XIII

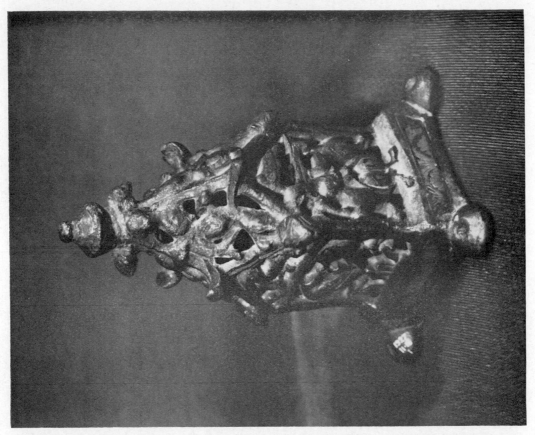

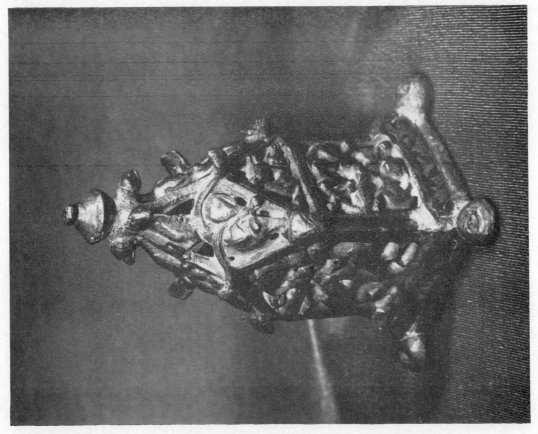

9. Detail of roof panels.

PLATE XIV

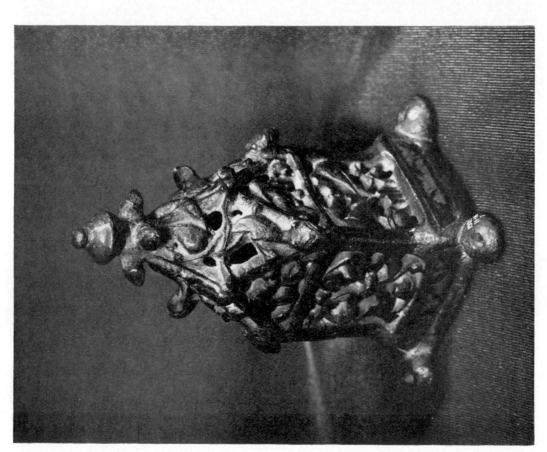

9. Detail of roof panels.

PLATE XV

10

Scale $\frac{1}{1}$.

PLATE XVI

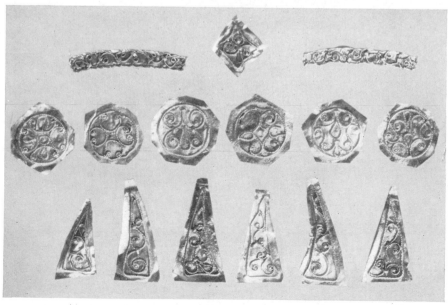

10. View of back and details of the gold filigree panels.

All Scale $\frac{1}{1}$.

PLATE XVII

11

11

12

13

14

15

16

17

18 and impression of seal

All scale $\frac{1}{1}$.

PLATE
XVIII

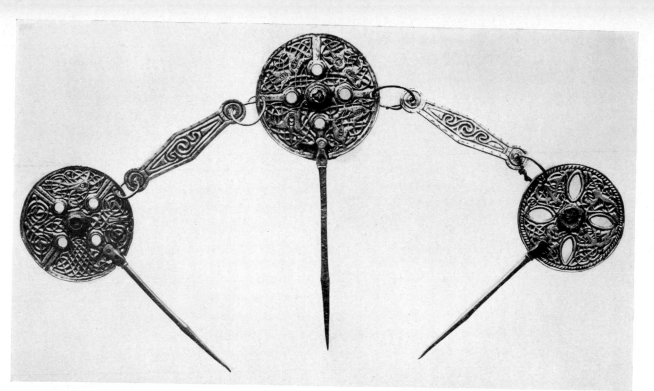

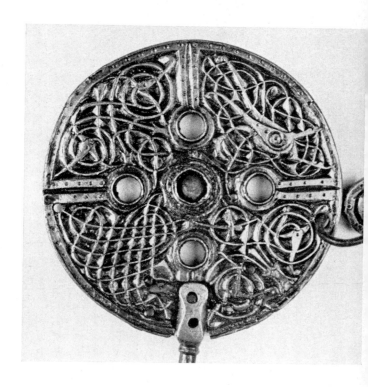

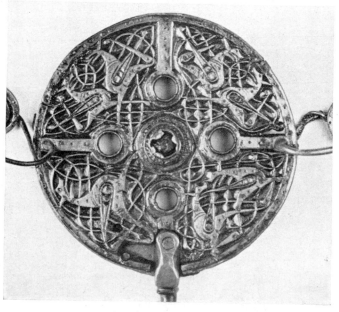

19. General view and details.

PLATE XIX

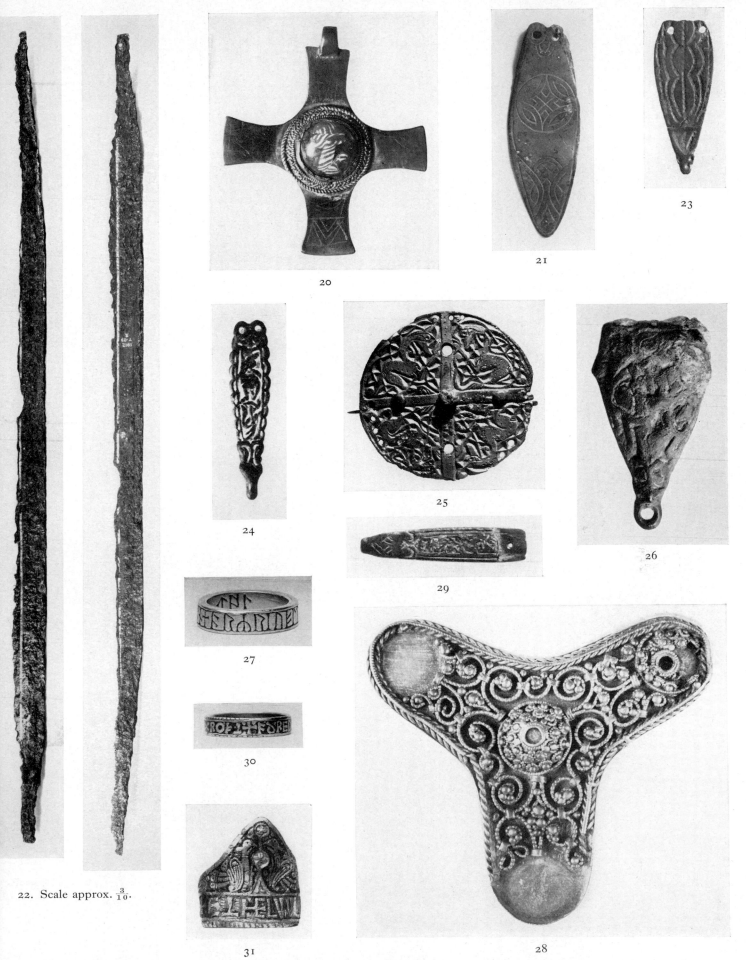

20

21

23

24

25

26

27

29

30

31

28

22. Scale approx. $\frac{3}{10}$.

All, save no. 22, scale $\frac{1}{1}$.

PLATE XX

32. Scale approx. $\frac{1}{2}$.

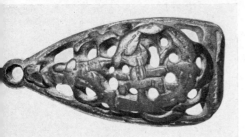

PLATE XXI

33. Scale $\frac{1}{1}$.

34. Scale $\frac{1}{1}$.

35. Scale, slightly less than $\frac{1}{1}$.

PLATE XXII

36

37

38

39

37–39. Scale $\frac{1}{1}$.

PLATE XXIII

40

42

41

All Scale $\frac{1}{1}$.

PLATE XXIV

43. Scale $\frac{8}{5}$.

44. Scale $\frac{1}{1}$.

PLATE XXV

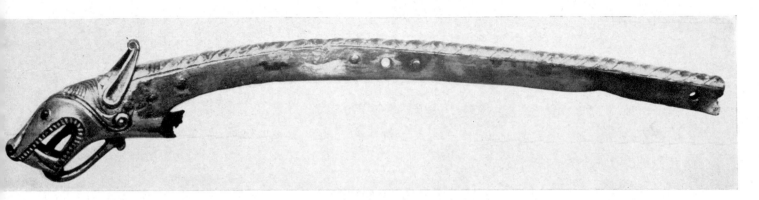

45

47

48

49

46

All Scale $\frac{1}{1}$.

PLATE XXVI

50. Scale approx. ¾.

51

52

53

54

55

Scale of 51–55 : ¹⁄₁.

PLATE XXVII

56

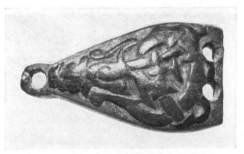

57

58

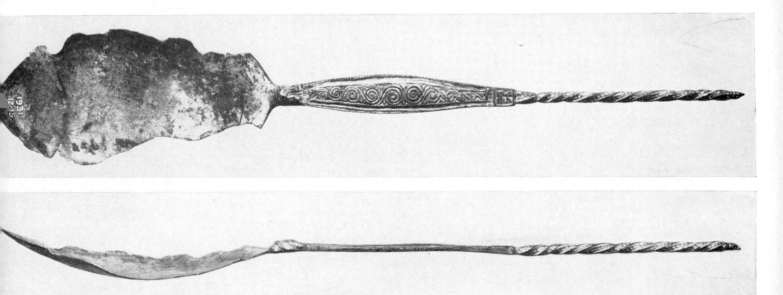

59

All Scale ⅟₁.

PLATE XXVIII

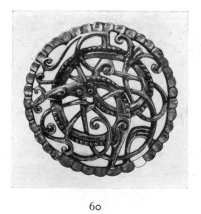

60

61

62

63

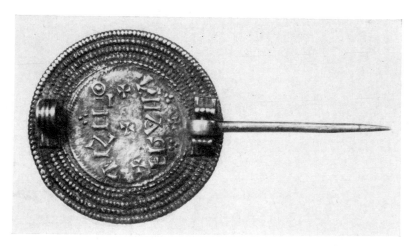

64

All Scale $\frac{1}{1}$.

PLATE XXIX

66

65

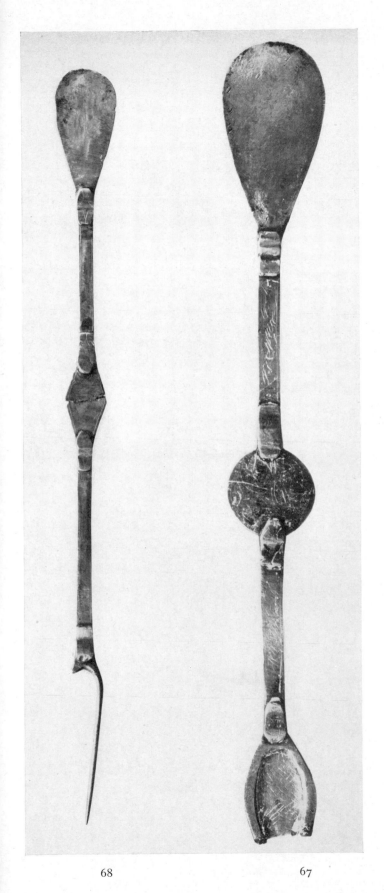

69

70

68   67   70

All Scale $\frac{1}{1}$.

PLATE XXX

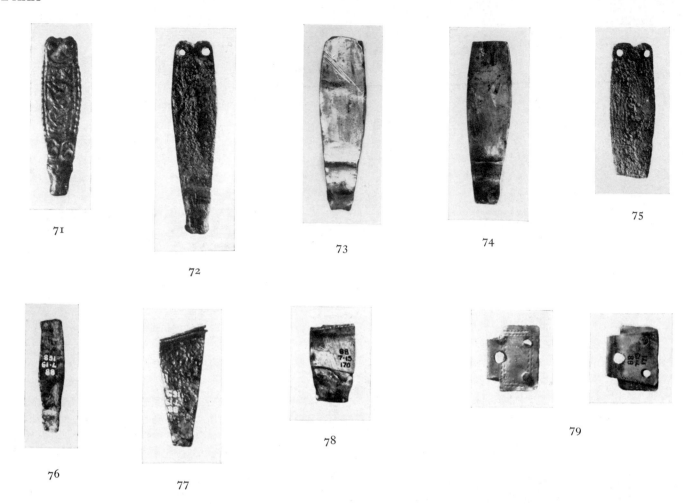

71

72

73

74

75

76

77

78

79

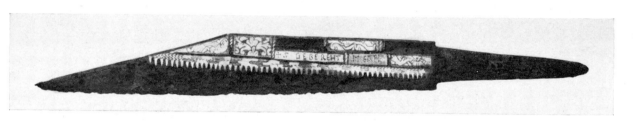

80. Scale ½.

82

All Scale ⅟₁, except no. 80.

PLATE XXXI

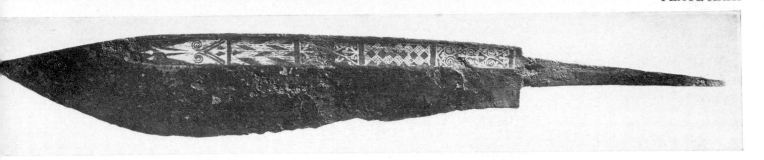

81. Scale $\frac{5}{7}$.

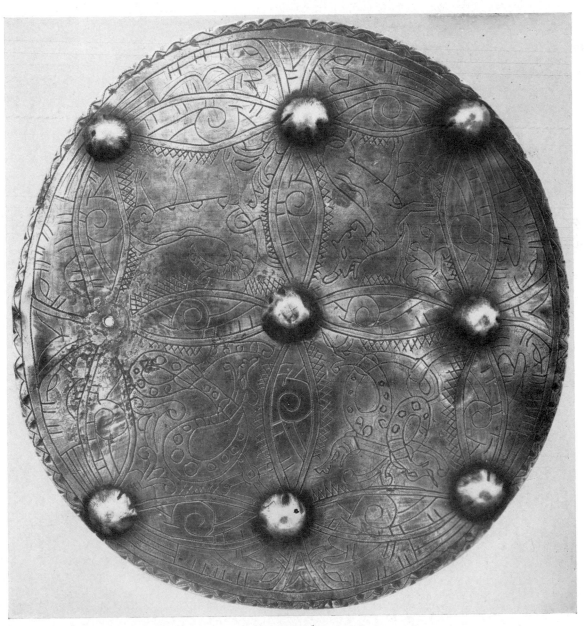

83. Scale $\frac{1}{1}$.

PLATE XXXII

83. Back

84

85

86 and 87

88

All Scale $\frac{1}{1}$, except no. 84 ($\frac{2}{3}$).

PLATE XXXIII

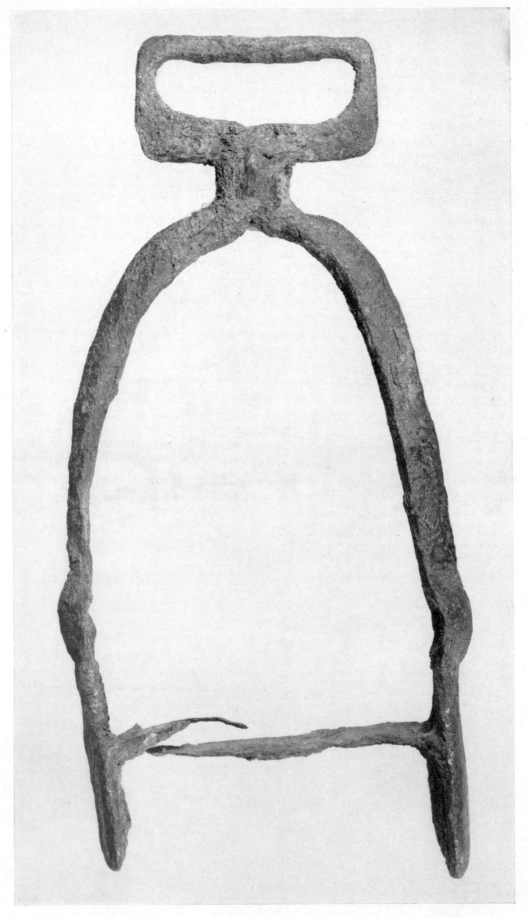

89. Scale ⅟₁.

PLATE XXXIV

90. Scale $\frac{1}{1}$.

PLATE XXXV

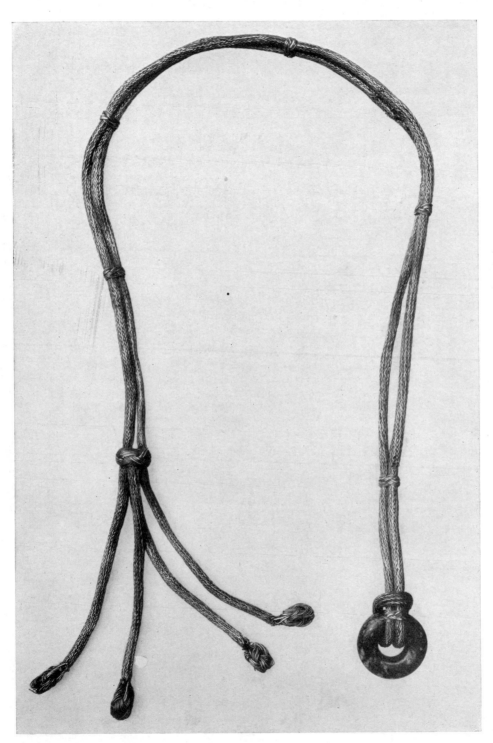

91. Scale $\frac{1}{1}$.

PLATE XXXVI

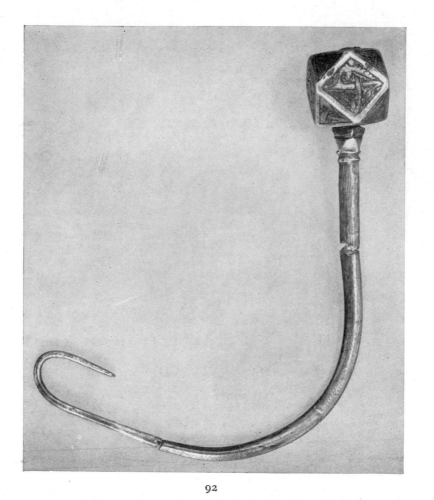

92

92. Details.

93

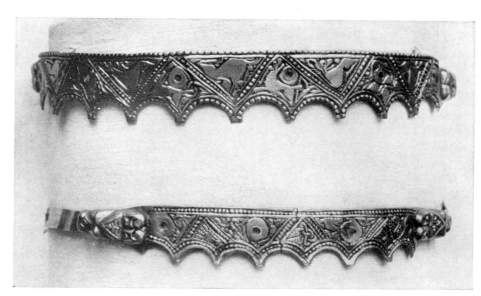

All scale $\frac{1}{1}$.

94 and 95

PLATE XXXVII

Terminals of no. 94.

Terminals of no. 95.

96

98   97

103

99–102

Scale $\frac{1}{1}$.

PLATE XXXVIII

104 and cast of seal.

105

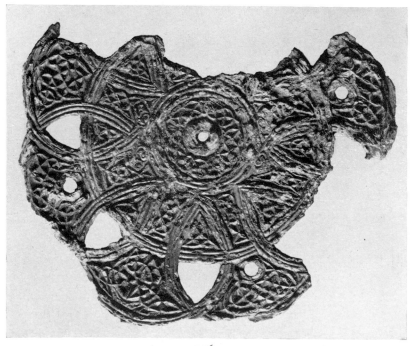

106

All scale ⅟₁.

PLATE XXXIX

107

108

114
109

110

111

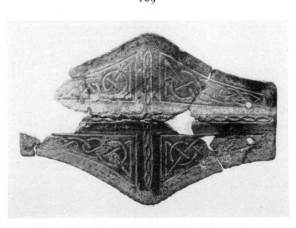

112

113

All Scale ⅟₁.

PLATE XL

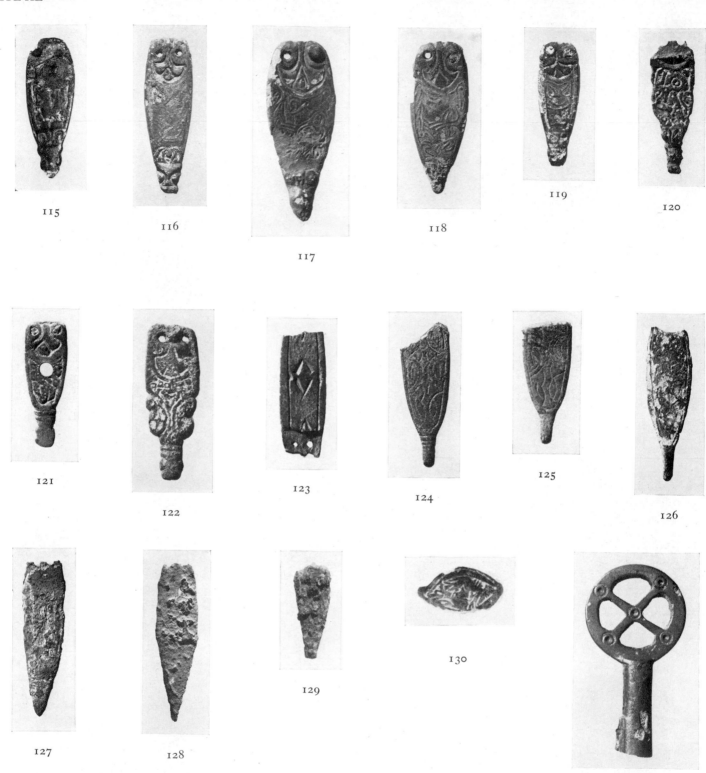

115

116

117

118

119

120

121

122

123

124

125

126

127

128

129

130

132

131

All scale $\frac{1}{1}$.

PLATE XLI

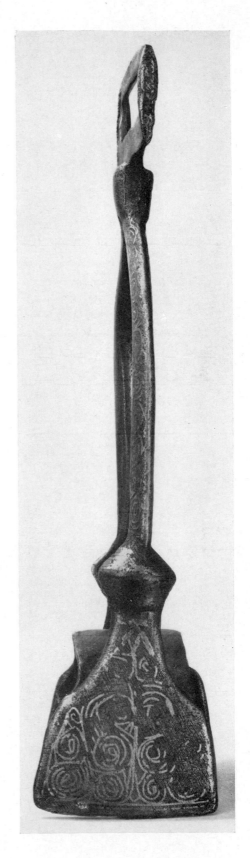

133

Scale $\frac{2}{3}$.

PLATE XLII

136

137

138

139

134

135

140

142

143

146

145

141

144

All Scale ⅟₁.

PLATE XLIII

147

148

149

150

151

152

All Scale ⅟₁.

PLATE XLIV

153

154 and 155

All Scale ⅟₁.